Penguin Books

HEROINES

Edited by Dale Spender

HEROINES

Edited by Dale Spender

Penguin Books

Penguin Books Australia Ltd
487 Maroondah Highway, PO Box 257
Ringwood, Victoria 3134, Australia
Penguin Books Ltd
Harmondsworth, Middlesex, England
Viking Penguin, A Division of Penguin Books USA Inc.
375 Hudson Street, New York, New York 10014, USA
Penguin Books Canada Ltd
2801 John Street, Markham, Ontario, Canada L3R 1B4
Penguin Books (N.Z.) Ltd
182–190 Wairau Road, Auckland 10, New Zealand

First published by Penguin Books Australia, 1991
10 9 8 7 6 5 4 3 2 1

Typeset in 10/12 Andover by Midland Typesetters, Maryborough, Victoria
Made and printed in Australia by Australian Print Group, Maryborough, Victoria
Designed by Ann Wojczuk

National Library of Australia
Cataloguing-in-Publication data:
Heroines: an anthology of contemporary Australian
    women writers.
ISBN 0 14 014697 0.
1. Heroines – Literary collections. 2. Australian
literature – Women authors. 3. Australian literature
– 20th century. I. Spender, Dale. II. Title. (Series:
Penguin Australian women's library).
A820.80353

For Carla Zampatti
a most contemporary woman

Acknowledgements

My thanks to the contributors whose imaginative responses have made this anthology possible, and who in the lengthy correspondence involved, have become 'pen friends'. My thanks too, to my inspirational editor at Penguin, Susan Hawthorne, who introduced me to many of the contributors and who has provided me with such stimulating and considerate guidance.

I am also grateful to the Rights Manager, Peg McColl, who has taken much of the stress out of 'permissions' with her scrupulous and sustained attention to detail. And for the first time I must acknowledge the benefits of technology closer to home; there is no typist to thank with this publication, only Ada, my Toshiba (and my computer consultant, Jeanette Bridgeman).

But without the support (and culinary skills) of family and friends – Ivy Spender, Cheris Kramarae, Kirsten Lees, Robyn Daniels, Rhonda Fadden, Renate Klein, Julie Steiner, Sara Gardener, Jill Hickson, Clare McAdam, and Ted Brown, this anthology could not have been undertaken; without the counsel, care, and infinite capacity of Lynne Spender to provide a sounding board, it could not have been completed.

Contents

DALE SPENDER

Dale Spender is a researcher and author–editor of more than thirty books. As a feminist she has been interested in the nature of authority – in how men get to speak more, and why their work carries more weight. Many of her publications have focused on the silencing of women in the spoken and written form and have been directed towards reclaiming the range and richness of women's voices, past and present. With the shift from print to electronic media she has transferred some of her concerns with authority to information technology; the co-editor of an international data base on women (WISE), she currently lectures in many countries on the need for a new discipline: Computer Crit.

The founder of numerous women's publishing ventures and the series editor of the Penguin Australian Women's Library, she is an internationally recognised scholar, teacher and public speaker. She is completing a book on women's language strengths (*Talking Comfort*) and working on the role of intellectuality and the issue of women's exclusion. Her publications include *Man Made Language* (1980) and *Feminist Theorists* (1983), which have been translated into Japanese; she has written widely in the area of women's intellectual history (*Women of Ideas – And What Men Have Done to Them*, 1982), education (*Invisible Women: The Schooling Scandal*, 1982), literature (*Mothers of the Novel: 100 Good Writers Before Jane Austen*, 1986) and women's personal chronicles (*The Diary of Elizabeth Pepys*). She has edited *The Anthology of British Women Writers* (1988) and *The Penguin Anthology of Australian Women's Writing* (1988). In press are *The Knowledge Explosion: Generations of Feminist Scholarship; Living by the Pen: Early British Women Writers*; with Kirsten Lees, a book on Dymphna Cusack and with Patricia Clarke, a volume of early Australian women's letters and diaries.

Introduction

A Product of the Times

The contemporary literary scene is one of energy, experiment, excitement – and change. There are so many creative writers heading in so many different directions, and challenging well-entrenched assumptions, that it can be a very difficult task simply trying to identify some of the penchants and patterns of the present period. And this in itself is a reason for putting together a contemporary anthology. For a collection of some of the most stimulating and satisfying current writing not only affords a rewarding reading experience it also helps to provide an illuminating overview of the contemporary scene. To take account of where we are is to have a better idea of where we are going.

But given that sweeping shifts and changes are the order of the day there is not much point in turning to traditional sources to find examples of the full range and diversity of contemporary efforts and achievements. The only really satisfactory means for sampling the entire scene, of gaining some impression of the transformations which are underway, is to look at the women and the various ways they are earning a living from writing in this changing era.

Yet to focus on all the forms that paid writing can take at the end of the twentieth century raises as many speculative questions as it provides insights and understandings. Which is why this is an unusual anthology. It is a product of the times in that it reflects many of the unique problems and practices that are making their presence felt in the world of print today. And it suggests that literature, and literacy, both closely associated with the printed word, are definitely not what they used to be. In sampling the range of paid writing in the current context, this anthology puts print into contemporary perspective; no longer the primary medium, print now shares the information spectrum with the screen – with the electronic media.

In representing the many models of contemporary women's writing – from a short story in the *Bulletin*, to lectures and public speeches, along with a television script, a musical, newsprint, drama and fiction – this anthology helps to identify the impact of the electronic media. It points to the processes and pressures that are currently transforming communication, and which are customarily labelled as the 'information revolution'. While it was not part of the original purpose of the anthology to enter the discussion on the implications of technology and the changing face of print, this is where an overview of contemporary women's writing undoubtedly leads. Many of the contributors to this volume have already left the traditional paths of the past and have set off in new directions, as they help to shape the forms of the future. They are at the 'cutting edge' of the information revolution.

Information revolution is a term which in recent years has entered the vocabulary of everyday life. More often applied to the work place (or war technology) it has come to mean changes in everything from banking practices, to satellite communication networks, fax machines and electronic mail facilities. But for all its wide associations, the term 'information revolution' has not usually been applied to literature: rather, a dividing line has generally been drawn between the electronic media, and the artistic and creative activities of the author. Apart from the occasional discussion about the relationship of writers and word processors – and the increased 'unaccountability' of screen editors[1] – in professional associations such as the *Australian Society of Authors*, the world of letters generally has kept a respectable distance from the information revolution. Or so it has seemed.

Revolutions, however, have a habit of challenging and changing some of the most cherished assumptions of a society, and the information revolution is no exception. One thing this collection makes clear is that whether they like it or not, contemporary writers cannot be isolated from changes in the channels of communications. So not even those who continue to believe that they are outside – or above – the encroaching influence of the new electronic media, can remain immune from some of the subtle and significant shifts which have been set in motion. And it is not just writers, but the 'readers' too who must also modify their ways.

If as yet, the effects of the information revolution on authorship – and the state of the art – have not become an explicit and central topic within literary circles, there is some evidence to suggest that writers themselves have not been slow to see the writing on the wall. For a survey and analysis of contemporary writing reveals that there are many authors who are conscious of the new demands of the era, and who are shaping their work accordingly. This contemporary anthology, which brings together the contributions of many outstanding women writers, gives some idea of the currents that are now at work in the literary mainstream; it provides insights about society, *and* about the information revolution which in the last decade of the twentieth century has become a fundamental feature of life.

Many writers from many different backgrounds, with many different styles, have contributed to this volume, and while a distinctive feature of the collection is the variety of the forms, this diversity must be placed alongside the common assumptions. It is interesting to note that another distinctive feature of the anthology is the shared response to the technological changes that are confronting authors.

Simply earning a living from writing is one of the perennial problems that authors face, and in this respect, the writers included here are again, very much a product of their day. For unlike writers of earlier periods, these authors have indicated that for many of them it is no longer the *publication* of their words which provides most of their income, but the *performance*. It is the presentation rather than the page, the image rather than the print-face, which is becoming the predominant form.[2]

This acknowledgement by authors is a striking illustration of the changes that are currently taking place in the literary arena. And this anthology helps to 'trace' the process of transformation. In bringing together these writers who are responding to changed circumstances and patterns of communication, this volume provides a sampling of the best contemporary writing, *and* an illuminating perspective on the information revolution. It shows how the medium of print is beginning to share space, and status, with the new electronic medium; it shows how the book is giving way to the image – which is one reason that many writers are finding that print does not pay as much as performance.

Not that the topic of the information revolution is taken up directly by any of the authors in these pages. But because they are all perceptive writers who engage with the shifts in political and personal processes, their work reflects contemporary collective and individual concerns.

From Page to Performance

The history of information media suggests that the latest development, the move from page to screen, will mean more than a minor change in the financial arrangements of authors, or a modification from reading to viewing among audiences. As the electronic media become more embedded in our way of life – in our work, domestic organisation, and leisure – it seems unlikely that any aspect of existence will be free from the influence of the information revolution. If past shifts in information channels are anything to go by, then the entire social fabric, right through to the nature of the individual, is on the agenda for transformation. And for many reasons, writers are at the forefront of this change.

For five centuries published writers have occupied a position of influence. For five centuries it has been the medium of print (and hence the published writers) which has shaped the 'truths' of the society, which has carried the information that has structured individual and community life, from one generation to the next. This power of being published – *of going public* – was recognised from the very early stages of print, so that access to publication has always been subject to some measure of control. From newspapers and magazines, to books – and academic journals – publication has depended upon some form of selection process, as indeed it does within this very anthology. Not everyone gets into print, and those who do, must meet certain criteria.

With the introduction of the printing press, only the very few – the privileged in church and state – had access to publication; the power of print was promptly perceived, and supervised. And while the number of authors, and the diversity of views, has expanded over the century it is still the case that print affords some measure of power and some means of persuasion. Published authors have been in a position to have their opinions reach a wider audience, and to exert considerable influence.

Understandably, in the past, authors have often 'led the way'. But as the end of the twentieth century approaches, all this is changing. Print no longer rules exclusively, and published writers no longer stand alone as the arbiters of views and values. As the page gives way to the screen, we become a society in transition; to go *public*, in the contemporary context – to be *published* – is often to perform. As writers and readers and society members, we might not yet be fully aware of the shift in focus that is taking place. But even if we have not consciously addressed all the issues associated with the innovations in custom and convention, it seems that we are already engaged in making the required readjustments.

As a community we are moving away from print literacy, which involves processing an alphabet, arranged in a linear pattern; and we are heading towards screen literacy and the processing of images. From reading in *silence* and as *individuals* we can find ourselves increasingly watching and listening to a writer's work – and often in the company of others rather than alone.

Each year there are more and more literary festivals, more and more events where 'readings' are given, and which can be 'recorded' on audio tapes, or video. Novels which in the recent past would have been savoured in solitude are now being read in part, and in public, by the author. Television 'Book Shows' and even feature films are making visual the work of many authors. And the new demands are so very different that even if they are not articulated by writers or readers, they are being taken into account as the trend to performance continues. It is possible that in the future this period will be seen as the time when rhythm and auditory features of the printed language changed, as authors became more conscious of the 'speaking voice' in their work; and as 'readers' became more accustomed to 'hearing' them in person, or on the radio or the screen.[3]

Of course this is not the first information revolution to have taken place. This is not the first time that there has been a change in the influential voices of the community – in the medium, the message, or the 'manipulator'.

There have been four major information periods in human history, with each one building on the form that has gone before. So the oral, for example, gave way to the written, as the primary information medium, and then the written to the printed word. And it isn't as if each medium has been discarded; while it may have lost its place (and prestige) as the official medium of information, it still had many communicative and creative uses. The oral, the written, and the printed form can all now be 'accommodated' and find a place in the electronic era.

But clearly, with each new medium has come a new context and challenge for authors; there are new concerns and possibilities and new demands made upon communicative skills, as the contributors to this volume reveal. And in the interest of trying to understand and appreciate the forces which are shaping the contemporary context, it is helpful to look at the responses of the past and the patterns of restructuring.

The invention of the printing press, for example, and the expansion in the availability of printed materials – newspapers and magazines as well as books – led to one of the greatest social revolutions that there has ever been. Understandably, many of the community leaders caught up in it were anxious and apprehensive about the nature of the changes and the consequences. There was considerable resistance to the introduction of print. Remarkable as it may seem to us now – reared as we have been with the medium – it is worth noting that along with the printing press came dire warnings about the damage that print would cause to the social institutions, and the community. As early as the fifteenth century there were complaints that books would mean an end to conversation in the family[4] and that they would threaten the fabric of social life. With everyone off reading their own book (or newspaper), engrossed in their own *private* world, doing their own thing and forming their own independent views, it was consistently argued (particularly by the scribes who could see their influence waning) that there would soon be a breakdown in shared values, an end to order and cohesion.

This was not all; it was widely held that books were dangerous, that they would give people ideas, that they would foment discontent and provoke the population to demand changes. And clearly such developments were undesirable. Precautionary steps were taken to prevent literacy from spreading; the working classes of Britain were discouraged from becoming literate, females were denied education (on the grounds that literacy and learning 'unfitted' them for the role of dutiful wives), and in the United States the act of teaching slaves to read was made a serious crime.

Despite these preventive measures, however, the reading public grew at an astonishing rate (suggesting how readily individuals could acquire the skills of writing and reading when they were considered so valuable – and subversive). And many were the members of the establishment who deplored the shift from manuscript to print, who protested at the dreadful drop in standards when literature went from being the privilege of the few to the political and pleasurable pastime of the masses. There was so much reading and writing going on that it was firmly believed (by a select few) in the sixteenth and seventeenth centuries, that society was experiencing a literacy crisis. The very reverse of our present problem (as we shift away from print), the cry of the time was not that people were reading too few books but that they were reading too many!

Currently as moves are made and campaigns are mounted to protect the book, to promote the reading habit (and overcome the literacy crisis of the twentieth century) in the attempt to preserve some of the organisational forms of the print culture, it seems strange to think that the introduction of this very same medium once prompted prophets of gloom and doom and fostered grave fears for the future of the social order. Even in the eighteenth and nineteenth centuries, regular warnings were issued about the dangers of too much reading and the risk it represented for public health; a 1795 tract clearly spelled out the message:

...susceptibility to colds, headaches, weakening of the eyes, heat rashes, gout, arthritis, hemorrhoids, asthma, apoplexy, pulmonary disease, indigestion, blocking of the bowels, nervous disorder, migraines, epilepsy, hypochondria and melancholy...
(Robert Darnton, 1990: 5)[5]

This was the price that the community would pay for widespread reading; females were held to be particularly susceptible to the perils of print. During the nineteenth century the medical profession lent its authority to the injunction that women's uteruses would atrophy and their brains would burst if exposed to too much reading. Novels were held to be the most damaging:

The reading of works of fiction is one of the most pernicious habits to which a young lady can be subjected. When the habit is once thoroughly fixed, it becomes as inveterate as the use of liquor or opium... The reading of fictitious literature destroys the taste for wholesome, sober reading, and imparts an unhealthy stimulus to the mind, the effect of which is in the highest degree *damaging*.

When we add to this the fact that a large share of the popular novels of the day contain more or less matter of a directly depraved character, presented in such gilded form and specious guise that the work of contamination may be completed before suspicion is aroused, it should become apparent to every careful mother that her daughters should be vigilantly guarded against this dangerous source of injury and possible ruin... We wish to put ourselves on record as believing firmly that the practice of novel reading is one of the greatest causes of uterine disease in young women.

J.D. Kellog, MD. *Ladies Guide in Health and Disease.*

While such edicts can be amusing today, they were taken seriously in their own time, and they stand as sincere expressions of a society that was trying to accommodate substantial change and find a way of coming to terms with the challenge of the new breed of writers and readers. And our own response to the electronic media is not fundamentally different from earlier reactions to communication shifts as Alvin Kernan (1990)[6] makes clear.

'Reading came to be feared in much the same way that too

much television viewing in late twentieth century America has become a kind of cultural bogey' (p. 130), he says, providing some of the parallels between the past and the present. The fear of the new, the unknown, and of the power of the medium and its authors, or 'manipulators', can lead to predictions about the collapse of society and the cost to individual and community health and well being.

Resistance has accompanied the introduction of each medium as the leaders of the old try to protect their position and practices, partly by discrediting the products of the new. So the scribes of the Middle Ages objected to the barbarism of the printing press and demanded to know how human beings could take on the word without carefully studying it, and writing it down, as they had done. Superficial knowledge, and a fragmented society with no proper values, would be the consequence of so many people reading so many different sources without appropriate supervision and guidance, they insisted. The new would disturb, and disrupt, and should only be allowed in small and 'controlled' doses and in suitably regulated educational and cultural establishments.

And the writers of the new form came in for their share of censure. The elite authors of the old school – Alexander Pope among them – objected vehemently to the new breed of authors, or scribblers, who were accused of catering to the lowest common denominator and of ruining the literary standards. Eliza Haywood, for example,[7] and other popular women writers of the eighteenth century were reviled for the way they were bringing literature into disrepute by producing popular 'pap' that was held to weaken the mind; ironically of course, many of these same writers who were once slated are now highly respected for their contribution to the world of letters. The question which arises is whether today's 'performance' and script writers, who are not now highly regarded, will constitute 'the canon' in tomorrow's electronic society.

But of course, in the new medium, the functions and features of authorship will be markedly different – as some of the pieces in this collection suggest.

At the moment, there is overlap. And while the two forms could be said to co-exist, it is the assumptions and expectations of the print medium – because of its historical primacy and power – which tends to be more entrenched, despite the challenges of the electronic age. Even in publishing where the new technology is transforming the old practices at a reelingly rapid rate, the hold that print has frequently persists. Some publishers do request that authors present their manuscripts in electronic form, even going so far as to specify particular systems, and discs; but most still accept typescript, or more commonly, 'hard copy' – the printed/electronic form.

But if there is one measure of the dramatic changes that have already taken place it is in the matter of handwritten manuscripts. The acceptance of such a document by a commercial publisher, is today, most unlikely: yet as recently as the late 1970s and early 1980s, the reputable British publisher, Routledge, for example, was still processing the occasional handwritten manuscript – from academics. Which prompts another provocative question; to what extent will the cost of the new medium, of software and hardware – as distinct from mere paper and pen – preclude certain people from becoming the future authors?[8]

None of the contributors to this anthology provided material in handwritten form; and although some of the pieces had been typeset (as in the case of Adele Horin's journalism), it is significant that the majority were the print-outs from personal computers.

But these switches in technological forms (from pen, to typewriter, and now to printer) and the switches in artistic forms (from page to performance orientation), are not the only changes that authors are facing. Audiences are also adapting, and society is changing, so that in the new electronic medium, *authorship* itself will have very different connotations and be subjected to very different forms of evaluation. That the writer is being deprofessionalised by technology, that the art of writing is being displaced by the proficiency and precision of a 'machine', is a suspicion that is steadily gaining ground. The signs of change are already present in this contemporary anthology.[9]

Author and Audience

In the period when the primary form of communication was oral, society was community based. If information was to be exchanged people had to be able to meet together, to talk to each other face to face, and the life of the society was organised around this principle. But each new medium has reduced the need for people to communicate directly and has allowed them to 'speak to each other' indirectly, across distance and across time, through written, printed, and now electronic media. This development which allowed people to be 'isolated', but still in touch, has had numerous implications for social organisation; historically the trend has been away from the accommodation of community needs toward that of the accommodation of the individual (who has access to books, post, telephones, and now the mass media).

In contrast to the oral medium, the written word – and then more dramatically, the printed word – allowed members of society to glean information without direct contact with another human being. Once they were literate, and if they had the economic means, it was a simple matter for people to take a printed work and go away and read on their own; to form their own opinions – and of course to transmit them to others through print or post. Which was the precise development that many of the authorities had feared.

This individualisation of society also provided improved opportunities for the spread of ideas. For through print, individuals could become independent of the authorities who in earlier times had been able to supervise the beliefs and practices of their communities. With the advent of print and post – of newspapers and letters as well as books – networks could be maintained among people scattered around the world; ideas produced in one place could be mooted and modified in another without any physical contact being made, and without any 'control' being exercised. (Of course, censorship, defamation and libel laws were soon placed 'on the books' as the new forms of control and constraint.)

The belief of the established leaders that print would promote the rise of the individual and lead to a demand for a more egalitarian society where everyone had rights, was more than justified. In some respects, individuality and independence are inextricably associated with the growth of the print medium, and have become the hallmarks of western society.

The concept of individuality, however, was by no means confined to the readers, the consumers – the audience. Writers also became increasingly individualised, and glorified. 'Authors' were no longer the semi-anonymous transmitters or recorders of received wisdom (as with the sacred texts for example) but became 'personalised' and 'appraised' within the print era. Texts were no longer produced in scriptoria – the rooms where manuscripts had been carefully written and regulated by a community of scribes – but were created, by a gifted and dedicated author, who, in romanticised terms, generally worked alone, and frequently in a garret, who was inspired by the muse and indifferent to the comforts of life. He was an artist, who more often than not – and at the expense of women – sought the recognition of *his* individual and creative genius from a grateful world.

The rise of print, individualism – and capitalism – are generally linked together and they all have implications for the author. For unlike the orators and scribes who went before, authors have been granted property rights over their words. Once there was a fixed text, as there is with print, discussions could take place about who owned it, and soon the concept of copyright came into existence. And along with it came the possibility of plagiarism – of stealing or using without permission the author's original words.[10]

Obviously, within this highly individualised context, where originality has been prized, the role and reputation of the writer has been of central importance. On the foundation stone of the romanticised artist – the rare and talented individual with distinctive if not unique skills – has rested the very idea of literature, with the few great writers producing works for the many appreciative audiences. The concept of a great writer and a great literary tradition depends upon the belief that the ability to be a good writer is a gift not granted to the majority of the community. But such arrangements are currently being questioned under the pressures of the new media, and it is disquieting to think that such a seemingly enduring edifice as 'the great tradition' could soon be dismantled.

From many quarters, however, there is mounting evidence that the print era as we have known it, and the literary stars as we have constructed them, are about to come to an end. For example, as we move into the electronic medium, the individuality and identity of the author is being progressively undermined; for there is no romantic cult of authorship and originality associated with the screen. In all the years of film and television, it would be difficult to name writers whose credentials and fame have been established through script writing. Rather, the teams of script writers who work together and who are often associated with 'soaps' and television serials, (not to mention the news broadcasts and the political speeches written by teams) may have more in common with the scribes of the old scriptoria – who also worked in groups and produced a combined and 'controlled' script.

And as the identity of individual writers can become submerged in writing teams, the issue of intellectual property rights becomes increasingly problematic; whose script is it anyway when so many people have contributed to it? And what effect does it have on copyright, and plagiarism?

But the responsibility for challenging the authors' ownership of text cannot be attributed to the direct influence of the electronic medium alone. Over the past decade there have been literary critics who have outlined their own version of the problem. The insistence that meaning resides solely with the readers (a not unpopular platform of much contemporary critical theory) and that authors cannot own their own texts, has also helped to diminish the scope and stature of authorship. (Other than that of the critics of course.)

Postmodernism could be said to be the *theory* of electronic media *practice*: with its questioning of sequence, unity, narrative, its emphasis on the juxtaposition of images – and its demotion of the writer, deconstruction of the text, and development of reader independence – postmodernism embodies many of the concepts and conventions of the computer era. It has been part of the process of decentring the word, of overturning the fixed canon of the great white men and of encoding the potential for the many different cultural groups, and many different societies to have their own many different literatures. This move from the fixed and universal centre to encompass the literature of women, of Blacks, of post-colonial peoples, can be seen by some as the collapse of standards, even as the end of 'white civilisation' as it has been known through the print medium. But it can also be seen as the emergence of a multiplicity of meanings which reflect the multiple experiences of the human condition; it can be seen as a realisation of the potential of the information revolution which allows for the democratisation of meaning, for the end of the distinction between culture maker and culture receiver, between writer and reader.

The premise that readers alone are the legitimate interpreters of the text can certainly lead to a democratisation of the critical process of meaning-making, and collapse of hierarchy of author and audience; but, of course, when everyone's view is as good as everyone else's, and when there are as many meanings as there are readers and no frameworks for making evaluative judgements, making meaning can become a meaningless activity.

To the leaders of the past who predicted that the results of print would be chaos and anarchy, no doubt the present crisis in meaning would represent the realisation of their worst fears. It certainly makes a mockery, if not an absurdity, of plagiarism; if words don't have any set meaning any more, how can you take someone else's meaning and pass it off as your own?

Whether contemporary critics are contributing to the decline in the powers of the author, or whether they are reacting to some of the pressures of the new age, there can be no doubt that print is becoming increasingly destabilised and writers – of literature and journalism – are becoming increasingly deprofessionalised as the electronic medium exerts its influence.[11] The shift of the literary and features editors of newspapers from private offices to open areas and VDU terminals, and the shift from the form of academic journals to electronic data bases, are but a few of the indicators of future directions.

Again, academics provide some intriguing examples of the trend towards deprofessionalisation. In the past, practices have been set up to ensure that the authors of academic articles are given due credit for their contributions. The ownership of ideas in academe has been given great prominence, and because it has been just as important to have a good name as a scholar (an international reputation no less), as it has been to have a good name as a creative writer, all sorts of systems have been devised to acknowledge the originality and to designate the property rights; hence an elaborate arrangement of footnotes and references. But the nature of data bases can put an end to all such individuality, to 'control' and to ownership of information.

While contributions to a data base can originate with an individual – who may be a well known and highly acclaimed academic associated with the development of a particular area of research and expertise – the material that such a person provides can be put into an electronic 'mixing pot' (of *hypertext* for example) so that the owner's identity and creativity can no longer be traced. And in the process of programming, even the original meanings might be substantially altered. For while it is possible and perfectly plausible for academics to check every aspect of their texts when handed over to a typesetter for publication in fixed form in a journal or a book, it can be very difficult to keep track of information and to see how it has been entered and used in a 'moving' data base. This loss of control over their own 'product' can be seen by academics as a threat to their territory, and to their professional status.

With typesetters, who were accountable, academics enjoyed a measure of control and professionalism; with programmers, who cannot be held comparably accountable, academics can be required to hand over their material to people whose values and beliefs may be very different from their own. And those who 'create' the programs are in a position to stamp their *own* shape and meanings on the data.

An author of information on witches, for example, may have intended them to be perceived as powerful and positive women who were persecuted by supporters of the new scientific revolution; but if the information scientist, responsible for the data base, does *not* share this view, the meanings of the academic writer can be lost. Entered under *satanic practices* or *wicked and wanton women*, the wise and resourceful witches of the original input might never again resurface. And this loss of the control of identity and meaning is part of the process of the deprofessionalisation of the author.

The passing of the permanent and set text is one of the salient features of the current revolution in communication, so it is not surprising that literary theory should be pre-occupied with the ramifications that this has for authors, audiences, and the nature of meaning. Traditionally, literary criticism has served for more than a century to describe and explain the processes, products and implications of print,[12] and in addressing the problems associated with technological developments, it could be that 'lit-crit' is in the process of becoming 'computer-crit' and is preparing itself to be able to describe, explain and evaluate the electronic media. As we become more familiar with the new channels of communication, and more knowledgeable about the place and purpose of literature and 'the great tradition' in the society of the future, more theories will emerge which take account of the combinations of print and screen.

In such a context this contemporary anthology can make a significant contribution. As a product of these transitional times it will mark the period where the focus turned more to performance than to print.

New schools of literary theory will no doubt emerge along with new concepts of literature, and they may bear little or no resemblance to the critical schools and the criteria that have been associated with the evaluation of the printed word. New insights will be forged about intellectual property, about plagiarism, copyright and payment (including royalties and public lending right) and new systems will be devised; and while the old ideas and institutions associated with print and the past may be modified, they will not necessarily be cast aside. Perhaps the linear model of information development will be replaced with a more interconnected one, in which all the forms – oral, written, printed and electronic – will exist in relation to each other. After all, as the emphasis moves from the fixed and recorded word to the moving image and the performance, it could be argued that we are back to sharing some of the values of an earlier era; the performances of William Shakespeare also had priority over the written word.

Content and Commentary

One of the starting points for this collection was the compilation of *The Penguin Anthology of Australian Women's Writing* in 1988; the aim then had been to represent the range of Australian women's writing but of course there was just so much material that in the interest of keeping the publication to manageable proportions, priorities had to be made. Preference was given to writers of the past who were often unknown (and invariably out of print) which meant that writers of the present were seriously under-represented. Clearly this was not a long term satisfactory 'solution', and to do justice to the full range of Australian women writers, an anthology devoted entirely to contemporary writers was required.

A further impetus – and rationale – for a volume of contemporary works came from a provocative short story written by Barbara Jefferis. Entitled 'The Drover's Wife', it dramatises some of the issues that are central in any consideration of Australian women's literature, and in the process of setting the scene, Barbara Jefferis also cleverly, and entertainingly, 'rewrites' the Australian heroine. This satirical and stimulating 'performance' which opens this collection, was the source for much of the substance and structure of the anthology.

Aware of the extent to which a male ethos has dominated Australian literature, Barbara Jefferis is a woman writer no longer content to allow the male view of the world (and women's place within it) to go unchallenged. Disturbed by the distorted representations of women she was forever encountering, she was stung into action; she 'rescued' the drover's wife from the pages of history and let her set the record straight with her own reply to her male authors: 'All very well for them to spin yarns and make jokes but nobody has written any sense about me.' protests Barbara Jefferis' drover's wife as she points out the poor treatment that she has received at the hands of men. And she starts by contrasting the tale she told Mr Henry Lawson, with the story he then made of it. Not that she accuses him of wilful misrepresentation; she just scathingly summarises the limitations of his view: 'He didn't mean me any harm, far from it,' she explains. 'But men can only see women as heroines when they do something a decent man would do for them if he happened to be around, like killing a snake or an injured calf, or hauling a rotten sheep carcass out of the well.'

It is the premise that men see women only in relation to themselves, and that they are reluctant to acknowledge women's resources, which is at the heart of much discussion about the image of women in Australian literature. In the words of the drover's wife who is a woman's creation, men can even deny the 'strength women have... because they think it takes away from' themselves; and this makes for a misrepresentation of the relationship between the sexes.

Like Barbara Jefferis – and the drover's wife – I am fascinated with the idea that women have a different version of their own lives, and that if given the opportunity they will portray their own resources, strengths, and relationship with the opposite sex, in very different terms from those of men. Which is why I wanted to know more about women's *heroines*.

So this was a suggestion in the guidelines given to the contributors of the anthology; it was not a prescription, but a request to keep heroines in mind. And the result has been more than rewarding; for not only does the anthology comprise a selection of outstanding pieces from contemporary writers, it also contains a gallery of remarkable female characters – women's heroines.

The Drover's Wife steps centre stage, to speak for herself, and Diane Bell provides the cultural backdrop for women's story telling. An academic, writing a scholarly article – which lends itself admirably to delivery and public performance – she uses her research and skills as an anthropologist to call up the foremothers of this ancient land. She weaves the narratives which connect her contemporary specialist knowledge with Aboriginal traditions and meanings. Self consciously analysing and challenging the boundaries of conventional academic writing, she blends the intellectual and the emotional as she presents some of the *sheroes* of Australian society.

It is 'Elizabeth' in all her many forms whom Diane Bell reclaims, reconstructs and reconnects with the Aboriginal heritage; as Lizzie, Eliza, Bess, Beth, Bessie, Liza, Isabella, Belle, Bethal, Liz, Libby and Elizabetta we hear women's voices putting together and passing on the traditions of the culture.

From Elizabeth Macarthur to the convict Elizabeth Foxall, from the poet Eliza Dunlop through to the contemporary poet, Elizabeth Riddell, and the feminist Elizabeth Reid, we witness a parade of women past and present as Diane Bell reinstates women in their community context.

The 'speaking voice' of Diane Bell resonates throughout her essay, and while slightly more sombre but nonetheless celebratory in tone – in keeping with the occasion – Jocelynne Scutt's Memorial Lecture for Peggy Martin also combines the intellectual and the emotional, with 'public speaking'.

Women orators who take the lives of other women as their subjects have not been prominent during the print period (although they had their counterparts in earlier times, particularly in women's communities, in indigenous societies or in religious institutions). But as greater efforts are made to acknowledge and appraise the contributions of women, there is a greater need for public testimony of women's achievements. The growing demand for lectures, speeches, and addresses, which recognise and respect the role that women play, affirms and extends the possibilities for writing and performing. Jocelynne Scutt's well researched and inspirational oration is an exemplary model of this contemporary form.

For Ruby Langford, the heroines are closer to home. Taking the women who have been most influential and most important in her life, she reminisces about her heroines' past and speculates on the fates of her daughters – her heroines for the future. Ruby Langford tells her own story, in her own distinctive tone; it is a voice which has not been heard often enough in Australian literature. It too is a narrative for performance; one which reaches back and touches the traditions that Diane Bell has traced, and reaches forward to link with the deliberate drama of Eva Johnson.

There is pain, and there is passion, in Eva Johnson's performance. The voices of three Aboriginal women reverberate with the discord of discrimination as they each confront their own individual crisis, their connections, and their collective struggle. As theatre, this piece is compelling. As a social document it is an indictment of many forms of oppression; yet it is not without hope. And it is this which distinguishes it from 'Northern Belle', Thea Astley's study of disintegration and dissonance; racism and the cost of human fears are the undercurrents in Thea Astley's short story.

The sense of loss which accompanies a cramped and narrowed life has often been the motif in women's writing, and the author invests this design with new force in the form of Clarice, in 'Northern Belle'. She contrasts the waste with the potential, the physical limitations of a small country town and the psychological limitations of small mindedness with the possibilities for a large and full life. The effect is harrowing. While Clarice does find some solace and sustenance in routine, regularity, her dog and her garden, in the end it is insufficient to protect her.

Elizabeth Jolley also adheres to some of the conventional images of women's writing: Miss Mallow – the spinster, who talks to herself and is not quite right in the head – is not an unfamiliar literary type. But here all similarity ends. For the voice of Miss Mallow can continue to be heard, long after the story has been read. A monologue – as is Miss Mallow's lonely life – this narrative breaks the boundaries of reality so that fact, fiction and sanity can readily be questioned.

A subtitle for 'Rambling Rose', by Barbara Hanrahan, could well be 'survival': this is another monologue, a monotone, where voice and meaning are mesmerisingly mixed. The passing of life is recorded without emphasis, without significance being given to some of the harshest blows that fate could inflict. Ironically, *Rambling* Rose holds herself tightly together, afraid to explore, experiment, excite.

The prose and the persona are just as skilfully interwoven, and just as disposed towards performance, in the 'parable' of Joanne Burns. But here we are faced with a heroine who does set out to determine the meaning of life – who seeks and samples and sifts and struggles, but who still finds no satisfaction in the prescribed solutions.

Georgia Savage's many and varied heroines, however, entertain more positive resolutions and speak out in defiant and lively style. While questioning the injustice of racism, sexism, ageism, and the rightful use of the meanings of the oppressed, the integrity, vibrancy, and the imaginative possibilities of these women, are never in doubt.

No anthology of heroines would be complete without the

'school ma'am', but Janette Turner Hospital gives the image a new twist in the person of Miss Lucia Davenport. 'Condemned' to the isolation of Northern Queensland for the error of her youthful ways, Miss Davenport 'pins' her hopes on her young students, Rebecca and Hazel. But yet another error of judgement permits crude male reality to intervene.

In more cerebral but no less amusing terms, Rosaleen Love also confronts a male reality; in response to the pervasive image of man as the origin of the species, she creates woman – 'Evolution Annie' – who tells the story of her *mother* (and father), thereby providing a different perspective on human history. 'Mother stayed at home and developed tools and the skills of reason,' Evolution Annie airily explains; 'Father and the boys went out into the world and got cold and wet and suffered broken bones and falls into chasms'... and came up against every conceivable threat and inconvenience. Having acquired some of the benefits of mother's reason and sanity, however, Evolution Annie and her sisters find that the world of men holds very little attraction for them. 'Staying home under the trees made excellent sense to us girls,' she says.

From an imaginative rewrite of the dim and distant past, Gail Jones takes her audience to an imaginative reconstruction of the impact of modern technology, and the media, on human consciousness. Intent on giving fictional form to philosophical issues, Gail Jones crafts 'Modernity' to explode with a clash of symbols, and of course, with a range of questions about progress, values, meaning – and violence.

Violence is also the critical element in Beth Yahp's version of the student riots in Malaysia – 'In 1969'. And the meaning of *mother* is questioned in this stunning short story which transports the audience to another world. Incisively she exposes the inhumanity of repression, and questions the price that is paid for the birth of the new, and for the 'political readjustment' of a society.

Finola Moorhead points the finger of accusation at a target closer to home. In a panoramic performance-piece she draws the parallels between witchcraft and the persecution of Lindy Chamberlain. A mother, accused, found guilty, imprisoned for infanticide on false and constructed evidence, Lindy Chamberlain was later pardoned. 'Miss Marple Goes to Ayers

Rock' has its elements of parody but its portrayal of a heroine is also essentially political.

Like Finola Moorhead, Roberta Sykes speaks on behalf of those who are victimised; meticulously and methodically she examines the accounts of white exploitation of Black resources and her calculations add up to some of the most heinous and horrendous practices that have ever been perpetrated. And in holding up her own heroines and insisting that their voices be heard, Roberta Sykes has herself become a heroine for other members of society. Among the many inter-connections in this collection is the link between Nora, the narrator in Georgia Savage's 'Photographs in Black and White', and the author of 'Black Women and the Continuing Struggle for Resources'; when given a school assignment on the women she admires, Nora chooses to write about the contribution and qualities of Roberta Sykes.

Adele Horin, too, has her admirers. As a journalist who is concerned that women's reality should be represented in the newsprint, her articles often necessarily deal with violence against women, and her position is one of having to report on the world of men, as women see it. When the news story is from the perspective of the dominated rather than the dominant – from the point of view of the victim rather than the exploiter – the effect, and the implications, can be startling. Sexual harassment, incest, murder, justice – all have their meanings changed dramatically when the 'source' is female.

Having spent many years weighing the worth of words – and often in newsprint – Elizabeth Riddell outlines the re-sponsibilities of the reviewer. She puts her theories into practice with an introduction to some of her own literary heroines. And in the form of 'Poor Johanna', Robyn Archer and Judith Rodriguez 'reclaim' another literary figure and weave together many of the strands of Australian women's writing with the presentation of their 'musical' which so impressively blends the past and the present, the myth and the reality.

When in the course of her research Judith Rodriguez found a snippet of newsprint – dated September 9, 1894 – which noted that upon death, a farm worker near Elmore had been found to be female, she wondered whether this event had any connection with such a character (Nosey Alf) in Joseph Furphy's novel, *Such is Life* (1903). Further research revealed that there was indeed a real counterpart for the fictional version and even that Joseph Furphy had met with 'Poor Johanna' who, disfigured in an accident, had taken to disguising herself as a man.

Robyn Archer and Judith Rodriguez have combined their considerable talents to recreate the story in which Poor Johanna has no supporting role but rather occupies the centre stage. And with its literary and historical overtones, its ballads, its bush setting, and its poignant and painful portrayal of one woman's plight, this performance piece simply calls for production.

Another marvellous contribution which awaits production is the script 'Roundabout' by Helen Hodgman. Written for the screen, it makes new demands, and provides new dimensions, for the reader of print. A seemingly riotous revel – which could be taken as part of the puff of the popular media – it can also be studied for its satirical and serious insights. But a full appreciation of its form and finesse challenges our conventional criteria for assessment; in contrast to our long tradition of critical practices in relation to print, we are but novices when it comes to finding a framework for the evaluation of soap scripts.[13]

A fantasy, and yet a reality, is the theatre piece of Sara Hardy, which portrays the meeting of Virginia Woolf and Vita Sackville West. As in this anthology an attempt has been made to include the many formative influences that have contributed to the current state of the art, it is fitting that Virginia Woolf should be given a place. Not just for her innovative achievements within the British world of letters, but because of the valuable legacy she has bequeathed in the form of her novels and non-fiction. Sara Hardy makes admirable use of literary allusion, of plays upon words and meanings from the 'original' when she casts Vita and Virginia in the role of heroines. Poised between print and performance, Sara Hardy weaves narratives and notions from the past into the contemporary scene, and makes her contribution to the rich patterning of women's literary traditions.

To map some of the direct – and indirect – interconnections

in the contents of this anthology could be a critical exercise in its own right, and one that cannot be undertaken in this introduction. But even a cursory examination suggests that despite the kaleidoscopic contemporary context, there are still common causes and concerns. While most of the current literary forms are included (with letters, diaries and faxes being the notable exceptions), and while they range from the reminiscences of Ruby Langford and Barbara Hanrahan, to the political analyses of Finola Moorhead, Beth Yahp, Jocelynne Scutt and Roberta Sykes, there are still strong links between these writers. While the search for identity reveals the great distance between the different cultural backgrounds, a gulf even between Eva Johnson's Aboriginal women, Barbara Jefferis' Drover's Wife, and Diane Bell's personal quest for an individual and collective past that has honour and integrity, it is possible to discern a shared sense of direction and purpose among the contributors. Sadly, they are sometimes united in adversity.

One of the themes which cuts across the work of the writers included here, is that of violence. Almost all the authors raise the spectre of some form of violation as they comment on contemporary society. And it is appropriate that the indefensible treatment of the Aboriginal and Torres Strait Island people, should be at the forefront of many of the denunciations of injustice and brutality.

Violence, however, is not new. While the violence against women may be given more media prominence in the modern world (see Adele Horin's articles, for example), it has been a reality of women's lives for centuries. One reason that 'Poor Johanna' for example, adopts male disguise is because it affords a measure of protection from male advances.

Within women's literature there has been a long tradition of women disguising themselves as men – particularly when travelling – with Fanny Burney making use of such a device in *The Wanderer* (1814).[14] More recently, and in Australian literary history, there was the case of 'Monsieur Caloche', a poignant tale by the nineteenth-century writer, Tasma (Jessie Couvreur);[15] and of course Kylie Tennant's heroine in *The Honey Flow*, as well as the author herself, dressed as a man when on the road. A slight variation on this theme – and one which allows the point to be made that human beings are treated differently depending on their dress – is presented in *Orlando*, Virginia Woolf's fantastic 'biography' of Vita Sackville West. In this novel the main character switches from one sex to another (throughout the centuries!) and dramatically demonstrates the manner in which 'clothes maketh the man'. So drastically different are the expectations and constraints that confront Orlando with the change of sex, that Virginia Woolf provides for herself a wonderful opportunity to satirically critique the origin of the inequality of the sexes.

When Sara Hardy dramatises the relationship between Vita and Virginia – partly with reference to *Orlando* and to cross dressing and sexual disguise – she draws upon layer after layer of motif and meaning in women's literary culture, using it to enrich the contemporary performance. And it is this blend of the old and the new, of the traditional with the technological, which characterises this contemporary anthology.

The electronic medium may be transforming the role of authors and the nature of their work, but currently the opportunities for writing – particularly for performance – appear to be many, varied, and expanding. With all the changes that currently are taking place in communications networks we are not only entering the era of instant world news (witness the Gulf War) but of world literature. Because Australia is an English speaking country – at a time when English is becoming more established as the international language[16] – and because it is a technologically advanced society (which is still extraordinarily wealthy despite economic difficulties), Australian writers are well placed to participate in the international literary community and to keep pace with, if not to help shape, some of the priorities and practices of communication for the future.

As the end of the twentieth century draws near, Australia is moving away from its single-image and limited identity (of the mate in the outback, the 'ocker'), and Australian women have unprecedented opportunities to make a contribution to local and global literature; they are opportunities which are being realised as the international success of so many testifies. Germaine Greer, Colleen McCullough, Jessica Anderson, Sally Morgan, Kate Grenville, Coral Lansbury, Jill Ker Conway, Anne

Summers for example, are among those who have enviable reputations and who are frequently 'studied' in educational institutions outside their own country.

With the rich cultural mix that is rapidly becoming the hallmark of Australian society, and with the remarkable range of contexts, and contrasts that the continent affords – from the wilderness to the metropolis, from the traditional lifestyle of the Aboriginal people to the information overload of the bureaucrat and technocrat, from the old to the new – Australian writers enjoy immense privilege in their access to creative resources – and catalysts. That women have used these advantages to forge such a dynamic and engaging literature – by means of pen and personal computer – is the reason that I hold them to be contemporary heroines.

---

1. That editors can change/delete/add to 'manuscripts' on screen, without such alterations being immediately obvious to the author, is a controversial issue which raises many questions about 'power' professionalisation and the 'producer' of the text.

2. The exception is of course, literary grants and prizes. Many of the contributors to this collection have been the recipients of state and federal grants, and the biographical notes help to indicate the number who currently enjoy the assistance of the Australia Council.

3. It has been suggested that the growing number of literary events and readings is evidence that print, and the book, is alive and thriving; but it could just as easily be argued that it is *performance* which is becoming the primary medium while the solitary and silent processing of print (and the book) is on the decline.

4. See Raymond Williams 1975, *The Long Revolution*. Penguin, for further discussion.

5. See Robert Darnton 1990, 'First Steps Towards a History of Reading', in *Australian Journal of French Studies*, Vol. 22, No. 5.

6. Alvin Kernan 1990, *The Death of Literature*. Yale University Press, New Haven.

7. For further information see the section on Eliza Haywood in Dale Spender 1986, *Mothers of the Novel; 100 Good Women Writers Before Jane Austen*. Pandora Press, London.

8. That women have been able to enter the literary profession in greater numbers than most other professions in the past, has often been ascribed to the fact that writing has not required any capital outlay. Paper and pen

has been cheaper even than paint – and artists' models – and much cheaper than training in the traditional professions of law, medicine etc. But if electronic presentation becomes the prescribed form of the future, for many women the cost of a personal computer and associated expenditure, could well become prohibitive so that the possibility of being a 'published' writer could be closed to them.

9. Some discussion of this phenomenon is beginning to take place in the academic world where tasks which were once seen as discriminatory and indicative of scholarship are now performed by software; 'spell check' for example, or reviews of the literature, and even programs which will 'lay out' manuscripts and present them according to the requirements of a particular house style, have all undermined the judgement and decision making scope of the author.

10. Mary O'Brien has pointed out that with capitalism, and the ownership of texts/ideas, came – *the footnote*; one of the means whereby intellectual property rights are established. (Private communication.)

11. I would like to thank Anna Yeatman for her comments in this area.

12. 'English' did not become a discipline at British universities until the end of the nineteenth century and it is from this base that most 'lit crit' and literary theory has originated.

13. It is interesting to note that Helen Hodgman is also a highly acclaimed fiction writer, winner of the Somerset Maugham Award and the NSW Premier's Prize.

14. For further discussion see Estelle Jelinek 1987, 'Disguise Autobiographies; Women Masquerading as Men' in *Women's Studies International Forum*, Vol. 10, No. 1; pp. 53–62.

15. See Lynne Spender, (ed.) 1989, *Her Selection*. Penguin, Melbourne.

16. Even within the European community English is enjoying greater popularity as the language or print – particularly with the end of 'foreign language rights' in that community; Departments of English as the International Language and 'Englishes as World Language' are also being established within different universities (e.g. University of Illinois, Urbana, USA).

❧ BARBARA JEFFERIS

Barbara Jefferis was born in Adelaide and began to
earn her living from writing in Sydney, in journalism.
She moved into radio, writing more than fifty dramas
and dramatised documentaries for the ABC, along
with serials, scientific and schools' programmes. She
has also been for many years a regular reviewer for
the *Sydney Morning Herald* and the *Australian*.

The author of nine novels – published simultaneously in America and England, and translated into
European and Asian languages – she has also written
a travel book, biography, and publications for the
Society of Authors (she wrote *A Guide to Book Contracts*
and *The Good, the Bad and the Greedy*, and as a very
active member of the Society she formulated its
Upfront Book Contract and played an influential part
in setting up Public Lending Right). In 1986 she was
made a Member of the Order of Australia for her
services to literature.

Barbara Jefferis has always been *a writer*. About half
of her fiction is contemporary, the other half set in
the remote past. She says 'It makes me wince to hear
it described as "historical". It's not, in the accepted
sense of being fiction that tries to reconstruct actual
people and events. What I do is, I hope, different –
subversive and more than a bit anarchic.

'I'm against all forms of gadzookery and the way
the past is patronised, as though people are
intrinsically quaint just because they've been dead a
long time. The received wisdom about women comes
from the printed sources, and *they* give us no more
than a picture of what women ought to have been, if

they had fulfilled the expectations of the men who made the rules.'

The questions Barbara Jefferis asks, help to frame a very different female tradition.

'Were women cravenly god fearing? So dumb that they couldn't see a correlation between the persecution of witches and the church ban on contraception? Did they really believe they had smaller souls than their brothers? Weaker intellects? Less courage? Inferior moral perceptions? What, all of them?' And these are not just issues of the dim, distant past: 'My *Drover's Wife* brings the same questions forward seven centuries. She has a proper sense of her own worth, and she knows the history of women – or of any single woman – isn't quite the way men have always wanted to hear it told.'

Among her publications are;

1953 *Contango Day*. Dent, London. Morrow, New York.

1955 *Beloved Lady*. Dent, London. Morrow, New York.

1959 *Half Angel*. Dent, London. Morrow, New York.

1961 *Solo for Several Players*. Dent, London. Morrow, New York.

1963 *The Wild Grapes*. Michael Joseph, London. Morrow, New York.

1967 *One Black Summer*. Hart-Davis, London. Morrow, New York.

1974 *Time of the Unicorn*. Gollancz, London. Morrow, New York.

1978 *The Tall One*. Gollancz, London. Morrow, New York.

Biography

1982 *Three of a Kind*. Sisters, Melbourne.

The Drover's Wife

It ought to be set straight. All very well for them to spin yarns and make jokes but nobody has written any sense about me. Nobody has even given me a name except one and he got it wrong and said I was called Hazel. The drover's wife, the doctor's wife, the butcher's wife. You wouldn't think of all the countries the one where women are the fewest would be the one where they don't exist, where men'll say 'the missus' sooner than give a name. Small wonder the Eyetalian got his facts wrong and said there weren't any women in the country for the first hundred years. I had to laugh. I don't know why; it isn't funny when you think about it.

I better say first who I am. I'm forty-six years old. I have four children, all of them boys. My womb has fallen, so've most of my teeth, but I've got a straight back and a good head of hair and I can match anyone on a hard day's work. I know seventy-three poems off by heart and I'm not afraid of the dark.

I was born somewhere on the stock route between Tibooburra and Broken Hill; nobody ever told me exactly where.

My father was a drover. Times there was no stock to be moved he dug dams or went fencing – hard grafting for very little money. He died quietly one night by his campfire without saying a word to anyone. I was twelve.

We weren't on the road with him. We had a shack out of Nyngan – my mother, my two brothers, my sister Bessie and me. Ma was a hard-handed woman. I never saw her after I cleared out with the dentist but sometimes still I dream I run into her. I'm glad to wake up.

The boys cleared out as soon as the first was old enough. We never did hear what became of them. We had a few acres and three cows and some pigs and fowls. It wasn't much of a life. Ma took up with a shearer when I was fourteen and *she* cleared out for six months. It was better there without her than with her. Then they both came back and the next thing was Bessie ran off with a Bananalander. I'd like to see old Bess again; I really would, but she was never much for writing letters so there wasn't anything I could do, not knowing where she was. She's forty-nine now, if she's alive.

That left me stuck there two years with them, like a bandicoot on a burnt ridge. I gave as good as I got but I took the first chance that offered to get out of it.

Now it's a matter of what each of them had to say – answering it. Take them as they came. Mr Lawson first. He didn't mean me any harm, far from it. But men can only see women as being heroines when they do something a decent man would do for them if he happened to be around, like killing a snake or an injured calf, or hauling a rotting sheep carcass out of the well.

He was a nice little bloke, Mr Lawson. No bother to anyone, quiet, deaf, drank too much. Every man I've had to do with from my own dad down to the drover drank too much on occasions, but very little was too much for Mr Lawson and it didn't seem to make him happier any longer than the time it took to get it down his gullet. He was a good listener – the best I ever knew in those dry times when there wasn't much listening going begging for ones like me who'd spend weeks talking to the flies on the wall. And he really listened. You could tell because he'd ask things, wanting more.

So I told him a lot. Talked too much – must've – because some of it he took and turned into that story about the snake, as though what I'd really told him wasn't true or wasn't fit. His snake story was true enough. Nobody goes to sleep with a black snake under a floor that's got gaps in it in a room that's full of children. Yes, I watched; I had a candle going and a green sapling close at hand and Alligator in with me because he was a champion snake-dog all his life till a big brown brute got him down at the dam. Mr Lawson made it a great and terrible night. It wasn't. I've spent great and terrible nights.

Like the one I told him about. Joe was droving and the baby was ten months old the time it happened. He was the one Mr Lawson mentioned that I had without anyone with me, only the old black woman, Mary. I was into my time and Tommy and Billy both in the cot together and me blind silly with the pain and the fear of what'd happen to them if I died, which can happen. And her ugly face came in at the doorway. I screamed, and that set the two kids screaming. Next thing I knew she had her hands on me, and she knew what she was doing.

Only time I worried was when she went off down the cow-yard with the bucket to get some milk for the kids. I thought

she mightn't come back, being who she was. It made me feel
a bit different about the blacks and Reg was as fine a baby as
the others had been, and fatter.

Until he was ten months old. One moment he was as bonny
as usual, the next he was screaming and going into a fit. I got
the tub and the hot water the way I'd been told but had never
needed before. It was no good. I got the dog in and threw the
tub of water on the fire and banged the door and left the kids
yelling in the dark hut with only Alligator to mind them.

He took another fit in my arms while I was catching Roley,
and another on the ground while I was saddling up. Then I
don't know how many more there were. Roley wasn't a fast
horse but he was a stayer and we would have made the nineteen miles in an hour and a half. We'd gone maybe ten miles,
perhaps eleven, when the baby had another fit and right at
the height of it everything stopped. I knew he'd gone.

I got down, holding him, and lay down with him behind
some bushes. I don't know how long I was there. When I do
remember again there was enough light, starlight I suppose,
to see Roley, off a hundred yards grazing. I was lucky he'd been
trained not to light out for home.

But I wasn't thinking of home. I could only think of the baby.
I was hugging him, crying and talking, kissing him, closing his
eyelids and then opening them up again, trying to push my
tit into his mouth. You do strange things when you're by yourself at a death. I must have been there a long time. He began
to get cold. I put him inside my clothes and caught Roley and
went home.

The dog got up when I opened the door, but the boys were
asleep with their arms round each other. It was near dawn. I
got the spade and went out. It took me a long time to dig deep
enough, being a dry year and my head full of strange fears out
of things I'd read about vampires and wolves' claws digging
him up. It was when I had finished and was making it all tidy
that I suddenly felt the pains, and there was no mistaking what
they were. I could have gone back, but what was the point?
The kids would have woke and asked about their brother. All
I could do was what the black gins do – scrape a hole in the
ground and squat over it, waiting for what was to come to
come. I would have given Roley and his saddle and bridle then

for a sight of Black Mary, but there was nothing there but small trees and the dry ground and the grey light that said it was nearly sun-up.

It hurt me a lot for a little thing no bigger than a small peach with the stone out of it. I covered it up and went back, gathering sticks on the way, knowing I'd have a wet stove to work at before I could boil the kettle and start the day. But later, when I had the fire going and the children were fed and playing round the woodheap, what with the sadness and no sleep and the sick fancies I had about wolves and that, I went back and scratched the soil off the hole and took the thing back with me and lifted the lid of the stove and dropped it into the heart of the fire. I don't know why I did that.

That was the story I told Mr Lawson a long time afterwards, or at least the parts of it that were all right to tell to a man. Funny the way he was more taken by a snake story, the sort that happens to everyone two or three times in a year. But that was the thing about him. Nervous. A nervous man who could never write about things as they really were but only about how they would have seemed to be if he'd been what he would have liked to be.

Gloomy, that, but I wanted to tell it just to show how wrong they are when they write about us. They don't understand the strength women have – won't see it, because they think it takes away from them. Not that I'm gloomy much, far from it. Wasn't it the dentist said I had a silly streak? Well, fair enough, if that's his name for someone who laughs a lot and can see the funny side.

Mr Lawson could laugh himself when he felt at his ease and had half a pint of tanglefoot under his belt, but it's a funny thing about humorous men – they don't go much on other people's jokes, only liking to work them over into something funnier for themselves.

He said another thing that wasn't right; he said 'As a girl she built the usual air-castles, but all her girlish hopes and aspirations are dead. She finds all the excitement and recreation she needs in the *Young Ladies' Journal*, and, Heaven help her, takes a pleasure in the fashion-plates.'

Who says they're dead? Who thinks that hopes and aspirations have anything much to do with expectations? Even the hardest times don't stop your fancies, don't stop a woman being broody, trying to hatch out stones like an old hen we had when I was a kid. And times haven't all been hard, not by a long chalk.

Hardest thing of all for women is that everything they do is for un-doing. It's not like sinking fence-posts or putting up a shed. *They'll* last, maybe fifty years if they don't get burnt. But the work a woman does hardly lasts a minute – if it's not mouths today it's moths or mould tomorrow, and the whole lot's got to be done over again. You have to laugh sometimes at the way your hard work goes down people's throats or under their dirty boots. Either that, or lash out with the copper stick. Best to laugh if you can and get on with it.

Another thing; didn't he notice the hut was papered floor to roof with pages from the Bushman's Bible? Perhaps he thought I put them up and never looked at them again. I put them up for two reasons – they were all pieces that were worth keeping to read again, and because they were the best thing I had for teaching the boys something a bit better than the simple rubbish out of school readers. Well, for three reasons, the third being that the walls looked better covered than bare.

If he'd looked he would have seen one of his own *Bulletin* stories. There was *Telling Mrs Baker* stuck right along under the shelf we kept the plates on. His idea of a good woman – a fool who'd believe anything she was told even when the truth was plain in front of her face. But I had it up there for the words, and the beautiful way he had of using them.

That's something I got from my dad. He had a way with words and a great belief in them. He used to say, 'No one knows what's coming after you die, or if anything's coming at all. Best you can do is stuff you head with words and poems and things to think about, just in case that's all you're going to have to keep you happy for ever and ever.' Well, he's gone now, so he knows what the answer is. It makes me laugh to think of him up there somewhere, spouting out all those verses from the *Bulletin*, loud-voiced.

Come to think of it, if you count hymns I know a lot more than seventy-three poems. Some of them must be by poets. Only a poet could have thought of 'blinded sight'. It doesn't make any sense but it's beautiful enough for me to think of it six times a day. And the one that says 'Before the hills in order stood.' I like that. I suppose it's because all around here it's so flat and there's no hills to make you lift up your eyes. I suppose the best thing you could take with you when you die is some words you've put together yourself into a poem. But you try it; it's not as easy as it looks.

I wish they had more poems from women. I don't mean I like them just because they're women's poems, but some of them really get into the heart of things. Everyone says Mrs Browning but for me they're like men's poems, written on ruled lines. Christina Rossetti – there's a name. I wonder if it's made up, like The Banjo and The Breaker and Ironbark and the rest of them. Not that she's in the *Bulletin*, but I bought a fourpenny *Goblin Market* once in Sydney. Something to think about in the next world, if my dad's right. And I know some others of hers, too. 'Sing no sad songs for me.' That's a fine poem, sad and funny too, if it means what I think it does.

The next one was Mr Drysdale. He did no harm, except to my vanity, which I wouldn't have if all my hopes and aspirations were dead. He knew the place, give him his due. He didn't sit down in George Street and try to imagine it. You can smell the dust and the ants squashed under your feet, and you can hear the crows when you look at it, even though they're not there. He made me into a black dress over a big belly. And the feet! Could have been size eleven. And a soft look like butter wouldn't melt to my face. But he knew it; he knew how the ground reaches up into you.

Then there was Murray Bail. I never remember seeing him, though he may have called himself something different then. He doesn't sound like one from our part of the country – more like a cow cocky, from the river areas. He must've known the dentist, but.

He never could tell the truth, the dentist. He'd never come right out and tell an honest lie, just say enough to give the wrong idea and then never a word to put it right. Like him saying about me, 'How can you tell by a face? That a woman has left a husband and two children.' I'd left a husband, all right, and *his* children, which is a different thing. Isn't anything a woman can do blacker than leaving her own kids, and that's what he was trying to make you believe.

He was a dirty man, the dentist – I didn't like him. I could tell what the night would be like by the way he came home. If his patients had been men, he'd come home wanting his tea. If they'd been women he'd come home with spit in the corners of his mouth and some of the things he wanted, in the dark with the blinds down, would've fetched him a bullet if he'd been an animal wanting them in the farmyard. Should've known, since that's the way I met him, over a rotten tooth that had to come out. Should have had more sense.

People said I'd never last, shut up in a backyard in a town. He had these two kids, poor little buggers. I was sixteen. Did what I could for them, them having no mother and him what he was. There were times I thought he was more than a bit mad – forever looking out to see who was looking in. He was very ignorant for all he had letters after his name and a brass plate. He couldn't read more than half a page of a book without getting bored and coming on words that were too big for him. I never knew him read anything much except for the racing pages in the paper and the labels on bottles, to see whether they'd thought up a better germ-killer than the one before.

All my life I never knew anyone who worried so much about germs. He was frightened of flies the way most people are of crocodiles, and a bit of fruit that hadn't been washed or a moth falling into his soup would give him something to talk about for half an hour. He says I was quiet. Well, I was while I was with him. Day to day things are for doing, not talking about, and he had nothing else.

He couldn't abide to see me chop wood or dig a hole to bury a bit of rubbish or a runover dog from the street. He'd do it himself in his good clothes and his white shirt with the sleeves rolled up and his chin stuck up on his starched collar like a sick calf trying to look over a paling fence. Poor job he'd make of it. I never knew him ever put on old clothes for a bit of hard yakka. Too afraid people would see him and think he was used to it.

That he was no bushman you could tell from the stupid thing he said, when he used a magnifying glass on Mr Drysdale's picture to see if he could tell who it was I'd gone off with. He said, 'It's my opinion, however, that he's a small character. See his size in relation to the horse, to the wheels of the cart. Either that, or it's a ruddy big horse.' Any fool could see there were two horses, and that the waggon had a centre pole, not shafts. But that was him – couldn't see what didn't interest him.

That holiday he talks about, up over Port Augusta, that was a disaster. It was supposed to be for me. He never for a moment stopped grousing – the heat, the flies, the dust, the snakes, the flies, the blacks, the cattle, the flies. Frightened. His kids liked it though. He says we only saw the drover once, boiling up on one side of the track. Gordon wanted to know where his cattle were. The drover just waved his arm, gave a grin. He was half-miling them and the grin meant the half-mile had got stretched and they'd be eating someone's good grass four days or more before anyone could cut the travelling brands out from those that belonged to the place.

We'd seen him five days before, a few miles up, and that day too I'd had a mug of tea from his billy with Gordon wandering off, too afraid of germs and the look of the thing. We didn't say much – just enough for him to know the two kids weren't mine and me to know he'd make it into Adelaide in a month with the cattle. It was how he looked – I knew he'd find me.

It's no surprise the dentist can't understand it. He could never see what it was about the country, so dry that days you could sit looking at it and your mouth would melt for the thought of a peach, maybe, or a tomato. He couldn't understand you could give up a board floor and a bit of carpet and some wax fruit under a glass bell for a shack with no floor at all in the kitchen and water that had to be carried half a mile when the tank ran dry. Lonely at times, yes, but it's quiet, and that's something.

There's more to a man than trimmed nails and a dark suit, and I'd rather have beer fumes breathed in my face than fancy pink mouth-wash.

He's never going to understand it, how I could find the drover superior. Put it down to my silly streak if you like, but we could *laugh*. We used to laugh over something or nothing, it didn't matter; just laughing because we felt good, because our skins liked each other, and our hair and teeth. Laughter doesn't last for ever any more than hair or teeth. But what I'm saying, when it all boils down and you've stopped laughing, he was a good man. Still is, even though his back's gone. And anyway, there are our kids, and bringing them up to know there are two or three more things in the world than how to break a horse and bring down a tree without smashing your fences.

Another thing he said, how a dentist can't afford to have shaky hands and how after I left him he sat for nights in the lounge with the lights out. Heart-rending, that is. Makes me laugh. The lights out and the blinds down too, I'll be bound, so's nobody passing could see the bottle on the table.

There's nothing better than rot-gut to give you a shaky hand next day, particularly if you're not eating right, and he'd never learnt to do for himself the way men learn in the bush. Truth is I worried about those kids of his when I'd left. Kay'd have been all right, but young Kev was a picky little kid, had a weak stomach.

After him, I thought I'd done with them talking about me, but then this Eyetie bloke. Dirty-minded. Hard to tell whether he's had his leg pulled or is trying to pull ours. I'll thank him all the same not to call me a sheep. You have to laugh, though. He's fallen for one of those stories they tell, round the fire. Voices carry a long way at night. I've heard worse than that. You can tell he's a foreigner by the words he uses, like 'inter-species reciprocity.' I had to first look it up and then sit and puzzle it out to mean taking a poke at a sheep. Any backblocker would have come right out with it, in four letters.

But once you've puzzled it out all you've got is the old story about someone off on his own having to do with a sheep or a pig or a cow. Only when they tell it here it's not a drover, not one of their mates, it's a half-mad manager or some rotten overseer. I don't say it never happened; they say everything you can think of happened somewhere or some time. So they say. But it's not the drovers' way. I don't have to spell it out, do I, more than that he can count on his five fingers?

It's funny to think this Eyetie chap, Franco Casamaggiore, isn't really different from any of the rest of them. Truth is there are many sorts of men, all the same; only one sort of woman, all different. We could be a lot fonder of them if only they'd admit how scared they are. Having their sex on the outside leads to a lot of boasting and worrying.

A lot of them cover it up by telling yarns. With our men it's some trollopy girl or a flash barmaid they took up with. With the Eyetalians it's animals. Same difference with the Greeks. It's rams with golden fleeces or it's white bulls or it's swans having their way with young girls. Our fellows don't go as far as that but often enough they talk about women as though they were animals – 'She's in pup,' they'll say, or 'She's running round Bourke like a slut on heat,' or 'Got to get home to the missus, she's due to drop her foal any minute.' Reason's plain enough; these are things you can own, use, brand – better or worse, batter and curse.

I'll say that for the drover; he doesn't talk about me as though I've got four legs and he doesn't think the way to praise a woman is to say she thinks like a man, acts like a man. Perhaps it's why I'm still with him, after so long. That, and the kids.

Worst thing ever happened to me was the day the baby died, losing two of them at once. And never knowing what it was I lost. Mary's black face came in at the door about a week later. I asked her about the thing I'd put in the fire. 'Inside... little man... all curled up,' she said. I'd never thought to look.

That started me dreaming. Dreams all mixed up with *Goblin Market* – golden head and long neck, dimples and pink nails. Laura like a leaping flame. One may lead a horse to water, twenty cannot make him drink. I would have called her Laura. More sensible to have called her Lizzie, for the sober sister. Put it down to my silly streak, if you like, but I would have called her Laura, and hoped she'd have some wildness and wisdom, like Miss C. Rossetti. I suppose I dreamed that dream twenty times before I wore it out. Oh well, dreams go by opposites, they say. Chances are it would have been another boy.

What I meant was to tell not so much about me and the drover and the dentist and the rest of them but about how women have a history, too, and about how the Bushman's Bible and the other papers only tell how half the world lives. You ought to be able to put it down in two words, or twelve, so people could remember. Women have a different history. Someone ought to write it down. We're not sheep or shadows, or silly saints the way Mr Lawson would have. There's more to us. More to me than any of them have written, if it comes to that.

The dentist was right about one thing, though. I'm not the drover's wife. Or only in the eyes of God if he's got any, if he's not another one with blinded sight.

DIANE BELL

Diane Bell was born in Melbourne in 1943; she grew up in Highett, Victoria, and left school the year before matriculation to attend Primary Teachers' College. Married at 22, then divorced, and with two children to support, she went to night school in 1970-71 to matriculate; it had to be humanities because she couldn't afford the practical class time for sciences. With her successful attempt at matriculation, Diane Bell gained entry to Monash University and, despite the demands of full time student, mother and breadwinner, embarked on what was to be a remarkable academic career.

From Monash University she went on to complete her Ph.D. in Anthropology at the Australian National University, and then to become Professor of Australian Studies at Deakin University – before being selected for the prestigious position of Henry Luce Professor of Religion, Economic Development and Social Justice at the College of the Holy Cross, Worcester, USA.

Running parallel to her academic appointment as Research Fellow in the Social Justice Project (ANU 1983-86) has been extensive work in applied anthropology. Diane Bell has worked as consultant to Aboriginal Land Councils, Legal Aid Services, the Australian Law Reform Commission and the Aboriginal Land Commissioner. She has given expert evidence in nine land claims and worked for the Aboriginal Sacred Sites Protection Authority.

Diane Bell's anthropological research has taken her

into Aboriginal communities where her concerns with women's religious beliefs and practices, land rights, oral history and social change, have been well expressed. She has made valuable links between Aboriginal women's customary law and the ways that Australian women's culture can be represented. She sees anthropology 'as a stance on life, rather than a set of prescriptions' and feminism, as the integrating framework for professional life and personal/political interest. 'If you ask me what I do, I say writer, anthropologist, feminist and the order is irrelevant because each shapes the other,' she comments.

A distinctive feature of her academic career is the emphasis she has placed upon writing and its potential for promoting social change; 'I write about the research I do because I believe academics have a responsibility to inform the public and I only research where I think there are important questions to be asked,' she says. 'I am concerned about the style of writing and continue to work at ways of making complex issues accessible. Much academic writing is for the privileged and not concerned with empowerment. I want to write of an Australia that offers dignity and fulfilment to all its inhabitants. I have always taken jobs which allow a considerable proportion of my time to be spent on writing and if I don't have that time, I get stressed.'

She also enjoys swimming, and cooking for ritual occasions.

She is currently working on a book, *Gendered Fields* (on gender and field work).

Among the books she has written or edited are:
1980/4 *Law, the old and the new.* Aboriginal History for CAALAS, Canberra.
1983 *Daughters of the Dreaming.* McPhee Gribble/Allen & Unwin, Melbourne/Sydney.
1984 *Religion in Aboriginal Australia.* (co-editor) University of Queensland Press, St Lucia.

1988 *Generations; Grandmothers, Mothers, and Daughters.* McPhee Gribble/Penguin, Melbourne.

1990 *This is my story.* (co-editor) Centre for Australian Studies, Deakin University, Geelong.

1990 *Aborigines and Australian Society.* UNESCO, Paris.

Sheroes of Mine

Soaring moments of triumph, tenderness, joy; searing moments of insecurity, guilt, betrayal... and how do I weave them into my known world? Am I the only one to stand on this spot? I'm an academic. Let me look to my scholarly heritage. History might reveal what led me here, but where are my female forebears? Some appreciation of genetics might explain my uniqueness, but why are other women in similar situations? The law might illuminate questions of my rights, but why does the burden of proof fall upon me? I'm a feminist anthropologist, that should help. Anthropology, 'the study of man', significantly reworked by feminists, gender accepted as an analytical category, now under siege, charged with inventing culture, anthropological authenticity critiqued, and women again lost, this time in a labyrinth of difference. There are only texts, the deconstructionists tell me. Well I yearn to rework the contexts that generate these wretched texts.

There are too many voices and too few speak to me. This world is not made in my image. It bears the names of male heroes: it is their deeds that are valourised. The language is larded with references to the male persona: only the aberrant is inscribed on mine. As a child I could look to female kin for guidance but their world is not mine. In private they railed against the injustice of their situation, their lack of opportunity, and their limited horizons, but they feared the consequences of breaking with tradition, of stepping outside the accepted space for wife, mother, sister, housewife, spinster, widow; they shied from pioneering hostile territory. In their homes, the homes of another, in institutions, homeless, alone, in the company of women, but rarely in a community of women, each generation it seems must reclaim their past. The process is private and familial, rarely public and national. 'Behind every successful man stands a good woman', was a consolation prize that was supposed to nurture us. Only the 'exception who proves the rule' was permitted to make it into the texts, but she cannot be a charter for commonplace behaviour.

Convention and canonising zealots have purged the public record of sustaining tales of proud, autonomous women, but by reading the texts against the grain, other pasts may be glimpsed, and muted voices may speak. Careful research reveals a host of women, some extra-ordinary, some ordinary, all of whom have shaped the spaces we now occupy: the shadowy spouse, the eccentric old maid, and the mad aunt, the witch, from these stereotypes emerge women who are persons in their own right. At each generation level we find women who have flown in the face of the tempest, shouted into the wind, and their voices, having been heard by those present, were blown away with the passing of the storm. Their fate is to be recalled in oral tributes and hearth histories. Fragments. If only all those lives were available. If only I could tap into those experiences, refashion them for the now, and be buoyed up by the knowledge that this was not virgin territory: my sheroes had already pioneered these spaces and their wisdom could guide, inform, empower, and nurture their heirs.

In this rich past, the narratives of my sheroes would interweave and interleave. The structuring principles, freed of chronology, could cycle through different relational moments and locate focal events in a landscape where the symbols speak to me, where I could abide. A country transformed by knowledge of other lives which, as women, are also mine. Desert landscapes of Central Australia are the only ones I know with this affection and confidence. My guides for these countries are wise in the ways of their land. Theirs is an ancient, dynamic civilisation superbly fashioned to the needs of the original peoples of this land. 'In the *jukurrpa*', my adoptive aunt is telling me, 'the *kurinpi* made this place, the old people told me. That's your place too Diane, you can follow-up for them; do the business; call out to the old people; they can hear.'

In this oral culture, it is the responsibility of the living to follow-up the narratives of the ancestors, and to find relevance in them for the living. There are no books: features in the landscape stand as testimony to the ancestral travels, and it is for the living to interpret the symbols. Old people living, and old people deceased, are brought into communication in ceremonial celebration when the ancestral past moves concurrent with the present, when the edges of identity are blurred, merged and finally forged into one. The brilliance of this Aboriginal religious philosophy of the *jukurrpa*, of the formative era when the ancestral beings pioneered the land, is the masking of its malleability. Known variously as the Law, the Dreamtime, and Dreamings, the *jukurrpa* heritage is made known through ritual re-enactment and subtly shaped to meet the needs of current generations. An all encompassing, enduring, sustaining, total world view, the *jukurrpa* is sensitive to gender, age, knowledge, human frailty, and has the capacity to accommodate change.

The narratives of the exploits of the *kurinpi* women vivify a tract of land extending from the Devil's Marbles to the Stirling Swamp in Central Australia. In the *jukurrpa* these women pioneered the land. At significant places in their travels they paused to perform particular rituals, to create and name features of the forming world. In significant encounters, especially with *ngapa* (rain), the *kurinpi* tracks criss-cross with those of other ancestors. Sacred sites, where ancestral spiritual power entered the land, are part of the heritage the living must maintain. They must follow-up the tracks, ensure the stories live, give form to the spiritual power in ceremony, and keep sacred places secure.

Within ritual recounting of the *kurinpi* narratives, a dilemma facing women is addressed, and possible outcomes explored. Here women may weigh their relationships with men as poised on a balance: tipping the scales for engaging with men is the desire for children and the company of a spouse, counterbalancing is the fear of the unpredictability of men, and men's challenge to the women's independence and autonomy. Stabilising the unsettling forces of this dilemma, is the constancy of the lives of the *kurinpi* women as ones of ritual observance and celebration of the bounty of their country.

In one account, two elderly, knowledgeable and respected *kurinpi* women, whose special power is manifest in their ability to turn red as they rub themselves with fat, travel from their swamp home in search of company. Once out of their homeland, they cease to name the country and travel more warily. They poke the ground with their spear-like sticks. As they pass from one swamp-land through another closer to Devil's Marbles, they enter a patch of tall spears. Fearing that perhaps someone might see them, they clutch their ritual packages, containing sacred objects, to themselves and continue. Several younger boys appear and dance flanking them. (This is the way of those who have responsibility through their mother's line for ceremonial performance and, in their travels, the *kurinpi* have already witnessed this ritual relationship.) The boys are carrying spears similar to the women's. The women teach the boys to throw spears in an overarm action.

The women wonder why the boys, who are also carrying ritual packages, such as are the right of older people, continue to travel with them. At the meeting, and while travelling with the boys, the women feel a mixture of shame and curiosity. Finally they reveal to each other the contents of their packages. The *kurinpi* attempt to leave, but the boys beg them to stay so they can show them everything. 'No,' says the women, 'You are too young and we are leaving.' Suddenly the boys disappear and reappear as initiated men. The women look on with amazement: these men are wearing their ritual headbands and armbands. Again the women hasten to leave and again the men beg them to stay. The women fear that these men might spear them for they now have long, strong spears such as men carry. The men follow the departing women who soon leave them far behind. 'Never mind,' say the men. 'We shall sharpen our spears, harden them in the fire, and spear the women when we catch them.'

The women say to each other, 'Come. Let them go their way. We have everything we need.' As the men travel they say, 'Let them go. We have all we need and can easily catch them later when we learn how to throw these spears.' As the *kurinpi* dance on, they see and join another group of women who are performing *yawulyu* (women's rituals for land, love and health). The men with the spears are unsuccessful in catching the women because they are not prepared to violate the restrictions of the women's ritual area. Each sex has residential and ritual spaces which are taboo to the other, and here the women are not only at a ceremonial site, they are also engaged in religious rituals.

This meeting with the boys has various connotations. Those which provide substance for reflection by current generations are the women's perception of themselves as social actors, and their relations to men. Before encountering the boys, the women had never felt shame. They had confidently and authoritatively known their country and their relationship to it. The ambiguous status of the boys is compounded by their transformation, without ritual, into men. Each is prepared to respect the ritual packages of the other, but the men rather fancy the women and decide to pursue them. The women continue to display their power by rubbing fat into their bodies and by producing colour changes. The men decide to use force and a new technology to win the women, but are thwarted when they discover the women have sought sanctuary in the company of other women.

In another account of an encounter of the *kurinpi* with men, the women do not escape, but are overpowered. In this *kurinpi* narrative, the women were returning to the camp after a day of hunting when some men began throwing stones at them. 'What is that?' asked the women. 'We want to get food, not to run away.' The women were unaware of the presence of the men. They continued home and on their way dug for grubs. One man ran after one of the women, stood on her digging stick, and asked the woman for food. They felt shamed because they had never met a man like that before. He told the women to get up and they would dig together. 'Don't be shy,' he said, 'We shall go together.' He gently took the woman by the arm and they continued together. But as they travelled and the woman left her country behind, she held back and tried to go the other way. The man crippled the woman with a spear, and as she lay naked, complaining of his cruelty, he began to beautify himself so that she would love him. He brought her animal skins to warm her body and sat with her. She tried to straighten herself but it hurt too much. She looked back to her country but knew she must leave with her husband.

As a sustaining women's narrative, this is a cautionary tale: men are so insecure that violence is the only way they can express emotion. As a vindicating male narrative, the wild are being made quiet: man tames nature. But when the text remains in its context, a key value is that women's power base is shown to be land and she acknowledges that, through marriage, men can disrupt her ties to land. The once kind suitor who took her by the arm, now spears her. Her tie to her country is also damaged. In being crippled by the spear-wound the woman is also deprived of her land. In the loss of land she loses her autonomy and power base, but he gains a wife to whom he can now afford to show affection, and from whom he now seeks love by beautifying himself. In her crippled state, she feels pain, loss of movement, and loss of land. As they continue together she sees his country, like a mirage, come up before her, and he begins instructing her in the wonders of his country. Through men, women may thus gain knowledge of another country, but the price is high. The reverse is also possible. Frequently men take up residence in their wife's country. On marriage men do not invariably succeed in carrying off young wives to another country: instead they may become part of the narratives of her land.

While travelling the *kurinpi* women take on the redness of the country. The rainbow-men they meet burst dangerously with all colours and use red of the ant-hill and green from the water to dull their brilliance. Women's and men's colours are not fixed in a colour spectrum, but are as fluid and as dramatic as the country itself, as ever changing and as unpredictable as the outcome of male–female encounters. Thus the dynamic of gender values is given metaphysical expression in ritual imagery. The rainbow-men, unsure of their ability to woo and win, decide to win then woo. They ask each other over and over again: 'Will she like me? Will we frighten them?' Once they make contact there is no standard response. Contact means that the stable, symbolically-ordered positions on the sexual axis are freed and negotiable. Like the shifts in colour, like the unpredictability of the country from which women draw their power, men constantly shift also. One brother uses soft words and beauty. He has been the confident one all along. The other uses physical force and soft words.

For the most part, in the narratives, the *kurinpi* are depicted as old, but they also appear as younger women. The desirability of women is not a function of age. They do not have a self-image of 'old hag'. Older women and men court each other and younger partners. What draws comment is the manifestations of knowledge of the *kurinpi*, not their age. The various encounters are not considered in temporal sequence, but like the women's ability to turn red and like the colours of the desert, are seen as co-existing in constant flux, and constitute an ever shifting, dynamic power on which women may draw. Different accounts are not considered as conflicting versions of the same story, but rather are taken as an illustration of the vagaries and complexities of male–female relations. At one moment in her life a woman may need reassurance that a relationship with a man will not bring violence, at another she may need the assurance that she has options; at one that his affections are true, at another that his infidelity is not to be internalised. It is not necessarily her fault if a relationship fails, but rather is one of the many possible outcomes of leaving the security of known territory, and, by way of a safety net, returning to her own country or joining a women's camp remains accessible throughout her life. As long as one remains in contact (directly or through ritual activity) with one's land, one may draw on all one's forebears for assistance, explanation, sustenance, guidance, and life itself.

Men have narratives, women have narratives: like the ancestral travellers, these accounts criss-cross, are negotiable, and co-exist in tension-ridden, knotty webs of contradictions. Women and men have their own ceremonies in which each celebrates their own connectedness to the past and gives form to their responsibilities. There are times when women and men share their narratives, each fleshing out their segment of the ancestral exploits in a joint ceremony; there are times when men are the guests of women; and others when women are the guests of men. No one context generates the evaluative frame for all texts, but the all embracing *jukurrpa* binds diverse experiences into a world view which holds explanation accessible through knowledge of the past, but cedes to the living the task of giving form to the *jukurrpa* design.

In what narratives might the newcomers to this land ground a sense of self, find a sense of place, explain the pain of loss of self in passion, seek the meaning of gender constructs, establish sanctions, maintain female solidarity? Western religions do not provide the comprehensive, interfunctional world view of the *jukurrpa*. The hierarchy is plain. Women have no female power to bestow names on the land, to generate explanatory texts, to celebrate sex-specific spaces sacred to women: to participate, women must seek concessions from patriarchal power; to ensure a proper marriage, promise to honour and obey. There is no public account of male violence as emotional insecurity: instead the narratives stress manly strength as heroic, sheroes are not canonised for making explicit their emotional needs. Frozen in non-negotiable texts of law and religion, the self-actuating woman is deemed deviant, a threat, insane, unnatural. It was not always thus. The biblical Eve, as the embodiment of original-woman, was but one persona of many contemporary narratives of women. In the gnostic texts of the late Hellenistic and early Christian period, there are multidimensional representations of women. The narratives of Lilith, in Hebrew folklore Adam's first wife, offer a lustier complex of passions. The Eve of Genesis is transfixed as mother-creator-destroyer. Feminist readings which valourise her anti-authority stance, her initiative, and her desire for knowledge, draw strength from the knowledge of the other persona.

The *kurinpi* provide the charter to create and recreate images of woman at every generation level. The living trace connections back to the *kurinpi* by reference to actual forebears who ultimately became assimilated to the domain of the mythical ancestors. One direct link is through naming. Each person has many names, some are taboo at particular times in a person's life, some may only be used by certain kin, some are ego-centric, others socio-centric. A personal name is bestowed as acknowledgement of one's heritage, and with it comes the power of those who bore that name in earlier times. When visiting a new land, one calls out to the ancestors by name and brings their past into the lives of those present. Within this schema, while in my own country, I move in a familial world where places bear personal names. My grandmother shares a name with me and her grandmother before her. In following-up through these grandmothers, I reach into the *jukurrpa*, imprint on the land, assert my right to access the *kurinpi* strength, and to read it back into the present.

So now, encouraged that there are other ways to know my world, I'm in search of narratives of sheroes to sustain my generation of women in contemporary Australian society. I'm evoking a personal name 'Elizabeth' and all her other representations, Lizzie, Eliza, Bess, Beth, Bessie, Liza, Isabella, Belle, Bethal, Liz, Libby, Elizabeta. Through her I'll trace the possibilities, the ambiguities, the contradictions and the contextualisations: she has no absolute Elizabeth manifestation, but can only be known through the forms I can give her and sustain by reference to the surviving evidence of her activities in this land. When I 'follow-up' her story now, she offers multiple readings of her Elizabethness, but I know in one of her selves, she stood where I now stand, and can speak to the dilemmas I now confront. When I, in my turn, draw on this heritage, I mould herstory into my history. She must not be lost to the next generation, for if she is, woman is also. She is woven in the tapestries of this land and the threads are testimony of her traces. I chose the name arbitrarily I thought, but then, as I began to write, I realised that Lizzie was my mother's mother's mother's name. She lived in England and it was her daughter, my grandmother, who knew this land. Maybe that trace has drawn me to the name, or maybe it is a long held belief that Elizabeth, as in Macarthur, has been poorly served by the histories of pioneering development of this land as a place for sheep and men, and I want to accord her shero status.

From Elizabeth Macarthur, 1766–1850, we hear an educated woman speak of her role in 'inventing' the social norms of colonial married life. This Elizabeth arrived in her new land in 1790 on the second fleet. Her husband spent many years in England and during his absence she managed their property, Elizabeth Farm. Her sons went to school in England, and after a separation of nine years, reappeared as men. Their transformation, like that witnessed by the *kurinpi*, announced a new relationship: these men would henceforth direct the business. 'Macarthur', an identity imprinted on towns, rivers, schools and bank notes, evokes masculine deeds: Elizabeth's has remained localised, imprinted on the farm.

In letters home, Elizabeth offers a social history of the new land, documents her preoccupations, explores how she relates to the new land and its black inhabitants, and projects a strong sense of self. The narrative is not one of unrelenting domesticity, but of naming her new world. Her first letters to her mother concern her child's health, make mention of that of her husband, and document tasks of household management. The mother–daughter tie, rendered invisible by family histories which trace descent through men, is strongly evidenced. As part of maintenance of women's lore, this Elizabeth writes to women friends: on marriage she offers the advice, 'choose an equal'. Communication with relatives in England was only possibly by sea mail, or in other words, the ritual exchanges of women were constrained by circumstance.

Elizabeth's sacred site, the place where her narratives now rest, the Mitchell Library, Sydney, will yield much of the shero activity of the colonial period. For all those Australian women who worked beside their menfolk in establishing farms; for all those women who worked alone; for those women who provided logistic support for their farmer brothers, fathers, sons and partners; could they not have 'shero Elizabeth', Mother of the Merino sheep industry? A contemporary shero, Eliza Forlonge, 1785–1859, who arrived in Australia in 1831, had already studied the sheep industry; had arranged for her sons to be suitably trained; and had hand-picked her flock. Pioneering a landscape further south, in what is now Victoria, she is remembered in a sundial at Kenilworth and a monument at Euroa, but not yet as part of a tradition of pastoral sheroes.

Convict women wrote new scripts in the land to which they had been transported, but the traces are faint, and rarely do we hear their voices. These women appear in routinely generated records, as statistics, rarely as full people. We know little of the everyday humdrum of making out in a foreign land. Their pioneering deeds in raising children, coping with the vicissitudes of male–female relations, mapping survival strategies, are subjects of speculation not an indelible imprint. And, their journeys in the new country were easily curtailed. Elizabeth Foxall, 1803–1840 arrived on the *Princess Royal* in 1828. Her husband had been transported a year earlier, but they were never reunited. With a vision of a better life, she attempted to marry a fellow convict and together they planned to open a small business. But their letters seeking the right to marry were intercepted, lost, misfiled, and her earlier marriage proved to be an insuperable obstacle. She died worn out, lonely and dispirited, aged thirty-six. The differences between her narratives and those of the 'Pure Merinos' illuminate the distance between convict and free.

Reclamation of convict sheroes is thwarted as names change and are mis-spelt, as these women move in and out of temporary liaisons and de facto relationships. Negotiating relationships with men of some standing was one route to security. Eliza Batman, 1802–1852, also Callaghan, Thomson, Batman, Willoughby, and near the end of her life, Sarah, comes to our attention through her marriage to John Batman. For a short time the marriage brought stability to her life. John, a native-born son of a convict, is remembered for his 'treaty' with the Aborigines in his attempt to purchase land at Port Phillip: Eliza's changing life fortunes tell us of the convict mothers of the nation. Eliza was transported for fourteen years to Van Dieman's Land in 1821, a long sentence for a woman. As an assigned servant she found ways of dealing with sexual abuse from her colonial masters. When she married John in 1828, they already had three children. He died of syphilis in 1839: Eliza, now mother of eight, fell on hard times. Her next marriage failed. Her only son drowned tragically. She cut a lock of hair and sent it to her daughter. The accompanying letter is the only self-authored trace we have of Eliza: the gentle Christian sentiments of that text contrast with the violent murder of Eliza in a drunken fight in 1852.

Arriving in Sydney on the *Superb*, in February 1838 from Ireland, my next tradition-generating shero, Eliza Dunlop, 1796–1863, took the opportunity to study local languages and songs of Aborigines in her new land, and to write poetry. Fragments of her Aboriginal vocabularies survive in the Mitchell Library, obviously a sacred site where many tracks intersect. Other traces of her travels are in court records of the Myall Creek massacre trials. This was the first occasion on which whites were successfully tried for murder of Aborigines. Outraged by the testimony of one defendant who said, 'Only one female and her child got away from us', Eliza wrote 'The Aboriginal Mother' which concludes with this challenge:

To tell of hands – the cruel bands – that piled the fatal pyre;
To show our blood on Myab's ridge, our bones on the stockman's
fire.

Relationships between immigrant and Aboriginal women in
the colonial period were fraught with misunderstandings but
also evidence flashes of sisterhood. The shero of Elizabeth Farm
was moved by Aboriginal women's gentle handling of their
babies, but thought their status akin to that of slaves. Unlike
the colonial model of upper class female gentility, the Aboriginal women worked at making tools and Elizabeth observed
them dexterously paddling about in boats. Two centuries later
Australian feminists are keen to make it possible for women
to work in traditionally male trades, and to improve working
conditions for all women. Appreciations of economic independence and notions of what are the proper activities of woman,
have undergone remarkable changes. Nineteenth-century
images of femininity entailed cultivating the gentle arts. For
Aboriginal women, convict women, immigrant women, poor
women, these were not sustaining skills or empowering images
for women.

Bessy Cameron, 1851–1895, encouraged to emulate the
model of the refined lady, found the colonial narratives hostile.
Born in Western Australia, given a good Christian education,
an accomplished pianist, chosen by Moravian missionaries to
teach other Aboriginal women, Bessy had come to expect more
of life than the paternalists had in mind for her. Her desire to
marry a similarly educated man was thwarted and, in keeping
with the missionary perception of her proper place, she was
married off to a peer. While 'marry an equal' was sage advice
from shero Elizabeth, shero Bessy did not share her privileges:
she was black and poor. Marriage limited her options for she
was now seen as the Aboriginal wife of an Aboriginal man,
not an educated woman pursuing a career. Torn from the
narratives of her place, and with no way of engaging with
those of her new situation, her life became one of despair. She
fought to stop her children being taken to be brought up
'white', as she had been. Traces of her travels are in the narratives of countless Aboriginal mothers, lamenting the stolen
generations, the children taken from Aboriginal mothers under

policies of protectionism, segregation and assimilation. If Bessy's narrative had been a cautionary account, could Aboriginal women have been empowered to keep their children? If the right to work had been seen as a measure of independence, not a demeaning of one's femininity, might there have been greater solidarity between Aboriginal and white women?

In the revitalised narratives of this land, Bessy's pioneering travels could cross over those of other women for whom the Christian religion was a major life context. Eliza Hassall, 1834–1917, grand-daughter of a founding 'hero' of the colonial regime, the Reverend Samuel Marsden (the flogging parson of Parramatta), never married, but dedicated her life to the care of her mother and the training of missionaries. With some intersection of narratives addressing the patriarchal impositions religion placed on women, the contradictory premises of Christianity may have been revealed. On one hand women's moral superiority was vaunted as a blessed brake on men's baser instincts, while on the other her spiritual unworthiness kept her out of office. Eliza Pottie, 1836–1907, evangelist and social reformer, offers another outcome of an encounter with religion and patriarchy. This shero, supported by her husband in her commitment to numerous women's causes, established a refuge for unmarried mothers. Or, we could hear from Kezia Elizabeth Hayter, a protégée of Quaker Elizabeth Fry. As an agent of Mrs Fry's 'Ladies Committee' this shero emigrated to Tasmania where she worked with women convicts. Her struggle with her 'guilt ridden vision of religion', is recorded in her diaries, surely one of the most common, yet vulnerable, store houses of women's lore. 'I have much to learn to subdue in myself before I shall be worthy to be the most obedient and gentle wife to you I desire to be', wrote this troubled shero of marriage in 1942.

The centrality of negotiating a space for self in marriage, of maintaining an identity, is a leitmotif of women's narratives through the nineteenth into the twentieth century. Shero Bessie Harrison Lee, 1860–1950, writing in *Marriage and Heritage* (1893) offered some alternatives. Raised by an Irish aunt from the age of nine, Bessie was counselled to 'be diligent', and to 'keep thyself pure'. It was advice she took to heart, but her clever interpretations of the charter of female purity entailed that men exercise responsibility in all their relations with women, exposed double standards in the bedroom and the workplace, and struggled with contradictions which confront contemporary feminists. Her ideas and strategies to relieve women of the burden of child rearing and male demands (domestic and sexual) were developed in relative isolation, but hers was an idea whose time had come. Twenty years later her ideas were echoed in the 'Votes for Women and Purity for Men' catch cry of the English suffragettes. Bessie remained childless through two marriages. Her first husband saw her as unique: her second travelled with her, and provided financial support. The narrative of this union charts a space in marriage which is woman-centred. When he proposed, Bessie objected that she would be no use as a farmer's wife. Reversing the roles, he replied: 'I do not wish you to be a farmer's wife. I want to be a missionary's husband.'

Other sheroes, advocating women's rights, brought to public awareness issues of special concern to women. Their honourable traditions, carefully reclaimed by the present generation of feminist scholars, trace paths which connect, overlap and enhance current shero activity. Elizabeth Hanretty, founding member of the Women's Employees' Mutual Association, which continued until 1917, was involved in Labor Party politics, and particularly the Anti-Conscription campaigns. Elizabeth Nicholls, President of the Women's Christian Temperance League in South Australia, in 1896 was advocating involvement in public policy including public positions for women. Sarah Elizabeth Jackson, 1890–1923, with an M.A. in Philosophy, found an educated woman 'has nowhere to plant the sole of the foot'. Eliza Fewings, 1857–1940, headmistress of Brisbane Girls' Grammar school, was fired after a complaint to the all male board. But she was not to be written out of the script of women's education. She immediately established her own school, which by 1903 was the largest girls' school in Queensland. Their narratives weave diverse themes – education, public service, unionism, temperance, peace, discrimination, alienation – into their separate worlds and their shared spaces.

Bessie Guthrie, 1905–1977, daughter of Jane Elizabeth, reared and privately educated by her Scottish spinster schoolteacher aunts, was advised, 'Never iron men's shirts'. Bessie's narratives have much in common with nineteenth-century sheroes and generated new contexts for contemporary sheroes. As designer, publisher, feminist theorist and activist, she pioneered new territory. War time paper shortages ended the work of her Viking Press, established in 1939, which published anti-war material and poetry including that of Elizabeth Riddell and Elizabeth Lambert. She was not deterred: in the 1970s she worked with the *MeJane* collective, Australia's first Women's Liberation paper. During the war she was head draughtswoman at Hawker de Havilland's experimental aircraft (gliders) factory. After the war she worked with the Young Women's Christian Association, not because of any commitment to Christianity but because of her commitment to the education of young women. She also worked to raise public consciousness of the plight of young women in trouble, provided them with refuge, and had one wall in her inner suburban Sydney home as a message exchange for girls in trouble. Like the *kurinpi* she understood the strength of shared experience; of female insights; and she worked hard to secure places. One of her sacred sites must surely be the Elsie Women's Refuge she helped to found. When Bessie died in 1977, women gathered outside her place to recall her work, women carried her coffin, and women sang over her. These mourning rituals for Bessie puzzled police who stopped the procession: Is this a funeral? Could women celebrate their own sheroes in ceremonies they created and managed? Was there no need for male approval?

The imprint of women's narratives on public spaces, decision-making, and resource allocation has been nourished, redrawn, reinvigorated, and recast by femtheorists, femactivists, and femocrats. These sheroes have rejoiced in the recovery of herstory and recoiled at the vehemence of the resistance to their vision. Just as it appeared women had a space, shifting fortunes destabilised their endeavours. Elizabeth Reid, a pioneering first, appointed as women's advisor to Prime Minister Gough Whitlam in 1973, transformed policies, was constantly harassed by media, starved of resources, and in 1975, when transfer of office was proposed, resigned. The continuing narrative of the journeys of that office, illustrate well the need for a secure site. But the traces of this generation of sheroes will not be lost. The narratives will be interwoven. Future political sheroes turning to the annals of the Women's Electoral Lobby (1972–), will learn that the founding sheroes were unaware of previous Australian feminist surveys of candidates for political office.

The contexts within which the texts are now generated have women-centred charters; have written the scripts critiquing patriarchal power; have exposed the contradictions of organised religions and the double standards operating in the worlds of morality, politics and economic reward. The collective memories are well documented and organisations provide foci for shero activity. There are places where a woman may plant the sole of her foot. Our writing sheroes, like Elizabeth Windschuttle, editor of *Women, Class and History* (1980), will ensure we are not cut off from our past. Nor will this generation remain isolated. Australian sheroes have an international context. March 8, International Women's Day, is their sacred day too.

Tracing the travels of my Elizabeth sheroes, we have coloured in the maps of women. Their narratives like those of the *kurinpi* deal with conflicts, tragedy, triumph, loss, victory, relations with men, the need for a place to abide. The outline of the map is known to heroes also, the critical factors and actors appear in any history: the sequential litany is known – Aborigine, convict, colonialist, sheep, gold, boom, bust, self-government, suffrage, federation, war, depression, war, boom, immigration, social movements and global issues. But women with knowledge of shero deeds may elaborate this design in a way which is appropriate for her needs, may bend and blend chronology. Shero narratives issue in many forms, today radical and socialist, liberal and marxist feminists pioneer the land. The needs of current generations are many, they shift, they defy categorisation, but somewhere, there is a shero whose story could sustain. Evoke a name, tease out the traces, celebrate the narrative, Shero …

Notes

The narratives are based on my research of Elizabeths in Australian History, but rather than reference the material in the text, I list below, in order of appearance of the shero, the sources on which I drew.

Elizabeth Macarthur, Dale Spender (1988: 11–33);
  M. Barnard Eldershaw (1988: 3–25)
Eliza Forlonge, Audrey Hudspeth (1988: 4–5)
Elizabeth Foxall, Babette Smith (1988: 71–6, 118)
Eliza Batman, Max Cameron (1987: 3–12)
Eliza Dunlop, Heather Radi (1988: 7–8)
Bessy Cameron, Heather Radi (1988: 58–9)
Eliza Hassell, Winifred Ward (1988: 30–31)
Eliza Pottie, Judith Godden (1988: 35–6)
Kezie Elizabeth Hayter, Miriam Dixon (1976: 68)
Bessie Harrison Lee, Patricia Grimshaw (1987: 139–47)
Elizabeth Hanretty, Margaret Allen et al (1989: 216)
Elizabeth Nicholls, Margaret Allen et al (1989: 270)
Sarah Elizabeth Jackson, Margaret Allen et al (1989: 269–71)
Eliza Fewings, Pat Noad (1988: 66)
Bessie Guthrie, Sue Bellamy (1988: 220–22)
Elizabeth Reid, Norma Grieve and Ailsa Burns (1986: 61, 63);
  Marian Sawer and Marian Simms (1984: 175–76)

Acknowledgements

I gratefully acknowledge permission of publishers Allen & Unwin to draw on material from *Daughters of the Dreaming* (1983).

Bibliography

Allen, Margaret, Mary Hutchinson and Alison Mackinnon 1989, *Fresh Evidence, New Witnesses: Finding Women's History*. South Australian Government Printer, Adelaide.
Bell, Diane 1983, *Daughters of the Dreaming*. Allen & Unwin, Sydney.

Bellamy, Sue 1988, 'Bessie Guthrie (1905-1977) feminist', in *200 Australian Women*, ed. Heather Radi, pp. 220-22.

Cameron, Max 1985, 'The rise and fall of Eliza Batman', in *Double Time: Women in Victoria - 150 years*, eds Marilyn Lake and Farley Kelly. Penguin, Melbourne, pp. 3-12.

Dawson, Madge and Heather Radi (eds) 1984, *Against the Odds: Fifteen Professional Women Reflect on their Lives and Careers*. Hale & Iremonger, Sydney, pp. 257-72.

Eldershaw, Flora (ed.) 1988, *The Peaceful Army*. Penguin, Melbourne.

Eldershaw, M. Barnard 1988, 'The Happy Pioneer: Elizabeth Macarthur', in *The Peaceful Army*, ed. Flora Eldershaw. Penguin, Melbourne, pp. 3-25.

Dixon, Miriam 1976, *The Real Matilda*. Penguin, Melbourne.

Grieve, Norma and Ailsa Burns (eds) 1986, *Australian Women: New Feminist Perspectives*. Oxford University Press, Melbourne.

Godden, Judith 1988, 'Eliza Pottie (1836-1907) evangelist and reformer', in *200 Australian Women*, ed. Heather Radi, pp. 35-6.

Grimshaw, Patricia 1985, 'Bessie Harrison Lee and the fight for voluntary motherhood', in *Double Time*, eds Marilyn Lake and Farley Kelly, pp. 139-147.

Hudspeth, Audrey 1988, 'Eliza Forlonge (1785-1859) pastoralist', in *200 Australian Women*, ed. Heather Radi, pp. 4-5.

Lake, Marilyn and Farley Kelly (eds) 1985, *Double Time: Women in Victoria - 150 years*. Penguin, Melbourne.

Noad, Pat 1988, 'Eliza Fewings (1857-1940) headmistress', in *200 Australian Women*, ed. Heather Radi, pp. 66-7.

Radi, Heather (ed.) 1988a, *200 Australian Women: A Redress Anthology*. Women's Redress Press, Sydney.

— 1988b, 'Eliza Dunlop (1706-1880) ethnographer', in *200 Australian Women*, ed. Heather Radi, pp. 7-8.

— 1988c, 'Bessie Cameron (1851-1895) Aboriginal Leader', in *200 Australian Women*, ed. Heather Radi, pp. 58-9.

Sawer, Marian and Marian Simms 1984, *A Woman's Place: Women and Politics in Australia*. Allen & Unwin, Sydney.

Smith, Babette 1988, *A Cargo of Women: Susannah Watson and the Convicts of the Princess Royal*. New South Wales University Press, Sydney.

Spender, Dale (ed.) 1988, *The Penguin Anthology of Australian Women's Writing*. Penguin, Melbourne.

Ward, Winifred   1988, 'Eliza Hassell (1834–1917) missionary training', in *200 Australian Women*, ed. Heather Radi, pp. 30–31.

Windschuttle, Elizabeth (ed.)   1980, *Women, Class and History*. Fontana, Sydney.

ROBYN ARCHER
JUDITH RODRIGUEZ

Robyn Archer

Robyn Archer was born in Adelaide in 1948 and
displayed a very early interest in music; in high
school she sang folk songs in coffee houses and after
finals competition success she appeared regularly on
Bandstand. During her university days she was
involved in drama and musical productions, and
though trained as an English teacher she was set on
a musical career – but one in which she would write
much of her material.

In 1971, after receiving her degree, she moved to
Sydney and into the club circuit, where she worked
as a solo singer/comedienne. With some teaching,
some experience as a balladeer in the cellars of a
hotel, and some success with *The Seven Deadly Sins*
(in which she sang 'Annie I', and where she became
familiar with the work of Brecht) she began to
establish her reputation as an extraordinary
performer.

In 1977 she released her first album, *The Ladies'
Choice*. Since then she has released four more albums
of her own music (including two Aria winners), and
written eighteen shows, which have had multiple
and international productions. In addition to other
honours she was recently awarded an Australian
Creative Fellowship and an honorary doctorate from
Flinders University.

Robyn Archer is aware of the double risk of being
both writer and performer. 'It's always slightly scary
going into rehearsal,' she says, 'because if someone

challenges the writing you are in a very vulnerable position.' But writing appears to be the way of the future. In a recent interview she said: 'I've been thinking that writing will become more important to me, but that's only as it should be. You can't perform for ever but you can write until almost your last breath,' she said in an interview with Peter Craven (the *Age*).

Robyn Archer's many performances include *Cafe Fledermaus, A Star is Torn, The Pack of Women*, and most recently *Le Chat Noir*. Among her books are:

1980 *The Robyn Archer Song Book*. McPhee Gribble, Melbourne.

1986 *A Star is Torn*. (with Diana Simmonds) Virago, London.

1986 *The Pack of Women*. Penguin, Melbourne.

1990 *Mrs Bottle's Absolutely Blurtingly Beautiful World-Beating Burp*. ABC Books, Sydney.

She has also written numerous articles for journals, newspapers and magazines.

Judith Rodriguez

Judith Rodriguez was born in Perth in 1936; her mother came from a Russian Jewish family, her father was an English immigrant, and her aunt was the leader of her own jazz band.

With an Arts degree from the University of Queensland, she left on a Walter and Eliza Hall Travelling Scholarship to Cambridge and later found her way to Kingston, Jamaica, where she married, and lectured in English at the University of the West Indies.

Four children and a divorce later, and after seventeen years as a lecturer at La Trobe University, Judith Rodriguez is now teaching writing at Victoria College and working on her own writing.

On being a mother and a writer, she comments: 'I've always "moonlighted", teaching writing outside my salaried job; editing, reading for publishers, reviewing and writing. I think it's the family role that makes it moonlighting. You're certainly tired the next morning. I always felt I was robbing Sibila and Domestica to pay whichever of the Muses would acknowledge what I wrote.'

Judith Rodriguez has been poetry editor for *Meanjin*, and is currently the series editor for poetry at Penguin.

With her interest in music, particularly libretti, her collaboration with Robyn Archer is not surprising. (They are also working on *The Hanging of Minnie Thwaites*, which contains many of Judith Rodriguez's lyrics.) She is also interested in art, especially print making, and in several of her eight collections of poetry, her own lino cuts appear. Among her publications are:

1976 *Water Life* (poems and lino cuts). University of Queensland Press, St Lucia.

1980 *Mudcrab at Gambaro's* (poems and lino cuts). University of Queensland Press, St Lucia.

1983 *Mrs Noah and the Minoan Queen*. Poems by Jennifer Strauss, Fay Zwicky, Antigone Kefala, Judith Rodriguez, J. S. Harry, Jennifer Rankin. Sisters, Melbourne.

1988 *New and Selected Poems* (with lino cuts). University of Queensland Press, St Lucia.

1990 *Jennifer Rankin; Collected Poems* (with biographical introduction). University of Queensland Press, St Lucia.

The Cold (poems). National Library of Australia, Canberra, forthcoming.

Poor Johanna

FOREWORD by Judith Rodriguez

In a year when I was supposed to be writing creatively, it is ever thus, I came across a snippet of newsprint that sent me into four months of feverish research activity.

Taking off from an interest in the Old Melbourne Gaol's 1890s hangees, I was reading up murders. So, though it was about a death, it was just luck the snippet caught my eyes. Low down on the page in a newspaper dated September 9, 1894, it noted that a medical practitioner called upon to certify a worker's death on a farm near Elmore, had found the worker to be a woman.

At once my mind went to Nosey Alf, Joseph (*Such is Life*) Furphy's woman disguised as a male boundary rider. Furphy finished his book in the late 1890s and published in 1903, but if Alf had a human model (and I was sure she had), Furphy might have met her years before. 1894 reports on the dead labourer included verifying details (her deformed nose, from being kicked in the face by a horse) and 'information', both true and false, far beyond the version Furphy shaped for his novel.

I asked Furphy expert, John Barnes, was there evidence in Furphy's letters of a live prototype for Alf? Exactly one letter mentioned 'Poor Johanna!' and his meeting her in Bendigo, leaving me in no doubt. I had been fortunate enough to make a wonderful discovery, the almost stranger fact that mothered Furphy's much-wondered-at strange fiction.

The article for academics is published in the periodical *Australian Literary Studies*. That was a duty. It was more exciting talking about it with Robyn Archer. Johanna should take the boards to tell her story, as she did in real life, with a 'lecture' that, like her life and Furphy's novel, must have been one long lie.

Notes to the second draft by Robyn Archer

Since the initial collaboration with Judith Rodriguez on her research to produce the first draft of *Poor Johanna* (this development kindly assisted by The Australia Council) in 1987, I have had many and varied ideas about the way the piece could go. I would like to develop it as libretto; even in its present form, there is the possibility of adaptation for a one-woman performance. The form in which it appears now runs close to that first draft, as a play without interval for four actors and a musician. Suggested doubling as follows:

JACK / JOHANNA
FIDDLER (MR McMANUS)

The figure of male authority:
MINISTER / DR HARSE / JUDGE SHADFORTH / Johanna's father, CHRISTIAN / JOSEPH FURPHY / COLONEL PRICE

Young Man:
TOM / NED / CRAVEN / DWYER / Johanna's brother, EMMANUEL / SOLDIER

Young Woman:
MISS TURNER / MUSIC HALL BAWD / DUFF / ROBINSON / Johanna's sister, THERESE / EMMY / SOLDIER

The device of Johanna's disfigurement ought to be stylised. A twisted half mask perhaps to cover one side of the face: something which can be easily removed for the flashback, and replaced again.

In design I've always felt there are great opportunities to create a stylish bush ambience both in sound and setting. Again I would prefer something simple and stylised, and have in mind the abstract sound/land-scapists.

In scenes 7 and 10, the speeches and directions in quotation marks are Furphy's own words from *Such is Life*, and the conversation in scene 7 draws heavily from that meeting in the book.

Poor Johanna is dedicated to the memory of my grandparents, Theodore and Agnes Wohling (RA)

SCENE I : A Sunday Afternoon Lecture

[*The sound of a small gathering of people. The fiddle plays the hymn, 'All Things Bright and Beautiful'.*]

MINISTER: Our pleasant Sunday afternoon, year of our Lord, 1892.

We continue to meet once a month in the spirit of love and community.

Refreshments afterwards – my good wife, and the ladies of the parish...

But to begin the proceedings, Miss Turner, Mr McManus to accompany – their delightful rendition, *The Banks of the Condamine!*

[MISS TURNER *and the* FIDDLER *take the stage. She sings sweetly.*]

The Banks of the Condamine (trad.)

Hark hark the dogs are barking
My love I must away,
For the lads they're all horse-breaking;
No longer can I stay.
I'm bound for the camp, love;
'Tis many a weary mile
To join those jolly horse-breakers
On the banks of the Condamine.

Oh Willie, dearest Willie
Don't leave me here behind
To curse and rue the day that
You ever learnt to ride;
For parting with my own true love's
Like parting with my life.
Why don't you be a selector
And I will be your wife?

I'll cut off all my yellow locks
And go along with you
Put on a pair of moleskins
And be a rider too;

I'll cook and boil your billy while
At riding you do shine,
And I'll wash your dirty moleskins
On the banks of the Condamine.

Oh Nancy, dearest Nancy
With me you cannot go
For the boss has just gave orders –
No females there, you know.
Your delicate constitution's
Not equal unto mine;
Then you could not ride an outlaw
On the banks of the Condamine.

[*The* MINISTER *leads applause.*]

MINISTER: A gift, a gift.
Thankyou Miss Turner – and Mr McManus
More later, I feel, if we may prevail...
And now, this wealth of talent in our small
parish – young Tom O'Connell – a recitation.
Come on Tom.

[TOM *gets up gawkily. It's obviously something he learned at school.*]

The Gallant Dane (Rodriguez)

There was a Dane who left the farm
    To sail against the foe
He'd chance his arm and take no harm
    And fetch up at Bendigo

He gave no thought to girls or gain –
Hip Hooray! for the gallant Dane

There was a Dane escaped shipwreck
    As after he could brag,
He strode his deck and risked his neck
    A-showing of his flag

Them foreign gunners saw him plain –
Hip Hooray! for the gallant Dane

There was a Dane dead in their sights
    Them gunners on their toes
Their gunnery was all my eye
    And also on the nose

They popped their shells and all in vain –
Hip Hooray! for the gallant Dane

And when the Dane, he reached our shores
    To settle 'mongst us all
It wasn't long ere they knew his song
    And the neighb'ring boys would call

God keep you safe and save you pain
Hip Hooray! for the gallant Dane

[*This is followed by a spirited rendition by the* FIDDLER *of
'Marching Down to Georgia', the marching song of the Victoria
Mounted Rifles, in honour of the main speaker. The audience
is encouraged to clap along.*]

[*Encouraged by the atmosphere,* MISS TURNER *leaps forward
without further introduction.*]

MISS TURNER:

'The Lost Doll' by Mr Lewis Carroll

I once had a sweet little doll, dears,
    The prettiest doll in the world,
Her cheeks were so red and so white, dears,
    And her hair was so charmingly curled.
But I lost my poor little doll, dears,
    As I played in the heath one day,
And I cried for more than a week, dears,
    But I never could find where she lay.

I found my poor little doll, dears,
    As I played in the heath one day.
Folks say she is terribly changed, dears,
    For her paint is all washed away,
And her arm trodden off by the cows, dears,
    And her hair not the least bit curled,
Yet, for old sake's sake she is still, dears,
    The prettiest doll in the world.

[JACK JORGY, *who is perhaps seated in the front row of the audience so that we cannot yet see his face, takes out a handkerchief and sniffs away a tear.*]

MINISTER: An unexpected treat.
    Most affecting, much appreciated...
[*He indicates that the audience should give her a hand. He may also affect to wipe away a tear, or sweat...*]
    ...And now to our main event, so to speak. A man of most unusual experience, a traveller, an adventurer, but nonetheless, a man who has been welcomed as a stranger to these parts, and has shown his willingness to assist our community in a time of drought and hardship. Members of the parish – our own gallant Dane, Mr Jack Jorgy.
[JACK *rises, shakes hands with the* MINISTER, *stands and turns. His face is horribly disfigured. One side is nothing but scar tissue, the mouth distorted. Apart from this, he is stocky and strong-looking. His clothes are decent, if a bit worn, and perhaps a little loose fitting. Nevertheless,* JACK JORGY *bears himself with dignity and pride. He is a performer.*]

JACK: I thank you, Reverend Sir, and I thank you, ladies and gentlemen, that you would spare your little leisure of a Sunday to hear the words of such a humble servant as I.
    For servant have I been, to God, King and Country, since I left my father's home, and so shall I continue to be, so long as God allows this body to serve me.
    For what else is a man put on this earth to do? A woman knows her life's destiny in the family – from the time she is a mere slip of a child, her

mother is preparing her, fostering her instincts to care and to nurture the near and the dear. She will cook, she will sew, she will teach and she will keep us healthy in our abode, until such time as she herself becomes a mother to her children, a companion to her mother, and fulfils in her life, the grander cycle that God in His wisdom has blessed this world of ours with. Like the rising and setting of the sun, like the inevitable changing of one season to another, year in, year out, so a woman is at one with nature, and life and death and birth. She is truly God's creature.

But a man, a man must choose his destiny. It isn't so easy as woman's lot. There are many pitfalls, and a man is in danger of choosing the selfish path, or the path that leads to disillusion and despair. And this is why I feel it is my destiny to speak to you one and all, that my life and my past may be a lesson to any young man who may hear me.

This is truly a glorious country, with land and luck aplenty. And I tell you that the backbone of this virgin continent is the man on the land. I know, for I was raised on the land, and I toiled by my father's side, and never was there a more honourable life than that which my father led, and into which he led me.

It has served me well all my years. And there's nothing in the cities, no great men of learning or politics or law, can persuade you otherwise. The sun, the seed, the stock, the seasons, these are the sustenance of the nation, and without them the people of the nation perish. There are times, we know, when a man may be forced from his precious piece of earth. He longs for the peaceful tilling of it, his chance to nurture in the way a woman might, to care in that same way for the beasts of the earth, that bear our burdens and make light work for us. But there are the times of War, when danger threatens home and hearth and country. Then it's off we go, my gallant lads, mates in arms, sharing our last pinch of tobacco and the snatch of an old tune in that foxhole we shelter in.

Yes lads and ladies, Jack Jorgy's done his time. For he travelled the world to see God's works, and he found that wherever he went men raised arms against each other to defend civilisation. I was in the Rifles in India, a hellish place for the European. The sun beat down on us so fierce we thought to melt away ere we took a shot at the devilish breed. Disease was rife, and deadly insects swarmed the hills where we waited for a crack at 'em. Yet when it was over, the victory was ours, we marched back to camp, wounds and all, with heads held high, for we had done God's bidding...

[JACK *strikes a noble attitude, salutes, and sticks his nose in the air. A* HECKLER *calls out.*]

HECKLER: Nosey!

[*Laughter.*]

HECKLERS: [*sing-song*] Nosey! Nosey!

[MINISTER *looks horrified at this cheekiness.* MISS TURNER *wriggles uncomfortably.* TOM O'CONNELL *turns round and glares, then giggles a bit with his face away from* JACK *and* MINISTER. JACK *looks at* MINISTER *who gives him an apologetic look.*]

JACK: ...no need for embarrassment, Sir, nor you, gentle folk. I am used to these silly jibes, made in such ignorance. I am impervious to their intended insult. For would I not be a foolish soldier who wears his medals in shame? For these scars were won in glory. I wear them proudly. My face is a testimony to the peril I undertook to defend my fellow man from the savage foe. What care I for good looks? Are these not sinful vanities? What use has a man for a handsome face?

HECKLER: Well you might've gotten a bit further down the track with that little sheila from Bendigo!

[*Loud laughter, including the* FIDDLER, *who fair rocks with delight.*]

HECKLERS: Jack Jorgy's as proud as a ram
But Jack Jorgy won't jump in the dam

JACK: [*coming over the top of them.*] ... that's right. I've never been one on looks. It's all the same to Jack Jorgy. Why, once upon a time I was in Camp at Queenscliff, lending a hand to keep the peace in this very country. Held the horse I did, with a right good hand, pride of the regiment, and all the Camp knew. Yet in comes the commander, takes one look at me and says, before the whole regiment – 'When did we start enlisting Chinamen in the Victorian Mounted Rifles?'

[MINISTER, TOM, *the* FIDDLER, *and* MISS TURNER *chuckle politely, but there is unseemly laughter from the rabble up the back.*]

HECKLERS:
[*to the tune of 'Click Go The Shears'*]
And as we turned to go,
It was twenty blinking Chinamen a-shearing in a row...

[*The rabble keeps up.*]

JACK: [*aside to* MINISTER] Look here, if they don't keep it down, I'm not sure I can continue. It's unseemly...

MINISTER: I'll grant you that Mr Jorgy, but they're not normally like this, the lads. They're a good bunch in this parish, and other speakers don't have this sort of trouble. You must look to your skills Mr Jorgy.

JACK: But listen to them. They're scarcely giving me a chance. I think I should stop and have done...

MINISTER: [*leaning closer*] Mr Jorgy, I don't like to remind you that I can hardly be expected to pay the full fee we agreed upon if you fail to give us the full speech, as promised. I'm sorry...

JACK: But, Sir, I simply can't tolerate such a loss – and it's not my fault after all. It's these louts...
I'm in need, Sir – my land, a lame horse,

lost my commission in the Rifles – earning an honest living is not easy these days. Surely you wouldn't? ...

[MINISTER *shrugs.* JACK *summons up a little extra force.*]

JACK: Good now, I'm glad we've had our fun – although I hasten to add that I hope we're not mocking the Chinamen too far, my boys, for there's many a noble soul hidden inside an unfamiliar kind of face. It's the heart that counts, and the work that builds. And God knows, the Chinaman can work – work with us to build this nation. Soldiers and farmers, that's what the nation needs, that's where our future lies – freedom and food, the two great essentials of life, and the men who choose these paths are our natural defenders. Where else does manliness lie? If not in these, where else?

Here is a man who's done both in his time, and here is dignity, and worthiness in God's eyes.

[TOM O'CONNELL *is quite stirred. He applauds and encourages everyone else to join him.* JACK *nods to the* FIDDLER. MR McMANUS *has a quiet word to* JACK. *They pose themselves, ready for a song.*]

Rise, Arise

Whene'er you see the dawn
Through gum trees grey and green
Whene'er you lightly tread the bush
That man has scarcely seen
Whene'er you cross the river's run
Which was not crossed before
Think you of the nation
That has ne'er been born before

Refrain

Rise. Arise!
Like morning sun in blood red skies
Rise. Arise!
The land is lovely to its lover's eyes

77

Whene'er you hear the cry
Of bright birds on the wing
Whene'er you hear the small child's voice
Alone, he freely sings
Whene'er you smell the springtime breeze
Wafting fresh scents by your door
Think you of the nation
That has ne'er been born before

Repeat Refrain

Whene'er you feel life's cruel
And death's the only fate
Just watch the wattle blooming gold
Beside the wooden gate
Whene'er you feel the world's too small
And has not room for more
Think you of the nation
That has ne'er been born before

Final Refrain

[JACK *has given a full throated rendition of this song, and the audience shows its appreciation.*]

HECKLERS: Bravo!
               Good old Jack!
               Give us another one, Jack Jorgy!

[*The* MINISTER *shakes him by the hand and is seen giving him his fee as they exit to applause and continued shouts for 'More!'*]

SCENE 2 : A Boundary Riders' Hut

The quiet sound of early morning in the bush – almost an echo of JACK's *previous song. Magpies are carolling. The stamp and breath of* DR HARSE's *horse tethered nearby. The sound of the other* BOUNDARY RIDERS *quietly at breakfast some distance away.*

DR HARSE *enters, bag open, sleeves rolled up, businesslike. He has just examined a dead body and is about to make his report. He takes his time to sit, takes out a notebook and reads aloud as he writes.*

DR HARSE: Tuesday, 5th September, 1893.

Summoned in the early hours by one of John Wiseman's boundary riders. The boy reported the death of one of their number during the night. Rode with him from Elmore to the boundary hut, some two hours steady ride over easy bushland. Post mortem revealed heavy congestion of the lungs and respiratory tracts, and severe infection. The body showed signs of a chronically weakened chest.

The condition of the hut is extremely poor. Dirt – or mud as it is now – floor, and many cracks in the timber walls. There are few comforts aside from the small cots these people use to sleep on. Bedding inadequate, and what is there, full of ticks.

Wiseman not a bad sort of chap, but it is a shame the way these men are expected to live, to do hard physical work for so little reward. Although of interest, these details of the report will, I am certain, be overlooked, when this morning's major revelation is...

[*The young* BOUNDARY RIDER *approaches with a mug of char.*]

RIDER: Doctor? Thought you'd like something.

DR HARSE: Thanks...?

RIDER: Ned.

DR HARSE: Thanks Ned. You all right, son?

RIDER: Yes, sir. It wasn't that much of a shock, if you know what I mean. Jack wasn't all that well for a long time.

DR HARSE: Why didn't...he...come to see me?

RIDER: He didn't seem to be much interested in living. You know how some of these old bushies get? Sort of...disappointed in Life, if you know what I mean.

DR HARSE: Jack wasn't all that old, you know – about fifty.

RIDER: Is that all? Sounded like eighty, but always had a young sort of face, apart from that mess on it.

DR HARSE: Yes, I know what you mean.

79

RIDER: Doctor, the other boys wanted me just to ask, make sure sort of thing, that it wasn't anything catching...

DR HARSE: No, it was bronchial pneumonia. Not catching. But I don't know how you'll avoid it yourselves in a place like this.

RIDER: Oh we're tough enough. Not like Jack. Bit of an old softie. Shirked it on the heavy stuff, but a great cook, mind you, and I wouldn't...

DR HARSE: Ned, I think it'd be a good idea if you sat down a minute.

[RIDER NED *squats.*]

I have to tell you something that's going to come as a bit of a shock to you and the lads. Your Jack Jorgy... was a woman.

SCENE 3 : A Musical Interlude

The chorus of the song comes from the headlines that heralded the reporting of the Heathcote court case. This derivation could be indicated by screen or by business with newspapers.

A music hall BAWD *appears*

> Chorus
> A remarkable deception, a sensational career
> An extraordinary case of personation
> Concealment of her sex, a woman's milit'ry career
> Masquerading as a man. Abomination!
>
> In Heathcote in Victoria it's 1873
> They've nabbed a person wearing pants
> they say that he's a she
> I can't abide that sort of thing
> it almost makes me sick
> For a woman must be pretty
> and a man should have a...
> (*Boom, Boom*)
>   ...good suit for Sunday!

Repeat Chorus

On Saturday they found a chap
in the bush near Ballarat
He was naked as a baby
all except for his cork hat
Now everyone could see quite plain
the measure of his...
(*Boom, Boom*)
...hand
Which only shows that it ain't the clothes
that always makes the man!

Repeat Chorus

Now when a country's young like ours
one has to make quite sure
That womanhood and manliness
are governed by the law
For what is going to come
of a nation bright as this
If a woman breaks the horsies
and a man sits down to...
(*Boom, Boom*)
...mend his trousers!

Final chorus
[BAWD *exits.*]

SCENE 4 : The Heathcote Court Case

MAGISTRATE SHADFORTH *enters. He winks at the* MUSIC HALL BAWD
as she exits.

SHADFORTH: All rise for me!
[*There's no-one else on stage so he sits.*]
Police versus Johnson.
Let the prisoner be brought in.
[JACK *is brought in by the* FIDDLER. JACK *is very different
from the last time we saw him. He is timid, confused, dejected,*

silent. SHADFORTH *scrutinises him at close cruel quarters.
Then he waves him away. The* FIDDLER *places* JACK *to the
side.*]

Call Thomas Craven.

FIDDLER: Thomas Craven!

[CRAVEN *enters.*]

SHADFORTH: You've been sworn in?

CRAVEN: Yes sir.

SHADFORTH: Do you know the prisoner, Mr Johnson, here?

CRAVEN: I know this person, your worship, but I do not
know the name.

SHADFORTH: Under what circumstances do you know the
prisoner?

CRAVEN: She was in my service for six months, your
worship.

SHADFORTH: 'She' you say?

CRAVEN: Yes, sir, she was called Johanna, but I've never
heard the 'Johnson' before.

SHADFORTH: She wore female attire whilst in your service?

CRAVEN: Yes, sir.

SHADFORTH: And can you give an account of her conduct
whilst in your service?

CRAVEN: Yes sir. Johanna was always very reliable, a hard
worker...

[CRAVEN *looks at* JACK *who nods gratefully, pitifully.*]

...and her conduct was very good. I never had
a complaint of Johanna whilst she was in my
service.

SHADFORTH: Thank you Mr Craven. You may go.

[SHADFORTH *looks at* JACK *and sighs, shakes his head.*]

I shall never know what possessed you, Madam.
Call John Duff.

FIDDLER: John Duff.

[JOHN DUFF *enters.*]

SHADFORTH: You've been sworn in?

DUFF: Yes, sir.

SHADFORTH: Mr Duff, do you know the prisoner here?

DUFF: Yes sir, that's Joseph

SHADFORTH: Joseph?

DUFF: Yes sir, Joseph Johnson.

SHADFORTH: And under what circumstances do *you* know the prisoner?

DUFF: I knew Joseph for about five weeks when I engaged him to work on my land.

SHADFORTH: What account can you give of the prisoner's conduct?

DUFF: I know of nothing against Joseph's character. He was a very good and willing person to work. He always worked very hard, and I had no complaints.

SHADFORTH: And the prisoner wore male attire whilst in your service?

DUFF: Yes sir. Well he couldn't very well wear a skirt could he, considering the kind of work he was doing?

SHADFORTH: Thank you Mr Duff. You may go.
Call Constable Dwyer.

FIDDLER: Constable Dwyer.

[DWYER *enters.*]

SHADFORTH: Proceed Constable.

DWYER: Constable Ernest Dwyer, Her Majesty's Police Force, country division, Her Majesty's State of Victoria...

SHADFORTH: Proceed Constable!

DWYER: As you please, sir.
The prisoner has been a known personage to me for some five or six months, I cannot be more accurate as to the date of the commencement of my acquaintance with her.
I made an arrest on the twenty-first inst...

SHADFORTH: Constable Dwyer, did you have any provocation for this arrest? Was there a complaint, a disturbance?

DWYER: No, please your magistrate, none whatsoever. The prisoner is a personage most mild of manner, and never was there less complaint about anyone in the whole district.

SHADFORTH: Then, Constable Dwyer, may I be so inquisitive as to enquire, why, after five or six months acquaintance you decided to make an arrest?

DWYER: Well sir, it's not right is it? And as things were quiet, I thought it high time to have something done.

SHADFORTH: [*banging gavel*] Quite right! Absolutely correct! Carry on!

DWYER: I found the prisoner working at chock-and-log fencing.

SHADFORTH: That's a fair load for a woman.

DWYER: Oh aye, never was a better worker at chock-and-log than Joseph here.

SHADFORTH: Do carry on Constable.

DWYER: I made the arrest and the prisoner told me that male attire suited her better than female. She told me, sir, that whenever she put on women's clothes people would call her for a man, and say bad names at her, so that is why she took to wearing pants and such, and also better to work in.

SHADFORTH: Yes, is there more, Constable Dwyer?

DWYER: Only that she intended to work the harvest, sir.

SHADFORTH: Thank you Constable Dwyer, you may go.
              And now I call on the prisoner...

FIDDLER: Ahem.

SHADFORTH: There's more?

FIDDLER: [*very loudly*] Doctor Robinson!

SHADFORTH: Ah yes, Doctor Robinson, you've been sworn in?
              [DOCTOR ROBINSON *enters.*]

ROBINSON: I visited the defendant in the lock-up Tuesday night last. I found the defendant to be a woman.
              Upon questioning her, I discovered that she had had an injury many years ago, and that when she dressed in the attire of her own sex, she was jeered at and called names by boys. With such disfigurement, she said, it was hard to come by employment. But if she dressed as a man, this problem did not arise. Thus she could earn more money by dressing as a man. I made some enquiries as to medical history, and her ability to stick with hard labour and she said she was well used to hard work and that she meant no disturbance or disrespect, but simply wished to

earn enough money to return to her homeland, Germany.

SHADFORTH: Thank you Doctor Robinson, for your time and your thoroughness. And now may we have the prisoner?

[FIDDLER *nods and gives* JACK *the arm up before* SHADFORTH.]

Well, Mrs Johnson, what do you have to say for yourself?

[JACK *stands mute.*]

Mmm. Not much one can say is there? Then let me state the court's view.

You are, by all accounts here, not a bad sort of woman, and in my opinion you do not warrant punishment. But it is not possible for you to go about in men's clothing. Not only is the morality of the matter to be considered, but I'm sure Doctor Robinson would substantiate the view that it is positively unhealthy for a woman's body to be thus encased in clothes that were never meant for such a form as God has endowed you with.

Now I understand that you gave away the clothes you had to wear as Johanna, when you were in Mr Craven's service?

[JACK *continues to look down.*]

Well come on, give us an answer. We all know you have talked with others. You do have a tongue. And I'm not such a monster am I now?

[JACK *is silent.*]

Do you or do you not have a dress?

[JACK *shakes his head.*]

The court is adjourned to three o'clock, by which time female attire will have been procured for Mrs Johnson. Then, providing Mrs Johnson keeps the peace, she will accordingly be discharged from our custody...

...in which she is remanded until the appointed hour.

[JACK *is completely downcast. He turns to* SHADFORTH.]

JACK: But...

SHADFORTH: I don't want to hear it, Mrs Johnson. You had your chance. And if it is about those boys, then you have the same recourse to the law as any other citizen of the colony. Should you suffer even the slightest mockery or abuse, you are perfectly entitled to bring the offenders before the court. Do you understand?

[JACK *turns away and walks out.*]

Court adjourned!

[SHADFORTH *bangs the gavel. He beckons the* FIDDLER.]

Psst!

[*He speaks surreptitiously to* FIDDLER.]

Call Doctor Robinson would you?

FIDDLER: [*shouting*] Doctor Robins . . .

SHADFORTH: Sssshhh!

Keep it down, you.

[FIDDLER *looks confused.*]

It's private.

[FIDDLER *nods knowingly and creeps out.*]

Blasted country constables. Blasted country courts. God, how I wish I were in Melbourne now. There's the place for you. There's life. There's a bit of variety. If I were there tonight I'd go off to the Halls, winking at Marie and tickling young Tess where she's best to be tickled; drinking my fill, and making a few bob on the side. Oh, the trouble those military get into – specially at the top. Top brass, and they pay their way.

But what's the country got to offer any more? There's no more bribes to be had in pure nuggets, no more bawds for the camps or the diggings. Scarcely a bushranger to be had anywhere. And why? The blasted law, that's why; made squires out of gutter-snipes, and governors out of thieves. All we've got left here is honest men, and ugly blasted women.

[ROBINSON *enters.*]

Robinson. Thank God. Something medicinal, quick, before I die of a lack of crime!

[FIDDLER *follows* ROBINSON *in.*]

And you. Come on. In a place like this I make no bones about who I drink with.

ROBINSON: I'm sorry to disappoint you Shadforth, but all my strong stuff's left at the asylum.

SHADFORTH: I'll sentence you to the blasted asylum. What in blazes is it doing there? The blasted nuns don't touch a drop!

ROBINSON: It's the diptheria. A whole family gone this week. And it'll spread.

SHADFORTH: God spare me this bloody country. Will it never be three o'clock?

[*Three o'clock chimes.* DWYER *enters with* JOHANNA, *in a dress. It doesn't fit. It's ugly.* JACK *is utterly degraded, can barely walk, let alone speak.*]

Good, that's more like it.

Now we'll let you go, Johnson, as long as you're on your way, and go about your business like an ordinary woman.

JOHANNA: Excuse me, sir.

SHADFORTH: Yes?

JOHANNA: It's difficult, sir, for me to be on my way anywhere, by any means. For I have no money, and dressed this way, no means of making any ...

SHADFORTH: Mrs Johnson, in Melbourne there are woman far uglier than you, making a sizeable living out of all kinds of professions. I'm not sure you try hard enough. Unlike a man, a woman always has a way.

[JOHANNA *tries hard to ignore the reference to prostitution. She is humiliated but tries to continue.*]

JOHANNA: I have no friends, sir, but in Adelaide. I have asked for neither pity nor assistance. I have always worked and always worked hard. But it was my men's clothes that allowed me to do so, and if you do not give them back you condemn me as surely as if you would send me to prison ...

SHADFORTH: You may leave, Johnson, and don't let us catch you this way again

JOHANNA: I even fought, sir, I was in pants as a boy, I have fought in the army. Surely ... ?

SHADFORTH: Off! Robinson, see her out.
              And you [*to* FIDDLER], for God's sake play us into
              tea time. The smell of justice even levels me from
              time to time.
              [FIDDLER *plays a plaintive tune.* JOHANNA *and* ROBINSON *exit,
              as* SHADFORTH *disrobes and prepares his costume for* CHRISTIAN
              JORGENSEN.]

SCENE 5 : A Family Scene

Interior of the Jorgensen Homestead 1859.

CHRISTIAN JORGENSEN *finds a chair, and sits to mend a boot. The fiddle
tune finishes or fades as the sound of girls' voices comes closer.*

Johanna's sister, THERESE, *enters first. She is followed by* JOHANNA,
fifteen years old, and handsome, dressed ordinarily in girl's clothing.
JOHANNA *carries a delicate tea-cup on a saucer.*

CHRISTIAN: What's this? Best china?
THERESE: Special, because the mother's out, and it's us
              who've made your tea.
              [THERESE *grabs her sewing and starts to work on it.* JOHANNA
              *carefully hands the cup to her father. The cup clinks on the
              saucer.*]
CHRISTIAN: It's true, we don't see these lovely things often
              enough. Thank you Johanna.
              [JOHANNA *smiles sweetly and sits at her father's feet as he sips
              his tea.*]
              It's good. It wouldn't be right for me to say it's
              better than your mother makes, but it's good.
              You're going to be a good wife, Johanna Jorgen-
              sen – strong in the field, good in the house, the
              kind of woman a man needs in a country like this.
THERESE: What about me?
CHRISTIAN: I'm sure you'll make a good wife too . . .
THERESE: I can sew.
CHRISTIAN: Indeed you can.
              [*He looks admiringly at* JOHANNA's *dress. It's not fancy, frilly,
              but well-made and elegant enough.*]

Very fine.

[*The girls look at each other and giggle.* JOHANNA *takes one of the boots and starts to polish it.* THERESE *is sewing.* CHRISTIAN *continues to sip the tea. We are aware of the sounds of the Homestead. The calls of crows, perhaps: something to suggest horses, something light, not a whinny, just hooves in the dust, exhaled breath.*]

You know, there won't be another cup like this in the whole colony, perhaps not even the whole continent. It was my mother's mother had this one from Copenhagen. It went to my mother, and should have gone to my sister, but my mother wanted your mother to have it – a good luck wish for the new world, and the new home.

No, the likes of us don't see the likes of this for sale in the colonies...

JOHANNA: Not even in the big towns, not even in Adelaide?

CHRISTIAN: I imagine such things arrive on the great ships from time to time, but never such as we could afford.

There are small things I miss about the old country; pretty things, delicate things that could belong as well to a farmer of modest means, as to a rich man. The value was not so much in its price, but in the pleasure it gave, the pleasure it gives.

[*He holds the cup lovingly, drinks lovingly.*]

JOHANNA: Are you sorry we came so far?

THERESE: That's a silly thing to ask.

[JOHANNA *looks at* THERESE, *puzzled, and looks back to* CHRISTIAN.]

CHRISTIAN: Johanna, it's not a silly question when it's the first time you've dared to ask it – but it would be silly ever to have such a doubt again. I tell you now, the poverty in the lack of a pretty piece of porcelain or a pewter spoon, is nothing, when you look at the riches that the new land has given us. Listen for a moment...

[*The sounds of the country.*]

What do you hear my lovely girls?

THERESE:	Nothing. There's nothing to hear.
CHRISTIAN:	Johanna?
JOHANNA:	I can hear birds – wood pigeon, cockatiel screeching. I can hear wind in the leaves, horse in the yard. I can even hear the sheep, the sheep in the far paddock…
CHRISTIAN:	And what do you think you would be hearing in Europe?

[*He puts the boot on the shoe iron and bangs a nail hard into the sole. There's a hard clang.*]

The sound of war, girls.

[*He bangs in more nails.*]

	A death knell for me, and for your brother Emmanuel. The sound of your mother crying because her men have been eaten up by Prussian greed. I think you'd rather hear your nothing, Therese, than have to listen to the sounds of war.
THERESE:	Yes, father.
CHRISTIAN:	As it is, we can now expect news of our own brothers and sisters consumed by that madness – every packet that arrives in Port Adelaide brings stories of such sadness. Johanna, you're old enough to remember yourself, the sound of those guns as they shot across our bows in the North Sea.
JOHANNA:	I don't really remember, father, it seems such a distance now.
CHRISTIAN:	The good Lord has seen to that – put the distance of seas and years between us and the troubles. I think of stories in the Bible about the chosen people and the promised land. Our own cousins are being forced into the army, abandoning their farms to the elements and whatever the women can manage. Here we plough and sow and reap according to the seasons, as God willed. And we're free to sing His praises in the purest and humblest way we know how. This land is hard, my girls, but it's God's country, and His blessing on us.

Look at you. Strong of face and figure, a rose in your cheek to fetch the finest young farmer in the district. Your brother out there can have his own land, and he'll farm too, and head a family like ours, strong and good in the name of the Lord. And you'll find husbands like him. Good men, who aren't afraid of back-breaking work, men who'll provide for wives who are strong in spirit, fair of face, as both my bright girls are...

[*The sound of horses, and* EMMANUEL *chiding them, the crack of the whip.* CHRISTIAN *keeps on at his boot repair.*]

Johanna, see if your brother needs any help. I'll finish this, and the tea, then come out.

JOHANNA: I'll put on the trousers.

CHRISTIAN: You'll do no such thing.

JOHANNA: But father, the skirts get in my way. I'm liable to get tangled in the harness or the rope.

CHRISTIAN: Johanna Jorgensen, I've told you before, what can't be done by a woman in her skirts, can't be done by a woman...

THERESE: See, I told you they don't like it – it's not just me telling you it's unnatural.

CHRISTIAN: My mother ploughed whole fields in her skirts. She harvested potatoes, she herded swine, and she held horse as strong as any man. And never once did man or woman catch sight of my mother's figure in men's clothing. Nor will they again of yours, Johanna. You're courting age, daughter, and there'll be no more of that trouser-wearing, not even for work with horses. It's time you started looking out for someone to wear the trousers in your own house.

Now see to your brother.

[JOHANNA *leaves.*

There's a silence between THERESE *and* CHRISTIAN *who concentrates on the boot. We hear voices and horses.*]

THERESE: How long do you think the mother will be at church?

CHRISTIAN: No telling. When the wives get together it's all talk along with the business.

THERESE:	You can't blame them. The mothers have precious little time between themselves. And they have women's things to talk over. I'm glad I'll be old enough to go with her soon.
CHRISTIAN:	I suppose that sewing of yours will be a boon to the ladies of the parish.
THERESE:	I expect I'll . . .

[*A sudden loud whinny. A crash of wood and hoof. Then a scream.*]

| VOICE OF EMMANUEL: | Father! Quickly, father! |

[CHRISTIAN *leaps for the door.*]

| THERESE: | Oh God, Johanna . . . |

[THERESE *puts down her sewing, but instead of following her father, she stays to narrate in song.*]

SCENE 6 : A Second Musical Interlude

During this song, the sequence portrays JOHANNA's *ten years at home after the accident.*

The song begins with a fiddle solo on the plaintive melody. CHRISTIAN *enters with* JOHANNA *in his arms.*
She is covered in dust, and on her face she wears a mask the same shape as the previous mask of her disfigurement, but this one is red and torn. She still wears the dress THERESE *made for her, but it is blood stained now.*

EMMANUEL *follows, keeping his distance and watching throughout the song.*

CHRISTIAN *gently puts her down, perhaps strokes her hair, then leaves.*

THERESE *is to one side, isolated in narrative spot,* EMMANUEL *to the other side as observer*

THERESE:	*Refrain*
	Child of the bush, unlovely tree
	Bright coloured birds may still gather in thee

Like the storm summer lightning
Fate stared in the face
To split thee and scar thee
and leave thee no place
To split thee and scar thee
and leave thee no place

[JOHANNA *removes the red mask and replaces it with the previous one.*]

For the wound would soon heal
but her face bore the scar
Of the twists and the turns
of an ill-fated star
Where menfolk prize women
to the ends of the earth
For face and for feature
instead of for worth

Repeat Refrain

[JOHANNA *tries to clean the blood from her dress.*]

Her sister was married, the loveliest bride
Johanna averted the poor face that cried
The children would mock her,
the word quickly spread
Of this poor Johanna who'd never be wed

Repeat Refrain

[*She fails to remove the stains and now begins to change out of the dress and into bushmen's clothes.*]
THERESE: [*continuing to sing*]

Her brother had land as her father passed on
Her mother went south, her old hope was gone
She had lost out to fate as a woman and wife
So Johanna determined the path of her life

[JOHANNA *leaves.*]

Child of the bush, unlovely tree
Bright coloured birds may still gather in thee

[*The* FIDDLER *plays a reprise as* EMMANUEL *approaches* THERESE.]

EMMANUEL: She's gone.

THERESE: It'll be for good this time.

EMMANUEL: I don't know how she's stuck it this long.

THERESE: But what in God's name will she do? How will she live?

EMMANUEL: She's left behind every single piece of her clothing – except the trousers, and the work clothes.

THERESE: She's left in them?

[EMMANUEL *nods.*]

No word?

[EMMANUEL *shakes his head.*]

Then she has only the Lord to protect her and look out for his poor blighted creature. We can do no more. She's gone against all our counsel.

EMMANUEL: Like a criminal ... [*yelling*] ... what else could she do?

THERESE: My husband listed things – the church, where she'd be safe from cruel eyes, where God could truly protect her ...

EMMANUEL: But Johanna needs the bush, the air, the open. She wouldn't let herself be caged like that, wrapped in skirts and cowls.

THERESE: It's sinful not to accept what God has determined for us.

EMMANUEL: I can't blame her, and whatever her fate, she is punished already. Our sister is like a soul in Purgatory. No matter how far away she moves, how much further on she moves, she wanders like a soul in torment.

She can never find peace.

[*He weeps.* THERESE *embraces him, and they leave.*]

SCENE 7 : A Pastoral

Dusk in the bush. The colours are of McCubbin's 'The Lost Child'; soft greys and flat peaceful greens. Sounds of birds settling for the night. The smell of eucalyptus, the chink of harness, footsteps.

The interior of JACK JORGENSEN's *place, poor but clean and tidy.*

JACK *enters. He wears bushman's clothes but they are 'uncommon neat and clean'. He has the paraphernalia of horse about him. He walks tired after a good day's work, puts down the gear and goes to the kerosene lamp on the table. Lights it.*

He is softly singing/humming: a girlish voice. He washes thoroughly face, hands and neck. He takes a book and sits, prepares a pipe, lights it, and takes up the book to read.

Outside at a distance, JOSEPH FURPHY *approaches. He is a well-dressed bushman, alert, observant. He stops to make an entry in his diary, speaking aloud as he writes.*

FURPHY: Friday, September fifteenth, 1877.
'Two strange horses in the paddock, the kerosene tins standing in the sheltered angle by the chimney; but the flowers are dead; the smooth-trodden radius round the door is no longer swept, except by the winds of heaven...
...cool white moonlight, flooding the level landscape, strange phenomena follow the footsteps of night...
...This is the time when mines cave in; when loose bark falls from trees; when limbs crash down from old dead timber; when snow-laden branches break, when all ponderable bodies, of relatively slight restraint, are most apt to lose hold...'
At last after reading of the court case in Heathcote four years ago, I believe I have come across this ill-starred individual.
'...heiress of infinite hope, how suddenly fallen...'

[*He packs the diary in his swag, straightens his clothes, goes up to the door, and knocks.*

JACK *is startled, then scared. He grabs up a heavy rolling pin and speaks in a gruff voice, very different from the light singing we have just heard.*]

JACK: Who's there?

FURPHY: A weary traveller, perhaps lost.

[JACK *is still fearful, resistant, but his desire for companionship wins over.*]

JACK: Moment.

[*As* FURPHY *waits outside,* JACK *puts on his boots and a coat which he buttons up very tight. 'He turned the lamp down till a mere bead of flame showed above the burner.' He lets* FURPHY *in. With face averted to disguise the scar, voice disguised, and sunken chested in order to conceal bosom, he merely nods* FURPHY *a greeting and offers him a seat.* FURPHY *notices* JACK's *pipe and takes out his own much fancier Meerschaum.*]

FURPHY: Thanks. Mind if I join you?

[JACK *nods again. As* FURPHY *prepares a pipe,* JACK *puts on a kettle.* FURPHY *suspects that* JACK *is the Heathcote Case, thus knowing* JACK's *secret all along. He watches* JACK's *every move intently.*]

                  Matches?

[JACK *throws him the matches and then sits back down, 'elbow on the table in order to shade with his hand the middle part of his face.'* FURPHY *lights up, tosses the matches back on the table, and leans back in his chair. He looks around the room.*]

                  You've got the place very nice, Mr Jorgensen...

[JACK *turns to him slightly.*]

                  ... it is Mr Jack Jorgensen isn't it? I've come to the right hut after all?

[JACK *nods.*]

                  Yes, the Wilsons on the next place told me. They said if I got confused, I was bound to end up at Jorgensen's. I'm Furphy, Joe Furphy.

[*He gets up to offer his hand, but his bum is barely out of the seat when* JACK *waves him back.* FURPHY *sinks back into the seat.*]

                  You've got a good size spread here.

JACK:	Eighty-three acres, few horse, few sheep, do the boundaries myself.
FURPHY:	Must get lonely.
JACK:	Used to live Shepparton way but it got too crowded. So I moved further on.

[FURPHY *is quick to cover* JACK's *cover-up.*]

FURPHY:	Know how you feel. Melbourne's got so you can scarcely take a breath – rich, poor, drunken Aboriginals. Ever been to Melbourne?
JACK:	Never. Not likely to either if that's how it is.
FURPHY:	What about the blackfellows? You see many of them round here?
JACK:	Never. Wiped 'em out. You know how they feel about anything that doesn't fit. Arrest it, or shoot it first – ask questions later, if there are any... Tea?
FURPHY:	Very kind.

[*The business of tea-pouring and giving it to him happens somewhere here.*]

JACK:	They got plenty of feed at Wilson's?
FURPHY:	Not as much as they'd like, not enough rain. I suppose that affects you. He told me they take your stock when the feed's good.

[*He sips his tea.*]

	Speaking of feed, didn't you blame Thompson and Cunningham for duffing in your horse-paddock, ten or twelve months ago?
JACK:	I didn't make any song about it.
FURPHY:	Of course not. Still you owe them an apology – which I shall be happy to convey, if you wish it. Warrigal Alf was the depredator. He was hovering about your hut that night like a guardian angel, while his twenty bullocks had their knife-bars going double-speed on your grass, and you slept the sleep of the unsuspecting. Ask Wilson; he'll give you the chapter and verse, without much pressing. He told me about it this afternoon.
JACK:	What's his other name?
FURPHY:	Who? Alf?

[JACK *nods.*]

Alf Morris, he's a carrier on these roads.

JACK: Why don't you call him so then? I hate nick-
           names. When did you see this Alf Morris last?

FURPHY: About two months ago. He was camped at the
           time in the Dead Man's Bend, at the junction of
           Avondale and Mundunbarra.

JACK: When are you likely to see him again? But of
           course, you can't tell. It's a foolish question. I
           don't know what's come over me tonight.

FURPHY: Most likely I'll never see him again. These wool-
           tracks, that knew him so well, will know him no
           more again for ever. He has gone four or five
           months' journey due north, in charge of three
           teams loaded with tools and cooking utensils and
           rations, and other things too numerous to par-
           ticularise, belonging once to Kooltopa, but now
           to a new station in South-Western Queensland.

JACK: And what's become of Kooltopa?

FURPHY: Old times are changed, old manners are gone; a
           stranger fills the Stewart's throne.

           Kooltopa's sold to a Melbourne company and
           is going to be worked for all it's worth. And I'm
           thinking of the carrier, coming down with the
           survivors of a severe trip, and the penniless
           pedestrian, striking the station at the eleventh
           hour. These people will miss Stewart badly.

[JACK *washes down the table and sets it.*]

           Do you see Wilson often?

JACK: Don't see much of anybody. It's a big spread,
           even for someone with a constitution like mine.

FURPHY: But you're lucky in neighbours.

JACK: Mrs is a good soul. She get over that child?

FURPHY: They didn't say anything. She seemed well.

[*He watches* JACK *at the table, looks around the room.*]

           Have you any swapping books?

JACK: Yes, you'll find 'Elsie Venner' lying on top of the
           upper shelf.

FURPHY: I've read it years ago, but we'll change. When I
           got my first swapping book, it was by Hannah

	More; now it's by Zola, and smutty enough at that ...
JACK:	I don't think it does a person good to read Zola.
FURPHY:	Not the slightest – that is, in the works by which he is represented amongst us. But do you think it does a person any good to read Holmes? Zola, even as we know him here in the Riverina, has this advantage, that he gives you no rest for the sole of your foot – or rather, for the foot of your soul; whilst Holmes serenely seduces you to his own pinchbeck standard. Zola is honest; he never calls evil good; whilst Holmes is spurious all through. Mind you, each has a genuine literary merit of his own.
JACK:	But don't you like Holmes's poetry?
FURPHY:	He has a range of about three notes; a flunkeyish koo-tooing to soap-bubble eminence; a tawdry sympathy with aristocratic woe; and a drivelling contempt for angular Poor Relations in bombazine gowns. Bombazine, by-the-way, is a cheap, carpetty-looking fabric, built of shoddy, and generally used for home-made quilts ...
JACK:	[*laughing*] No it's not! It's very good dress-material: silk one way, and wool the other; and it's mostly black, or maroon, or ...

[JACK *grabs up the food and offers it to* FURPHY.]

	... tucker?
FURPHY:	I'm most grateful.

[*They eat for a while in silence. Then* FURPHY *sits back.*]

	I thought food like this only came from having a woman in the kitchen.
JACK:	Then you might have to revise your thoughts, Mr Furphy.

[*There's almost a suggestion that* JACK *knows* FURPHY *knows, and she's giving him the clue that she's not going to talk about it.*]

	Perhaps a little accompaniment will assist my revision?
FURPHY:	

[*He takes out a Jew's Harp from his pocket and plays a bit while* JACK *continues eating. He finishes as* FURPHY *finishes a tune.*]

JACK: Do you like music?

FURPHY: Like it? I would give one fourth of the residue of my life to be a good singer and musician. As it is, I'm not much of a player, and still less of a vocalist; but I'll give you a song if you like. How sweetly everything sounds to-night. Bee-o-buoy-bee-o-buoy-bee-o...

JACK: [*interrupting*] Do you like Jew's Harp music?

FURPHY: Not if I could play any better instrument – such as the violin or the concertina; though I should in any case avoid the piano, for fear of flattening the ends of my fingers. Still the Jew's Harp is a Jew's Harp; and this is the very best I could find in the market. Humble as it looks, and humble as it undeniably is, it has sounded in every nook and corner of Riverina. Last time I took it out, it was to give a poor, consumptive old blackfellow a treat; and now, you see, I tune to please a peasant's ear, the harp a king had loved to hear. Bee-o-buoy-bee-o-buoy-bee-o...

JACK: [*interrupting again*] I'll give you a tune on the violin if you like.

FURPHY: Thank you, Jack

[JACK *goes to a case and from it takes a 'dusty, dark brown violin'. The* FIDDLER *begins a tune 'weary, wistful, melancholy'.* JACK *carefully takes the violin as if testing, dusting, tuning. He never lifts it to play.* JACK *simply holds it and sings.*

'*And such a voice. Rich, soft, transcendent, yet suggesting ungauged resources of enchantment, unconsciously held in reserve.* [FURPHY] *sat entranced, the subtle tyranny of the vocal harmony admitting no intruding thought other than a regretful sense that the song must end.'*]

The FIDDLE *plays the first Refrain.*

JACK: [*singing*]

        There was a time when I had hopes
        As strong as any man's
        That I would find the tender heart
        And hold the dearest hands

Refrain
Further on,
When disappointment clouds your sky with grey
You must move further on
And hope that you may find a brighter day
You must move further on
Until you find yourself some foreign shore
Where you'll be safe once more
Till you move further on

The birds upon the native tree
May travel light and free
But slowly on this earth I go
A heavy heart for me

Repeat Refrain

[*The* FIDDLER *continues to play this Refrain.*]

FURPHY: [*visibly moved*] Jack, 'don't you know it's wrong to bury yourself away here in melancholia seeing you're as gifted as you are.' Let someone else look after the place for you. 'No man's skill is sufficiently comprehensive to encompass such musical proficiency as yours and leave the merest flap available for anything else. I can see through you like glass. I could write your biography. And believe me, you're no more suited to this sort of life than you are to preside over a school of stoic philosophy. You're a reed, shaken by the wind. Be a man, Jack. Turn your face southwards or eastwards, and challenge your future with your violin and your voice.'

[JACK *looks at him with a 'wild shrinking look'. He 'walks slowly to his bed and lay down with his face toward the wall', fully clothed, boots and all, sobbing. Lights fade as the* FIDDLER *finishes the tune.*]

Morning

[FURPHY *is alone, on his roll, in his underwear; he gets up, washes, looks around. He finds the table set for a modest breakfast. There is a note. He reads aloud.*]

'Breakfast's on me. Goodbye. Gone courtin'.'

[FURPHY *takes out his diary, pulls the blanket around him, and writes, reading aloud.*]

'She needn't a done it! O she shouldn't a done it! Why should she go?

But she aimed at independence – independence!

A fine word, but a poor reality!'

[*He looks around the hut.*]

'This idea of independence is much too common amongst people ... you overlook the divine command to do our duty in that state of life in which it has pleased God to call us ... But who could blame this poor one, keeping his face averted ... Man must be subject to sale by auction, or be a wearer of Imperial uniform, before the susceptibility to insult perishes in his soul ... Strange to think that man should depend so entirely for his dignity upon a nose ... But such is life ... '

[FURPHY *addresses the audience, perhaps he starts to dress himself.*]

'Did you ever reflect upon how much you have to be grateful for in the matter of noses? Your nose may be your dram of eale – your club foot – your Mordecai sitting at the king's gate but you would look very queer without it.

In your morbid state of hypercriticalness, you may wish that indocile, undisguisable and most unsheltered feature had been made a little longer, or a little shorter, or a little wider, or not quite too wide. Or perhaps you wish the isthmus between your eyes a little higher, or the ridge of the peninsula a little straighter, or the south cape a little more or less obtuse. Or possibly you wish that the front elevation did not admit so clear a perspective of the interior of Ambition's airy hall ...

Check that rebellious spirit. Your nose is good enough ... better probably, than you deserve; be

thankful that you have one of any design at all ...'
For here was ... 'Pygmalion's masterpiece fallen
heavily, face downward, and then sprung to life,
minus the feature which will least bear tampering
with.'
[*He puts down his diary and picks up the note.*]
    Gone courtin' ... and they say he dodges the
women like a criminal.
[*He takes his things and leaves.*]

SCENE 8 : A Courting Scene

*Emmy enters with a tray of tea-things: pretty china, crocheted doilies.
She begins laying them out. There is a knock. A voice calls 'Coo-ee'.
Emmy smiles, but doesn't look up.*

EMMY: Mr Jorgensen?
VOICE: That's what they call me.
EMMY: Moment.
        [*She fiddles with the table a little longer, then leaves and returns
        with* JACK *following. He is spruced up, carrying a small bunch
        of flowers.*]
EMMY: [*not looking at him*] They're beautiful. Put them on the table.
        [JACK *puts the flowers down and stands awkwardly, but not
        defensively as with* FURPHY. *He seems much more open in*
        EMMY'*s presence.*]
        Well Mr Jorgensen, are the flowers to speak all?
        [*She turns and faces him for the first time.* JACK *almost
        involuntarily turns his face away.*]
        No greeting, Jack?
        [*He goes towards her, and with face still at an angle, takes up
        her hand and kisses it, head bowed.* EMMY *removes her hand
        gently and lifts* JACK'*s head, turning the face full towards her.
        She kisses* JACK *on the scarred part of his face.*]
JACK: I don't know how you can bear it.
EMMY: I have eyes that see through to the heart. The
        heart wears its scars differently Mr Jorgensen,
        and I'm not frightened of what I read in your
        heart.
        [JACK *kisses her hand once more.*]

Sit down, the tea won't be long.

JACK: I've not seen these before.

[*The tinkle of china once more as* JACK *fingers the cups.*]

EMMY: Thought it was about time I brought out the family finery for you. After all, you've become something of a regular.

JACK: Something of a nuisance, I fear.

[EMMY *looks him square in the eye.*]

EMMY: Never think that Jack Jorgensen, for it's not so. Here, there's a copy of the Bendigo Independent. I'll fetch the kettle.

[*She leaves and* JACK *starts to read. He finds something that makes him read more intently. He sinks in his chair.* EMMY *returns.*]

Jack, what on earth is it?

JACK: Have you read this?

EMMY: What?

JACK: Edward de Lacey Evans?

EMMY: I know, such a scandal!

[*She has a wicked look in her eye as she stops with the tea-things and comes close to* JACK.]

Imagine, Jack, just imagine, if you for instance, should be suddenly found to be a woman?

[*She bites her lip as she giggles, her eyes wild with naughtiness, as the* FIDDLER *strikes up his jig.* JACK *looks increasingly horrified as* EMMY *goes into her song.*]

EMMY: [*singing*]

> *Chorus*
> Good Evans de Lacey, you're cunning and racy
> You wooed 'em and wed 'em and some say you
>   bed 'em
> Don't know how you did but your wife had a kid
> And they say you're a woman and all
>
> They say you came from Plymouth
> on the Ocean monarch line
> Handsome, friendly, educated,
> singing very fine
> In eighteen hundred and fifty seven,
> they called you Nellie Tremayne

But on the trunk you travelled with
'Edward' was the name

Repeat Chorus

They say that at a party
you were very good at jigs
They say that at the mining camp
you were champion of the digs
But the boys could never figure out
why you wouldn't change your clothes
For you were always stylish
from your hat down to your hose

Repeat Chorus

You slept with Mary Montague,
Mary Evans was your bride
You married Sarah Moore eight years
in childbirth she died
You married Julia Marquand
and lived in Ballarat
And the wives all say they never twigged
So what do you make of that?

Repeat Chorus

But now it's come to Courts of Law
they say you're raving mad
And your wives were nymphomaniacs
all wanting to be had
They say it's not incurable
The remedy's easy and neat
Chaste abstention, lots of rest,
a diet that's replete

Last Chorus

[EMMY *is having a good time with this jig, she gets quite carried away with her dance now, and maybe another Chorus.*]

[JACK's *had enough. He puts the paper down and starts to leave without saying goodbye.*]

JACK: I must move further on
[JACK *exits.*]

[*The* FIDDLER *is really on fire with the jig now. Suddenly* EMMY *looks around, laughing, and sees that* JACK *is gone.*]

EMMY: Jack ... Jack?
[*The* FIDDLER *continues to play as* EMMY *shows her agitation, her sadness. She runs after* JACK.]
          Jack!
[*The* FIDDLER *segues gradually to the militaristic beat of a march which becomes the aforeheard 'Marching Down to Georgia'.*]

SCENE 9 : The Victorian Mounted Rifles

As the FIDDLER *plays 'Marching Down to Georgia', a soldier enters casually. He puts his rifle against the table, and begins to clear the things. He whistles along with the tune. A second soldier enters with* JACK *now dressed in his Mounted Rifles uniform.*

SOLDIER 1:   There, Jack, give us a hand, I've cleared most of it.
SOLDIER 2:   Good thing too. They say Price is a stickler for order. Wouldn't take kindly to the mess all mucky.
[*A bugle call announces assembly. The* FIDDLER *stops. The three soldiers line up.* FIDDLER *barks a few orders.*]
FIDDLER: Attention!
          Present arms!
          At ease!
          Stand easy!
[*They place their rifles in front of them. They wait some time. They shoo flies. One spits. They begin a conversation out of order, out of the corner of the mouth.*]
SOLDIER 2:   What d'ya reckon he's comin' here for?
SOLDIER 1:   Price?
SOLDIER 2:   Yeah!
SOLDIER 1:   I've heard it's the riots in Melbourne.
SOLDIER 2:   Riots?

JACK: Melbourne?

SOLDIER 1:   Yeah, reckon they'll have us down there, show a bit of muscle to the rabble. Whadya reckon, Jack?

SOLDIER 2:   Tell ya what, if we go to Melbourne, there's a bit of muscle I'll be exercisin', but it won't be on the rabble ...

SOLDIER 1:   Yeah. Eh Jack, look ...

SOLDIER 2:   Yeah Jack?

[*As* JACK *turns to look, they rub their crotches, make prickish gestures.*]

SOLDIER 1:   Gotta bit of flex there, Jack?

[*They both laugh.*]

FIDDLER: Attention!

[COLONEL PRICE *enters.*]

PRICE: At ease!

Right. Well, you've probably heard a lot of rumours flying around. Here are the facts! Things aren't too bright in Melbourne. There's a heap of whingers and bludgers down there, who aren't prepared to pull their weight in the colony, and we're pulling in a few reserves just to let them know, short, sharp and shiny, that if you want the benefits of a country like this, you don't get 'em by hanging around street corners, and making trouble.

SOLDIER 1: [*aside*] Told ya.

PRICE: Shut your face, soldier, the same applies to you!

SOLDIER 1:   Yes sir!

PRICE: We got unionists on the one hand, shearers on the other, businessmen clamouring at the doors of the banks, and what do they want? They all want more! So do the women, even mothers are marching in the street – troublemakers. Meanwhile, the thieves are having a field day, in and out of pockets, in and out of front doors left wide open while the owners grizzle up and down the street for a hand-out.

SOLDIER 1:   Charming.

PRICE: If you don't shut your mouth, boy, you'll arrive in Melbourne in irons!

SOLDIER 1: Yes sir!

PRICE: Now, we're going down there to show these mongrels a thing or two. It's no picnic, so don't start thinking this is a holiday. There'll be no time for booze, or dipping the wick, so get that out of your heads once and for all. Now let's see you. They don't like volunteers down there, none of them, so you're all going to need a sense of authority on your side. And it starts with your appearance.

Attention!

[*The* FIDDLER *begins the marching tune again as* PRICE *inspects,* SOLDIER 1, SOLDIER 2, *then comes to* JACK.]

Since when did we let Chinamen enlist in this bloody corps?

SOLDIER 1: Please sir, it ain't a Chinaman sir, it's Jack Jorgensen, sir.

[SECOND SOLDIER *giggles.*]

PRICE: I don't give a shearer's curse what it is, it's a mess! What have you got to say for yourself?

[JACK *looks down.*]

SOLDIER 1: Please sir, Jack don't talk much, keeps to himself sir, but if you don't mind me saying so sir, he's bloody good with the horses, and he's even better in the cookhouse.

PRICE: If he's such a dandy, why doesn't he press his bloody uniform? And it's three sizes too bloody big anyway!

[PRICE *turns away.*]

JACK: [*to himself*] I have to move...

PRICE: Present arms!

[*The other two go through their motions with precision, but* JACK *has lost heart. He fumbles.*]

JACK: ...further on...

PRICE: Shoulder arms!

[JACK *drops out of line.*]

On the spot, two, three, four, left, left, left right left...

[*The two* SOLDIERS *start marching.*]

SOLDIER 2:   Come on Jack, what's the matter with ya?

JACK: ...up country perhaps...

[JACK *starts to remove his uniform.*]

SOLDIER 1:   You don't want to worry about what he says,
Jack. We'll have a ripper time down the big town.
Think of those girls, Jack. Jesus, wouldn't they die
for a look at you?

SOLDIER 2:   God's gift to bloody women

SOLDIER 1:   Well, we never got to see it, but I bet it's a foot
if it's an inch!

[*They both laugh.*]

PRICE: Quick march! Left, left, left right...

[*The two* SOLDIERS *march off, laughing, whistling, followed by*
PRICE *and the* FIDDLER *also marching off.*]

[JACK *continues to remove his uniform and hang it or fold it.*]

SCENE 10 : Poor Johanna

When JACK *turns back to the audience in old bush clothes, his health
has obviously deteriorated. His breath is short, very wheezy. He gasps
as he speaks, his chest is sunken.*

Bush ambience once more. He hears a bird call. He smiles

JACK: What happens when a bird loses a wing? Other
birds are powerless to help. Perhaps it gets by,
perhaps it soon dies. Perhaps a child nurses it
back to health and strength. What of the tree that
loses a branch? Can it grow another? Can it
survive in any case? Perhaps a woman cares for
it, prevents the rot.

[*He goes to harness, handles it.*]

But what of humanity?
'Did the British think less of Lord Nelson –
did Lady Nelson think less of him for the loss of
his arm and eye? even the conceited German students value scars on the face more than academic
honours. It's effeminacy to brood over such things ...'

109

But 'a woman's first duty is to be beautiful. If
Lady Hamilton had been minus an eye and an
arm she would scarce have attained her unfor-
tunate celebrity...'
When women are loved, why are they loved?
Look at me. Look at my state.
And ask if there is anything in the way men prize
beauty? Is my present station at all to do with this?

[*she indicates her face.*]

'My face is remade to the order of the hoof; and
my life proclaims the might of the beast. For one
restless horse suddenly noticed me crossing the
yard; now turn away, since his rolling eye
crushed my entire life.

I am a victim of chance, a moment's ill-fortune...
A minor horsekick may exhaust itself in one
minute or less, but it leaves an indelible scar on
its victim...

And isn't history a mere record of blundering
horsekicks, followed by fleshly servitude to the
irremediable suffering thereby entailed? There
lives no-one on earth today who holds the flim-
siest gossamer of security against a pauper's
grave...

[*Birdsong, the rustling of leaves.*]

Do I leave with nothing then?
No family, no friends, no single soul who sees
what I truly am, and what I might have been?
Poor Johanna,
living in a land where she is no uglier than
the twisted drought-stricken gum,
singing with a voice that's sweeter than
the magpie-lark
and stronger than the Currawong in flight.
How poor is this?
When a woman loves her life,
what is it loved for?
Here, I am as beautiful as any living thing.

[*The* FIDDLER *starts to play 'Rise, Arise!'* JOHANNA *starts to
breathe deeply again.*]

Our virgin continent!
How long has she tarried her bridal day!
[JOHANNA *begins to stand tall, breathe easy. She takes up the song.*]

Rise, arise!
Like morning sun in blood red skies
Rise, arise!
The land is lovely to its lover's eyes

[*The* MINISTER, FIDDLER, TOM O'CONNELL, *and* MISS TURNER *return.*]

Whene'er you see the dawn
Through gum trees grey and green
Whene'er you lightly tread the bush
That man has scarcely seen
Whene'er you cross the river's run
Which was not crossed before
Think you of the nation
That has ne'er been before

Rise, arise!
Like morning sun in blood red skies
Rise, arise!
The land is lovely to its lover's eyes

[*Applause. Calls for more.*]

MINISTER: Thank you, one and all. I'm sure Jack Jorgy would
              love to oblige, but as you can all see he's had quite
              enough...
              Let us all join in the final hymn.
[*They all sing the hymn 'All Things Bright and Beautiful'.*]

JANETTE TURNER HOSPITAL

Janette Turner Hospital was born in 1942, in
Melbourne, and later moved to Brisbane, where
she attended the University of Queensland. She
was a secondary school teacher before leaving with
her husband for USA and Canada in 1967. For many
of her years overseas she has been a full time writer.
The winner of the prestigious Canadian Seal Award
for her first novel, *Ivory Swing* (1982) and twice
nominated for the British Booker prize, she is often
described as one of the most intellectual of
contemporary writers. She is a lecturer in the English
Department at La Trobe University for a term each
year.

Of her writing life she says: 'As I approach my
fiftieth birthday, I find myself drawn back more
and more strongly to the rich material of my
Queensland childhood and early adulthood, though
of necessity, I observe this past through the filter
of many geographical and cultural displacements.
(At the moment of writing, for example, I have just
returned from living in a town in South India where
westerners are rarely seen; I am spending the
summer months working on a novel in my home
in Canada, where the lives of my two grown-up
children, in nearby cities, are a source of constant
absorption and pleasure; I leave shortly for Australia
again, and expect to finish the novel while I am in
Brisbane and Melbourne.) For some time now I've
been spending an increasing part of each year back
in Australia; I also spend part of every year in
Boston, a city I love passionately, and one of the

places which certainly feels like home. A sense of living simultaneously in conflicting cultures is more or less constant with me.

In my writing, I explore lives whose present is geographically displaced from the past, but whose past, by reason of its intensity, constitutes a sort of hyper-real present, a translucent layer on the actual present. I explore the 'weather' which results from the interaction of these two 'fronts'.

I also find myself compulsively exploring the issue of trauma, especially – but not exclusively – in the lives of women: the way trauma imposes a life-long agenda, insists that its alumnae go on and on negotiating its terms and its legacy. I probe around those lives which have lost the negotiations (I've had close ties to several of these in real life), and to those which keep on surviving the skirmishes. I'm looking for the secrets of survival. The quest seems urgent to me.

There is a related issue which absorbs me: the issue of moral courage and moral cowardice. The person who has been in a state of absolute risk is perpetually tantalised (in a moral and metaphysical sense) by that moment when the intervention, or the failure to intervene, of another, makes a difference so overwhelming that it can never be adequately conveyed to someone who has not experienced such a crisis. To me, this is the most interesting question about any human being, the question of moral integrity: in a crisis, would he/she go out on a limb for another? Or would he/she slink into the shrubbery of safety and rationalisation and the averting of the eyes which is the time-honoured self-protective device of the majority?

It is surely the moral question we secretly ask ourselves about ourselves, because we don't *know*, we cannot know, until absolute danger faces us, how we would behave.

I find myself, in my fiction, putting very ordinary people into maëlstroms of moral dilemma. Willy-nilly, they are forced to make choices they would give anything to avoid making. In a sense, I write to find out what they will do.'

Janette Turner Hospital's books are:

1982 *Ivory Swing*. McClelland & Stewart, Toronto.
1982, Hodder and Stoughton, London and Sydney.
1991, University of Queensland Press, St Lucia.

1983 *Tiger in the Tiger Pit*. McClelland & Stewart, Toronto.
1982, Hodder and Stoughton, London and Sydney.
1990, University of Queensland Press, St Lucia.

1985 *Borderline*. Hodder and Stoughton, London and Sydney. 1987, University of Queensland Press, St Lucia.

1987 *Dislocations*. University of Queensland Press, St Lucia.

1989 *Charades*. University of Queensland Press, St Lucia.

1990 *Isobars*. University of Queensland Press, St Lucia.

In Canada her books are available from McClelland & Stewart; in the United Kingdom from Virago; in the United States from Bantam, W.W. Norton and Louisiana State University Press. They are also available in a number of European translations

The Last of the Hapsburgs

This is all you can see: the young woman, the Pacific, the stands of sugarcane beyond the dune grasses, and four miles of sand so firm that when Cabrisi's horse (the one that went wild, the brumby) when Cabrisi's horse gallops here, you can barely see hoofprints.

The young woman leaves no footprints at all. She stands with her feet and ankles in the erratic line of froth, at that point where ocean and shore eat each other, and reads the Port Douglas beach. Cabrisi's horse, nostrils flaring with the smell of her, rears: a salute of sorts.

'Caedmon,' she says – here, the naming of creatures is all hers – 'you beautiful show-off!' Of course he knows it. So bloody beautiful that a cry catches in her throat. Caedmon whinnies again, a high and jubilant note, and brushes air with his delicate forelegs. Another sign. The beach is thick with them, but who has time enough for the decoding, the translating, the recording?

Surf rises from her ankles to her knees. *Sing me North Queensland*, it lisps with its slickering tongues.

I can't, she laments, hoisting up her skirt. *I can't*.

She would need a different sort of alphabet, a chlorophyll one, a solar one. The place will not fit into *words*.

Surf rushes between her thighs. *Sing me North Queensland*, it commands.

The young woman lifts her arms high above her head and faces the ocean. She begins to dance. She sings. When the sun slides behind Double Point, she climbs the hill at the end of the beach, still singing. She finds the track, and eventually the road, and walks until a Holden utility brakes in a skirl of dust. 'Stone the crows, Miss Davenport,' the driver says. 'You all right?'

She looks at him, dazed. Her sodden clothes give off steam. She says vaguely: 'Yes, oh yes, perfectly all right, thank you.'

Driving on, the man shakes his head and mumbles to himself, not without affection: 'Strange bloody old chook. A looker once, probably. Quite a looker, lay you a quid, back in her prime.'

Miss Davenport, the woman thinks, blinking, as though she has just stumbled across something she had misplaced. Miss Davenport the schoolteacher. And not young at all, how odd.

Before the avocadoes and kiwi fruit and mangoes, back in the time of the sugarcane, Wednesday afternoons used to roll in with a dreadful humid regularity. They would float up from Cairns, cumulus, wet, fuzzy, drift past Yorkey's Knob and Port Douglas, and settle onto Mossman. *Wednesdays come several times a week*, Miss Davenport wrote to her sister in Brisbane. *I do think sport is very much overrated by the Department of Education. Why can't we have a compulsory afternoon of thinking instead? Or of daydreaming?*

Technically supervising the girls, Miss Davenport wilted under a parasol. *Deliquescence,* she thought. (She had a habit of fondling words.) *We are all gone into the world of fog,* she thought. Deliquescence: it had a damp sound, soft on the tongue. Miss Davenport mopped at her face with a lace-edged linen handkerchief. Flies molested her. She kept a fascinated eye on Rebecca. Already she had misplaced Hazel.

Rebecca and Hazel, she wrote to her sister, *have the gift. They are consummate artists. Houdini pales in comparison.*

Ida, her sister, lived in a flat in Toowong. Two years earlier, Ida had retired from one of Brisbane's more exclusive schools, and since then heraldry had engulfed her, the branches and twigs and epiphyte creepers of the family tree curling through her sleep, *gryphons rampant* and *fields azure* blooming in her waking thoughts. She wrote to vicars in Sussex villages and mapped her way, vine by vine and knothole by knothole, into the past. Not that this meant she neglected the scrapbooks. Far from it. At Christmas, both she and Lucia still worked on the travel book, refurbishing a June day in an Italian village here, resetting a sentence there. Emendations were also constantly made to the archival records of the more remarkable students.

You never know, Ida wrote back on the subject of the present specimens. *You just never know. Can any good thing come out of Mossman? As always, the answer is: who can possibly say? For you and me, Lucia, life is what we can catch in our scrapbook nets. That and only that, my dear. So pin your Rebecca and your Hazel right through their pretty wings with your fountain pen.*

Catch as catch can, thought Miss Davenport, dissolving beneath her parasol. There was a coded reproach in Ida's letter, but Ida had earned a permanent right to the little slinging privileges and arrows of sisterhood. Ida had hushed things up and smoothed things down the time Lucia's life had quite shockingly spilled out of handwritten page into messy event. Afterwards, of course, the private girls' schools were out of the question. Afterwards, Lucia had to be grateful for appointments in such places as Childers and Mt Isa and Mossman.

Miss Lucia Davenport could not see Hazel, but she could still see Rebecca working her way into invisibility. At each cheer or catcall, as though the noise itself offered camouflage,

Rebecca would move a foot or two closer to the cane.

Between Miss Davenport and the cane was a paddock full of brown stubble and dust and hockey sticks *where ignorant armies clashed by*... well, where eleven local girls vied with eleven from Cairns High in the regional semi-finals. Boys wolf-whistled from the sidelines. Boys leaned on their bikes and laid bets on the outcome of the game. Boys lay on the grass for the very best view of Dellis's panties.

Miss Davenport saw Rebecca reach the cane. For a few seconds, Rebecca's hair was a black swatch against the purple tassels of the ripening stalks, then the girl disappeared.

Hazel had disappeared during the first ten minutes of the match, but that was different. The methods were different. Hazel had the spooky powers of a gecko lizard. You could stumble across Hazel in the middle of an empty paddock, sitting cross-legged on the ground, as unobtrusive as grass. 'Hazel!' you might say, dumbfounded. 'How long have you...?' But because of something in Hazel's eyes, you never quite finished your question. And Hazel never answered you. She hardly ever spoke at all. She had another name which nobody could pronounce, though sometimes you heard it when one of her younger siblings came for the lunch. (In Hazel's family, the kids had to take turns; Hazel was the one who carried the much-creased brown bag and made the decisions.) *Joanna Goanna*, the boys called her, taunting.

Miss Davenport squinted and surveyed the entire paddock from the cane to the school buildings. It was quite possible that Hazel was there somewhere, watching the hockey game, willing them all to believe she was the magpie in the poinciana tree.

Rebecca had vanished.

Miss Davenport kept her eye on the magpie which looked right back and commanded: *Sleep, sleep, sleep, sleep*...

'The last of the Hapsburgs,' Charlie said. 'That's what people call them.'

'Who?' Miss Davenport asked.

'Her parents. That girl's. The one you go on about.'

'Rebecca Weiss?'

'Yeah. Her mum and her old man, one hundred per cent

bonkers. Joe Hawkins at the Commonwealth Bank started it. He sees them once a month, they're rich as Midas, got most of it stashed somewhere in their place up the Daintree, Joe reckons. Not in their bank account, that's for bloody certain. They got *investments* in Sydney and Brisbane, that's what Joe reckons. They bring Joe their piddling deposits once a month, a bloody joke, typical Ikey. The last of the Hapsburgs, Joe says, and it caught on. Whoever the hell the Hapsburgs were.'

'Austro-Hungarian emperors,' Miss Davenport said. 'Rulers in Europe from the thirteenth century to the First World War.'

'Yeah?' Charlie laughed. 'Well, there you are. Bloody peculiar, that's all I know. Mind you, anything you want to dream up, you can find up the Daintree. It's a zoo up there.' Charlie ticked off the fingers of his left hand with the index finger of his right: 'Crocs in the Daintree itself, and in the rainforest, you name it: Japs who've been lost since New Guinea, boat people, hippies, paddocks of mary-j that stretch all the way up to Torres Strait, greenies, Jesus freaks, Martians, dinosaurs, and the last of the Hapsburgs in their castle.'

'Castle?'

'Yeah. Well, good as.' Charlie O'Hagan drained his beer and signalled for another. 'And I should know, I been there once.' He leaned back on the stuffed leather banquette and laced his fingers behind his head. Lucia Davenport noted the strain in the fabric of his trousers when he did this: the creases, the protuberance, the welt of muscle along the thigh. Charlie closed his eyes and breathed deeply, and from off the top of his fresh-tapped beer he blew the froth of that up-the-Daintree circus.

'Two storeys high,' Charlie said. 'And I don't mean it's got an under-the-house. I mean, two floors all inside, the way they have in England. And the roof has pointy things, castle things, whad'ya call 'em?'

'Spires?' she asked. 'Minarets?'

'Minarets, yeah.' Charlie opened his eyes and smiled a slow smile. He drank a golden mouthful and let the golden word and the liquid slip pleasurably together, making a tour of his veins. 'Minarets,' he repeated, in love with the sound of them, the idea of them. 'Yeah, minarets. That's what it's got. Twenty or thirty sprouting out of the roof like bloody pawpaw shoots.'

'Oh Charlie.' She laughed, pushing a puddle of beer across the table with one finger, accidentally brushing his hand. 'You and the blarney stone.'

'They got more rooms than you could shake a stick at.'

'How many rooms?'

'And servants,' he said, rising to a warm and beery eloquence, 'with velvet bloomers like your grandma used to wear.'

None of this, alas, could be put in the letters to Ida. It would never do, it would be sheer lunacy, to submit Charlie to a reading by Ida. Charlie, alas, had a reading audience of one. But there, he was without fixed form or narrative limit; in secret genre, he flourished as extravagantly as climbing pandanus up the Daintree.

'And in a room smack in the middle of the mansion,' Charlie elaborated, 'in a bloody *wardrobe*, no windows, that old codger Weiss turns Daintree fungus into gold.'

Charlie O'Hagan, Mossman cop, married man, father of a good Catholic brood (several of whom learned their English-FrenchHistoryGeography from Miss Davenport, high school arts teacher) met with Lucia as often as possible. Not in Mossman, needless to say. And not in Cairns, which would not have been any safer, bars having at least a thousand ears, especially where school teachers and policemen were concerned. No. Luckily Charlie had connections and they met offshore in the floating tourist hotel. They drifted as whim took them: Green Island, the outer reef, the Whitsunday Passage, wherever. They left no wake.

Miss Davenport leaned across the table in the dimly lit bar. 'Do you mean he's an alchemist?' she asked. 'Rebecca's father?'

'Yeah,' Charlie said. 'That's the word, I reckon. Makes this dynamite dope out of fungus, pure gold in Sydney. Got his private fleet of hippie runners, that's what we reckon. We turn a blind eye. But we'll bust things up quick as a wink if we ever have to.'

'But you *wouldn't*, Charlie, oh you wouldn't, would you? You can't believe a word of all that, it's just talk. And they're so shy, they're so harmless, and Rebecca's so... Anyway, you're not that kind of policeman.'

Charlie O'Hagan put down his beer and coughed. 'Yeah, well. Don't spread the word. Do me in, if they find out what a softie ... ?' He grabbed her hands, slopping beer on the table. Policeman and school teacher slid into collision on slick leather. Ignoring the waitress, Charlie O'Hagan sent his rough cop's tongue on a voyage inside Miss Davenport's mouth. 'I gotta get you into bed,' he said. 'In the next five minutes, or else.'

Without coming up for air from the kiss, Charlie O'Hagan snapped his fingers, and the manager pulled up anchor. Four stars streaming, the hotel tacked into the wind, making for the steamy place where the Daintree spills into the sea.

The boys thought Rebecca was ugly, plainjane, a real dog, a praying mantis, a barbwire tangle of sticklimbs and sharp points, so of course Rebecca believed them. Miss Davenport thought she was striking in the manner of Virginia Woolf, the kind of girl whose gaunt cheekbones and deep eye sockets will become memorable – though perhaps not ever in Mossman.

On a certain Friday in the not-quite-so-wet part of the year, gangly Rebecca, who wrote unsettling English compositions modelled on Dostoevsky, hung about Miss Davenport's desk.

'My, uh, father and mother,' she said in her oddly formal, oddly desperate way, 'wish to, uh, invite you...' Shyness scrunched Rebecca's eyes tightly shut. 'They, uh, told me I had to invite you for *shabbas*.'

Miss Davenport, not entirely precisely clear on the subject of *shabbas*, answered carefully. 'When is that, Rebecca? *Shabbas?*'

'It's uh, tonight,' Rebecca said. 'For tea.'

Miss Davenport raised surprised eyebrows. She was touched. Rebecca, however, twisting the damp edge of her school uniform in her hands, gave every sign of hoping that her invitation would be turned down. Miss Davenport bit her lip, compassionate. The last of the Hapsburgs, Charlie whispered in her ear. She saw minarets. Curiosity, alas, overcame her.

'That would be lovely, absolutely lovely, Rebecca. I'd love to come.' Rebecca's lashes fluttered across despairing eyes. 'But how will we ... ?' Miss Davenport began to ask.

'On Fridays, uh ... they, um, my parents drive down.' During the week, Rebecca boarded at the Methodist parsonage next door to the school. 'We have to, uh, be back by sundown.

They'll be waiting for us, uh, at the Post Office.'

He's like a goblin, Miss Davenport wrote to Ida. *So is the mother. And only alchemy could keep that car functioning. The drive takes an hour, and the forest starts smothering everything once you're fifteen minutes north of Mossman. It's like moving inside green yeast.*

There were no minarets.

There are two storeys, Lucia wrote to Ida. *But it's rather like a dollhouse, or a farmhouse in the Black Forest, and very beautifully made out of cabinet timbers. Mr Weiss built it himself, and the mother weaves tapestries on a loom. They take carvings and weavings to Kuranda and Cairns to sell. Poor as church-mice, I'd say. Hardly any furniture, but everything handmade and wonderful to touch. And everywhere, floor to ceiling, there are piles and piles of books. I've never seen so many books.*

At table, there were candles, and place settings for five.

'Rebecca,' Mr Weiss said in his heavily accented voice. 'Ask Leo if he will please come down and join us with our guest for *shabbas.*'

Rebecca, expressionless, looked first at her mother, but her mother was ladling vegetable stew. She looked at her father. She twisted the hem of her skirt in her hands.

'Rebecca?' her father asked, his eyebrows raised.

Rebecca climbed the silky-oak staircase, trailing a hand up the banister. She disappeared for a full two minutes. Miss Davenport spoke warmly of Rebecca's writing.

'Yes, yes,' Mr Weiss said, nodding. 'In the beginning, God *spoke.* There was a word and it contained everything. Everything.' He nodded and nodded, beaming at her. 'The word,' he said. 'The word. We are grateful to you.'

Rebecca came slowly downstairs. 'Leo is unable to join us, Father,' she said.

'Ah.' Mr Weiss sighed and bowed his head. 'But perhaps only to be expected, yes?'

Candles were lit, bread broken, wine drunk. Mr Weiss spoke of music and books, of Mendelssohn and Isaac Babel... Would Miss Davenport, perhaps, be teaching Babel's stories in the English class?

'Actually,' Miss Davenport confessed, embarrassed, 'to tell you the truth, I'm afraid I'm not familiar with... I haven't actually had the pleasure...'

'Yes, yes, *Red Cavalry* and *Tales of Odessa,* ah *there* was – as Babel called himself – the master of the genre of silence.' Mr Weiss spoke of things not lost because the silence preserved them. He spoke of the words of silence and the silence of words. He talked with manic excitement and speed, as though he were some necessary counterpoint to the masters of silence.

Mrs Weiss did not speak at all.

'Rebecca,' Mr Weiss said when the plates had been cleared, 'will you ask Leo if he will play for us now? For our guest? The Mendelssohn, tell him, he cannot refuse us.'

Rebecca did not look at Miss Davenport, but Miss Davenport watched Rebecca's face, in profile, floating upstairs at the top of her shoulders. It was like a mask, like a waxwork image of Rebecca.

They waited. Mr Weiss spoke of Mendelssohn, of silence, of darkness, of how all that mattered could be preserved if one got far enough from distracting noise and light. 'Getting far enough away, that is the secret,' he said, nodding, nodding. 'Silence and darkness. Although such problems for the violin, poor Leo, *ach!* You have no idea of the problems, the rainforest, the heat, the moisture, *oi vay.*'

'Father,' Rebecca said in a low voice, descending. 'Leo says he will play, but he will not come downstairs.'

'Ah, ah!' Mr Weiss raised his wineglass to the stairs. 'He will play.'

Mrs Weiss folded her hands in her lap and closed her eyes. Rebecca twisted her skirt in her fingers and studied the table-cloth. Mr Weiss began rocking gently backwards and forwards, eyes closed, a smile on his face. 'Ah,' he sighed blissfully. 'Mendelssohn.'

Miss Davenport heard the usual forest noises, the calls of nightbirds, the cicadas.

And then, she wrote to Ida, *I don't know how to explain this, but I heard it too. I definitely began to hear a violin. At first it was so faint that I thought I was hearing the echo of Mr Weiss's hope, but then it was Mendelssohn, unmistakably. The first movement of the violin concerto. When it ended, Mr Weiss was crying.*

Lucia did not mail this letter to Ida.

'Rebecca,' Miss Davenport said, as they walked west, late the next Wednesday afternoon, on the road that led to the Mossman Gorge. Dust rose in little mushroom clouds around their sandals. 'Who is Leo?'

'Dad's oldest son. He used to play in an orchestra.' Rebecca looked at Miss Davenport and then away. 'Second marriages. They both had other children but there was no one left. I was born out here. After ... all that.'

It was a three-mile walk through tunnels of cane in a swooning heat that dripped across the forehead and down the neck and gathered wetly in bodily creases. Then they would climb into the shadow of the Divide, where the gorge was full of deep green pools and falls and ferns.

Rebecca had been alarmed by the invitation. 'What if someone sees?' she asked nervously. She was afraid of being called teacher's pet; she feared open spaces and long exposures. Lucia had had to wait for her half a mile along the road.

Lucia imagined what Rebecca might write in her diary: *She watches me all the time, and today she asked me to go swimming at the gorge. Help! Some of the girls think she's queer.*

Rebecca said: 'I suppose you think we're crazy?'

'No, Rebecca, I don't.'

Heat, cane, dust, steamfoghaze. It was like walking through dreams. Miss Davenport's voice came sleepily, drugged. 'You'll win scholarships, Rebecca. To university. You'll escape from here.'

Rebecca stopped then, turning, swaying a little in the haze. 'But this is where we've escaped to,' she said.

They walked. At the end of the road, just before the wet mouth of forest licked up unpaved grit and dust, the Reserve slouched against the mountain, a sorry place. Some Mister Government Man, well intentioned perhaps, had hacked clear a crater between forest and canefields, a pitiless saucer of red dust in which he had planted twenty fibro huts on low stumps. Men sat on the wooden steps, children chased each other in the compound.

'There's Hazel,' Rebecca said.

'Where? Oh!' Miss Davenport waved and called. A hush and a stillness fell abruptly on the children playing tag. Thirty or more faces, the faces of men, women, and children, stared silently.

Hazel, barefoot but still wearing her school uniform, did not move.

'Hazel?' Miss Davenport called again, less certainly.

Hazel came forward slowly, her bare feet sending up dust signals, her eyes down.

'Hazel,' Miss Davenport said. 'Rebecca and I are going to swim at the gorge. Would you like to come with us?'

Hazel rubbed one bare foot against the other leg and studied the busy columns of bull-ants emerging from pockmarks in the earth near her feet. She touched the black juicy bulbs of an ant body with her big toe, and the three women watched a file break rank and follow its leader across the mound of Hazel's foot. Fifty ants later, Hazel looked from Miss Davenport to Rebecca and back to Miss Davenport. Since the invitation was not withdrawn, she bit her lip and giggled a little and put a hand over her mouth to cover her shyness. 'Okay,' she said, from under her hand. She giggled again, and blushed. She called something back over her shoulder and flicked her hand in a curious way. It was as though she had pulled a switch: noise began, the men looked away, the children went back to play.

Miss Davenport the schoolteacher and her two pupils left the bare saucer of the Reserve and crossed the shade line.

The change was abrupt. The light turned green, the temperature dropped, webs of lawyer cane lay in wait. Below the falls (they were only ten feet high, but aggressive) the pool was as green as the matted canopy above. Hazel tossed her tunic and blouse over a rock and dived in, a shallow arc, from the bank. She was not wearing underwear. Rebecca and Miss Davenport registered this with mild shock.

The Methodist minister's wife, Lucia mentally wrote to Ida, *donated the uniform and shoes. Hazel, no doubt, would have been too shy to specify further needs, and it would not have occurred to the minister's wife, or any of us, for that matter...*

Rebecca took off her uniform and folded it neatly.

Ribs like corrugations on mother's old wooden washboard, Miss Davenport saw herself writing. *So painfully thin, I couldn't bear to look. For a moment, Rebecca seemed to be assessing the disadvantages of walking back into town with wet underwear, but then she entered the water with tentative steps until only her head was visible.*

Perhaps she could not quite subject herself to open comparison with voluptuous Hazel.

In the green pool the two heads floated with their dark hair fanned about them: waterlilies on lily pads. A languid steamy contentment suffused Miss Davenport. Back on the hockey field, in the sticky heat, she had thought only of coolness, water, the gorge. Rebecca had been an afterthought, an impulse: Hazel another impulse. But sometimes... *All manner of thing shall be well.* She saw the words in black floreate script on parchment. She smiled.

Green coolness, she had been thinking on the hockey field. The gorge, the falls, the pool.

She had not thought of the matter of clothes at all, how it complicated things. And now, after all, it was irrelevant again, for all manner of thing would be well.

Miss Davenport, with a careless rapture, took off all her clothes and walked into the water.

The pool, from dark subterranean places, was chilly, a shock to the body for whole minutes. Time must have passed, though the three women were not conscious of it. They did not speak, but they were aware of each other. Birds piped and flashed their colours, the falls kept up their subdued chatter.

This is where we have escaped to, Miss Davenport thought. One is safe in water.

One is helpless in water.

Afterwards, she could never understand how there was no warning, no transition. Just peace, and then chaos, the jarring laughter and catcalls, the five boys standing on boulders.

Joanna Goanna's tits! they whooped. *Cop those black tits! Plain-jane hasn't got any tits, she's flat as a bat. Oh 'struth, cop that! You can see old Dried-up Davenport's pussy!*

The boys, Miss Davenport noted, were in an intense and spiritual state, a kind of sacrilegious ecstasy, leaping from boulder to boulder around the pool. Like kings of the wild, they stood high on the great black rock and pissed into the water. Then one of them, Ross O'Hagan, eldest son of the local police-man, an ordinary boy who sat at an ordinary desk in Miss Davenport's English class, that boy turned his back and pulled down his shorts and squatted. A turd emerged slowly and hung suspended from his hairy anus. It was long, amazingly

long, making its celebrity appearance to a chanted count. One!
the boys chanted. Two, three, four, five...

Miss Davenport, Rebecca, and Hazel watched, mesmerised.
The turd had attained the count of ten, a plumbline reaching
for water. Eleven, twelve, thirteen... It detached itself at last
and fell into the pool with a soft splash. Cheers went up, and
more whoops of laughter, and then the boys were off like
possums, flying from rock to rock. They scooped up the bundle
of female clothing, and ran off.

Miss Davenport was able, for a moment, to think of the value
her nylon panty would have as trophy: a relic almost, handed
from boy to high-school boy until it passed into legend.

Water lapped at their shoulders. Polluted water. Hazel, inured
to indignity perhaps, was the first to move. She clambered onto
the boulder below the falls and let the water hammer her. Once
she slipped, and fell back into the pool, and climbed out again;
she submitted her body to the punitive shower.

But what comfort could Miss Davenport give to Rebecca
whose face had put on its whitewax look-alike mask? How
could she unsay the sentence that had been spoken, become
an Anti-Circe? In her teacherly mind, she rehearsed possible
spells: *This says more about the boys than it does about us.*

But it would not serve, she knew it. It might be true, but
it would not serve. That steaming fact, dropping stolidly into
the pool, spoke a thick and dirty language. The acts of men,
even when they are boys, Miss Davenport thought, are shouts
that rip open the signs that try to contain them. We have no
access to a language of such noisiness. Our voices are mice-
mutter, silly whispers.

We will have to stay here in the pool forever, she thought.
We are dead ends, the last of a line, masters of the genre of
silence. We will have to invent a new alphabet of moss and
water.

Hazel, wet and comfortably naked, walked out of the pool.
Miss Davenport shook herself as a terrier does. We'll have to
cover ourselves with something, she thought briskly. We'll
have to walk back before it gets dark.

RUBY LANGFORD (GINIBI)

Ruby Langford was born in 1934 on an Aboriginal mission, Box Ridge, in Coraki on the north coast of New South Wales. At eight years of age she left the mission to escape an Aboriginal protection roundup. She was raised in the town of Bonalbo, and left school in second form; as she says, 'The rest of my education was in the school of hard knocks, just like every other Aboriginal mother.'

Much of her life story is contained in her highly acclaimed book, *Don't Take Your Love to Town*, published by Penguin, which is now a recommended school text. For Ruby Langford this represents not just a personal achievement but a considerable advance for the Aboriginal people: 'My story is about twentieth century Aboriginal life,' she says. 'About the way we live today. And it's probably the only information that a lot of students get that puts the Aboriginal point of view. Because Koori history and culture is almost never taught in schools, and if it is, it is usually as it is seen by whites, and not from an Aboriginal perspective.'

Ruby Langford is currently working on her second book, *My Bundjalung People*; in it her aim is to trace the history and culture of her people, for her own satisfaction, and for the benefit of Koori and Gubba alike. She has returned to the mission station where she was born and she is working with her adopted daughter – a photographer and a descendant of the stolen generation. 'I think it is the first time ever that Kooris have tried to document the history of the Bundjalung,' she says. 'The people on the mission have given us permission to do a photographic exhibition and with *our* words and images, at least it means that this version of Koori culture won't be misrepresented by whites.'

Politics is a primary part of Ruby Langford's reason for writing. 'In doing the Bundjalung people *we* are gaining expertise, and we are educating the Aboriginal people as well,' she comments. 'Aboriginal people get so little recognition in this country that it's vital that both Kooris and Gubbas learn about our plight, and our contribution. Aboriginal images have been used to promote the country for tourism and yet we are an exploited people. We don't have the same rights as whites – not in health, housing, or employment.'

Through her writing Ruby Langford takes the opportunity to challenge and change some of the racist images of society; 'We are sick of being forever stereotyped as lazy, layabout drunks and no-hopers. You just have to look at the television to see how the negative image of the Aboriginal people is maintained. You won't see many Kooris in ads or on the soaps. They even use other Blacks – "exotics" from far away places – but no indigenous ones. It's time the original inhabitants of this land had their full image presented.'

Ruby Langford is very active in achieving this end. Apart from giving many lectures (in which she reads and performs much of her writing) she has contributed extensively to anthologies, and has written a paper, 'The Oppressed People' in 1990, *Writers in Action*. (Writer's Choice, Sydney University).

Koori Dubays [1]

My Mother: she gave birth to me!
26 January, 1934

My recollections of my mother are from when I was a little girl; her voice softly telling me that when I was a baby she only used Palmolive soap on my skin because that kept it smooth and soft. And because I was the eldest of the three girls in her marriage with Dad, I was prompted to ask, 'What about Gwennie and Rita? What soap did you use on them?'

'Well,' she said, 'Gwen was a Lux soap baby, and Rita, the youngest, was a Palmolive girl just like you.' That ended my childhood curiosity for a little while, and pleased me greatly. For I thought... Rita and I are dark, and Gwennie is real fair, and I wondered if that had anything to do with the selection of the soaps, because everyone knows that Palmolive is a dark soap, but that Lux is white! You see, I was a very questioning child, a 'stickybeaky kid', and I wanted to know it all. There were other things too that I had a burning desire to know. Boy, what a stickybeak I was.

And I listened in great wonder. When my mother would tell me about the olden times when they used to travel in real old buses to dances in different towns. That in those days the dances were olden-time dances, and they had an MC who made them all form a circle, and when the music started up they all moved off together and became one swirling mass of dancers. The music was played on an old button accordian and gum leaves, a guitar, an old violin and a mouth organ. Hurricane lamps hung on nails at vantage points around the hall, giving the old wooden place a soft warm glow.

I remember some of the dances too. There was the Pride of Erin, waltzes, quicksteps, and the progressive barn dance. And the old sets. We kids were allowed to dance inside the circle so the grown ups couldn't tread on us. We were only little you see.

I remember the Master of Ceremonies and another bloke, standing at the back of the hall and giving a rendition of,

Oh Mr Gallagher, and Mr Sheen...
You're the biggest, ugliest 'B' I've ever seen...

And they would sing these ditties back and forth, insulting each other amid much laughter from all the dancers.

Gwennie and I won a pair of spoons for our dancing. We were good little dancers too. And there'd be big open fires lit out the back of the hall, with women bustling round making tea and cocoa, and slicing up damper to eat. It was a very happy atmosphere.

Then on the way going home, how sleepy Gwennie and me would be; so sleepy that Mum and Dad bedded us down in the port racks on the bus, with a blanket and a pillow under our heads. And that's where we stayed, snuggled up, until we reached home. I remember the bus's motor humming, and people singing; it made us real contented as we nodded off to sleep.

Going back in my thoughts, I can recall Mum searching for bush tucker, for buninny and binging (meaning porcupine and turtle in the Bundjalung lingo). How she would take us kids to a swamp, and settle us down while she got into the water, tucking her dress up into her bloomers and then wading around feeling with her feet until she got a binging and wrung its neck, killing it. Then she'd throw it onto the bank where me and Gwennie waited with a chaff bag to put them into.

Back at home a fire was lit in the old fuel stove. She'd lay the turtles on their backs to cook inside the oven while we waited patiently for a good feed. Other times she got us bunya nuts from the bunya pine trees and broke them up with a tommy axe and roasted them for us in the hot coals. They were good tucker too. Filled our little bellies up.

All these memories are of a long time ago. I didn't have much chance to get to know her well, my mother. Because she ran away and left us on the mission and I was too young to understand why.

We never saw her again until we moved to Sydney. By then we were teenagers. She'd had another family to the man she had run away with. She worked hard and raised that family properly. Although she never raised us, her own children to Dad. My two sisters never forgave her. She died and there was only me and her other children there to mourn her. But I loved her because she gave me life. She brought me into this world and I did love her for that. She always called me *my girl* and she'll always be a heroine in my eyes. And I do know that my father was terribly heartbroken when she left, but that old hurt healed itself, because they became friends before she died.

Mother Nell: she raised me, 1944

After Mum left us, people sent word to Dad who worked in the scrub timber-getting. He knew the old Abo Protection Board would take us and put us in a home to be trained as servants to white people, so he took us three girls back into the bush with him. While he worked we were looked after by Uncle Ernie Ord, tribal doctor and clever man; he caught bush tucker for us, made ashes damper, and told us stories of all the bush animals and birds. He gave me my totem because I was the eldest: willy wagtail. He said it would tell me good news, or bad; it was my messenger bird and would watch and warn me.

Dad took us to live in Bonalbo with his brother, Uncle Sam and his wife, Aunt Nell. The first time I saw her I knew I would love her. She was a big robust woman who wore an apron with a notepad and clothes pegs in the pockets. The pad was for writing shopping lists, and the pegs, for pegging clothes on the line.

I was eight years old and I tried to be just like her. Mother Nell, we called her, this gracious, kind woman. And she and Uncle Sam never referred to each other as Nell and Sam, only as Mother and Father. And she was ten years older than him. But I never heard them argue, never.

She taught me how to milk a cow, and how to crack a horse whip; how to cook, and how to make home-made butter. She also taught me how to love and respect my elders. And not to talk at the meal table – only grown-ups talked at the table.

She taught me the magic of listening to Old Jack Sperring's dance band on Thursday nights; she taught me how to whistle the cows up. She taught us how to laugh, and love; and how to be humble.

If I had ever had the choice of a mother, she would have won the toss.

Mother Nell had one child to father Sam, called Judy. She

was a change of life baby, and Mother Nell ended up with a tumour in her stomach. She wasted away to nothing but I'll always remember her laughter and her love because she raised me to be what I am.

In my mind's eye, when things get too much for me, I remember this big robust woman, and feel ashamed of my petty whinges. I feel honoured to have known and shared a piece of her life with her.

I went home to Bonalbo in 1986 for a school reunion. Me, and my two sisters, and Mother Nell's other daughter, Shirley. And we went to our old street, where our old house used to be. But there was not a thing left of the old house. Just all the memories we'd shared with Mother Nell. We walked sadly away, with our memories in our hearts.

Mum Ruby Leslie: she helped me, 1950

When I was seventeen and having my first child, this lady was to be my baby's grandmother. I wasn't married to her son though. I left Sydney (and the rag-trade, where I had learnt my trade) and went to live in Coonabarabran until I had the baby. It wasn't just because I was unmarried and pregnant, that I left Sydney. In those days unmarried, pregnant women were looked upon as tarts. And I knew I wasn't one of those. I left because I didn't want to embarrass my dad. He was a dear father to us girls.

His last words to me were, 'If it doesn't work out, Ruby, you come right back here.' I was young, and very inexperienced about most of the facts of life – partly because it was a taboo subject when I was a girl; you didn't even talk about menstruation in front of men.

Mum Ruby was an old hand at having babies. She was one of 'the stolen generation'[2] who had been put into Cootamundra, and it was to her I turned with all my questions about pregnancy. 'How will I know when it is time to go to the hospital?' I would ask her. 'Well,' she replied, 'You'll get these real bad pains, like backache, and they'll get harder and harder to bear until you'll feel like you want to push down and give birth. It takes hours though, OK?' I found this information a blessing as I didn't know a damn thing about child-birth. But Mum Ruby knew. She'd had seven kids of her own.

Her family lived with her and her second husband in a tin shack on the Gunnedah Hill, in Coonabarabran behind the mission. There were several Kooris living in these fringe dwelling camps on the hill, with exotic names – like French's Forest. And where Mum Ruby lived they called 'Leslie's Leap' or 'Leslie's Lookout'. We sure had deadly names for our shanty towns.

I ended up having four children born in Coonabarabran and no matter where I was, Mum Ruby came. Even when I was out in the bush working at ringbarking, or burning off. And she always took the rest of my kids and looked after them, when it was time for me to go into hospital for my next birth.

Mum Ruby has a special place in my heart, because she taught me to have strength, and a will to win, and not to let anything beat me. She also taught me how to swing a (kelly) axe, and chop down trees which were then left to dry out for the winter fires. She taught me how to make a bough shed to shade us from the summer heat; how to cook in an old camp oven the best rabbit stews – and how to set the rabbit traps to catch them with.

I could ramble on and on about this old girl, with her smoke-dried hair from the open fires. She was quite a lady. And I'll always be thankful for everything she taught me about life and giving birth. I'm her namesake, Ruby.

Neddy Pearl: my best mate of 37 years, 1950

While I was living on the Gunnedah Hill, Mum Ruby introduced me to Nerida Chatfield, who was one of the Koori women who lived in a tin shanty at the foot of the hill. It was right where the well was that supplied our drinking water. She had ten kids, and she was ten years older than me, and we became firm friends. When my eldest son Bill was born, she was the only visitor I had. She came into the ward with a hand-crocheted bonnet and bootie set, all done in blue, for my little son. He was so small – only weighing 6lb 10oz – and she had to remake the bonnet to fit his head.

Billy's head was the butt of many a joke when he grew into a big teenager. Back in those days he called Neddy his pin-up girl, but I lost Bill when he turned eighteen. He drowned in eight inches of water having an epileptic seizure. And eight months before I buried his sister, Pearl. That was in 1969 and 1970. And Neddy Pearl still has that big safety pin that Bill pinned on her jumper when he christened her his pin-up girl, twenty years ago.

For eleven years I lived in Coonabarabran and did bush work. After I came to Sydney to live in 1962, Neddy's and my roads crossed many times over the years. When I started to write my autobiography in 1984 – finishing it in 1987 – Neddy played a starring role in it. Because we shared many adventures in life together as 'titis' (sisters); we even shared our boyfriends.

We nursed each other through our grief over the death of our kids. Neddy lost four. I lost three.

I love her just like she was one of my sisters. All the sorrows and joys we shared. We will grow old together, and still be best mates.

Neddy nearly lost her arm when she had a run-in with a train. As she was about to board, it moved, throwing her between the tracks, and almost cutting her arm off.

All her family have gone their own way in life. She used to live down the south coast, but she's moved over to Fairfield Heights now, which is not so far away from me. So we'll be able to get together, just like the old days. And reminisce about old times, and all the happiness we shared. We won't look back with anger at our losses but will go forward with hope, and laughter – because that's all we had to begin with.

Kath Walker (Oodgeroo Noonuccal): she was an inspiration to me, 1989

I picked up a book of poems that my sister Rita gave me, called *My People*; it was published by Jacaranda Press in 1970. I like poetry, but when I started reading 'No More Boomerang' and 'The Ballad of the Totems', I cracked up. This Murri woman was a deadly writer. And I couldn't put it down. She's been socking it to the Australian public about our Aboriginal history, through her poems, for years. And she's been an inspiration to me, ever since I first picked up that book of poetry.

I didn't have the chance to meet her until January 1989 at the Black Playwrights' Conference, at Macquarie University, Ryde. And I met her son, Vivian too. I sat spellbound each day, watching the rehearsals of the twelve plays they were performing there.

There was Bryan Syron, Mudrooroo Narogin (Colin Johnson), and Archie Weller, Bobby McLeod, Richard Walley, Rhoda Roberts, and Justine Saunders and Bob Maza. There was a big mob of them; playwrights, actors, producers, and artists. It was wonderful. I felt honoured that they had invited me to attend.

Then Kath's play was performed. And her grandson – of about ten or twelve – played the didgeridoo. I had never seen all our people come together to perform before, though I knew how talented they were as artists, dancers and performers. And they were outstanding.

We were introduced, Kath and I. And we chatted whenever we got the opportunity. Some of my books, and those of others, were on sale there. And people came up to get me to autograph them. It was an experience, I can tell you.

We attended a premiere on the last day when the performers were given awards for their work. It was an honour to meet Kath; she's my favourite poet. You can have all your Henry Lawsons, and Keats, and Wordsworths. Kath Walker – or better still, Oodgeroo Noonuccal – will do me fine. Because she's a champion of her people.

My Daughters
Dianne Ridgeway: My Old Lady, 1989

I had five daughters; now I have four and Dianne Joyce Ridgeway is my eldest now. I call her 'My Old Lady'; her husband calls her 'Little Ruby' because she's fat and cuddly like me. She was married at sixteen, and she is thirty-five now. She has two children: Steven and then fifteen years later, a baby girl called Nikita Pearl. 'Pearl' after the sister Dianne lost.

Out of all my kids this woman is the battler. She's the home maker, gardener, chief cook and bottle washer. All my kids were close, but the three eldest were the closest – and she's the eldest now. All the worrying for the others seems to have fallen on her shoulders. She's like an old mother hen, looking after her chicks. Always out to help anyone she can, she's never had any of the luxuries of life, just the bare necessities.

Her eldest child is called Steven after his dad. He's six feet three inches tall, and a basketballer. He was the only Koori picked in an otherwise all white team to tour America in December 1988. Now he's doing his Higher School Certificate and wants to become an exchange student; he wants to go back to America and study art.

Money has always been tight for this family. But they'll make it, if there's a way.

Aileen Rita: my second eldest daughter, 1989

She was married to one of the 'Mutineers on the Bounty Mob'; his surname was Quintal. But the marriage broke up, and now she's divorced.

My two grandchildren of the marriage are still on Norfolk Island with their father; perhaps I will be able to visit them one day if the funds are available. Aileen lives in Bidwell, out in the western suburbs. As a matter of fact, all my kids are westies. With the exception of my youngest son, Jeffrey.

Aileen has two children, Stella and Mathew. She waited a long time for a home. I call her and Jeffrey the 'docile Libras' because they are docile until someone stirs them up!

But what I love about Aileen is that when I had major surgery on my stomach, two and a half years ago, out of all my kids *hers* was the last face I saw before going in to the operating theatre at eight o'clock in the morning. And it was the first thing I saw when I opened my eyes many hours later. She was just sitting there quietly, waiting for me to wake up.

I've never forgotten that.

Ellen Linda: my third daughter, 1989

Ellen was born in 1960. She's thirty now. Mother of four, one son, three girls; with my twentieth grandchild, a girl was born recently.

I remember her when she turned fifteen and left high school, saying 'I'm your only daughter without a boyfriend. No one wants me.' And then one day, a bloke named Ronny Nicholas came into my lounge and asked could he take my two girls, Pauline and Ellen, and their girlfriend Karen who was his sister, away up to the Entrance for a weekend. A bunch of teenagers were going, and he said he would take good care of them. He looked responsible enough, so I said yes.

Ellen was never able to say again that no one wanted her. They've been together ever since.

Ellen, out of all my girls, has the same personality as David, the second brother who died. Always laughing and going on silly.

I knew one day I would have to write something about all my girls because they are great mothers and home makers, and I am so proud of all of them. But I don't let them know that, 'cause it keeps them on their toes, aye! They are forceful women, and don't put up with bullshit from anyone. But the thing I like most of all is they are endowed with the gift of loving and helping anyone who needs help. They are special people, my four women.

And by the way, Ellen has blessed me with my own name-sake. Her eldest daughter is named Tara Ruby Maude. I'm thrilled about that too.

Pauline Anne: my youngest daughter, 1989

I nicknamed her Porkie Pie years ago. She's twenty-seven now, mother of three girls; she had them very young, just like me. And of course, she's neurotic – just like me! This one is the peacemaker of the family – although she's been known to cause a few blues of her own too. She was a caterer at the Royal Easter Show for years, and then a home care worker. But now she's an Aboriginal Education/Liaison Officer at Doonside High School.

This is the one who is a real Jeng-Waller – which means 'mouth almighty' in my lingo. Always having a go at me because she says I favour the boys more than the girls! 'But I'm not angry,' she says. 'I know why you do it. To make us responsible for ourselves and our kids. And to be strong like you.'

Aye! She's pretty right about that. But wrong about me favouring the boys. Because I love them all equally and I'll always be there for them if they should ever need me. They all know that. It's because boys are more helpless than girls, aren't they? Every woman knows that. But my four daughters are all heroines to me, and always will be.

Pam Johnston:
Boomali Aboriginal artist and mother

I first met Pam, when the people at Penguin and I were trying to decide on a cover for my book; I had a say in the design, and I wanted a cover by an Aboriginal artist, something to show that it was Aboriginal writing. Someone gave me her phone number so I rang and made an appointment with her. She came with a friend and took photos of me, and I explained how I'd love to have Mt Lindsay in the background, near Mulli Mulli country. But of course I would have to get permission from the tribal elders because Mt Lindsay was the home of the Hairy Man spirits.

She and another Koori artist, Danny Eastwood, had a go at the design. But Penguin rejected the roughs, and settled instead on a Mimi spirit design that I'd found in a book.

In all my travels, I've met a lot of people, but none like this woman. This mother is from the Gamilori tribe. She completed her MA last year, and never have I come across another Aboriginal woman so committed to our culture. Never. She doesn't just promote herself, she promotes her *people* and her culture. She's very community-minded. Not like some, only looking for glory for themselves.

Tireless in her efforts, she's worked in refuges, and teaches art and culture to our boys in Long Bay Gaol. As well as helping to run Boomali Aboriginal Artist Gallery in Chippendale. The first ever Aboriginal owned and controlled art gallery in

Sydney, it shows all paintings – urban, tribal, and community. They have even begun to sponsor gaol art too. All the paintings are covered by copyright so the artists can't be ripped off, as they have been in the past.

Whenever I have lecture engagements in town, she shanghais me, and I get the chance to watch this human dynamo Gamilori woman at work. It leaves me breathless, just watching her.

She has done so much for our people, everything to do with our history, art, politics and culture, as well as being very articulate in her presentation. Pam is unfailing in her efforts to fight for the rights of our people. She's a heroine to me because of all that, and she's opened up her heart and home to this old woman. And in my way, it takes a special kind of person to do that.

---

1. Dubays – women.

2. In the late nineteenth century *Aboriginal Protection Acts* were proclaimed in various colonies. It was proclaimed in NSW in 1883 and repealed in 1969. It is estimated that in that period 20 000 children were stolen, mostly half-castes, to be trained as servants.

❧ BARBARA HANRAHAN

Barbara Hanrahan was born in Adelaide in 1939, and was brought up by her mother and grandmother. Novelist, short story writer and artist, Barbara attended Adelaide Teachers' College; from 1957 to 1960 she studied at the South Australian School of Art and from 1960 to 1963, she continued with evening classes in print-making. In 1963 she left for London where she attended the Central School of Art.

She travelled between London and Adelaide for many years before settling in her home city; and she wrote fiction, produced paintings and prints, and lectured in the arts in colleges in both Australia and England.

She has had more than twenty-five solo exhibitions of her paintings and prints in Australia, England and Italy; and she has had eleven novels published since 1973. (Most of her book covers are her own artistic work.)

In 1968 she turned to writing and reflections on life when her grandmother died. *The Scent of Eucalyptus*, an autobiographical novel, was published by Chatto & Windus in 1973.

Among her publications are:

1974 *Sea-green*. Chatto & Windus, London.

1980 Fontana/Collins, Sydney.

1977 *The Albatross Muff*. Chatto & Windus, London.

1978 *Where the Queens all Strayed*. University of Queensland Press, St Lucia.

1979 *The Peach Groves*. University of Queensland Press, St Lucia.

1980 *The Frangipani Gardens*. University of Queensland Press, St Lucia.

1982 *Dove*. University of Queensland Press, St Lucia.

1984 *Kewpie Doll*. Chatto & Windus, London.

1985 *Annie Magdalene*. Chatto & Windus, London.

1986 Beaufort, New York.

1987 *Dream People*. Grafton, London.

1988 *A Chelsea Girl*. Grafton, London.

1989 *Flawless Jade*. University of Queensland Press, St Lucia.

Rambling Rose

Granma grew beautiful sweet peas and was a great drawer of jugs; she'd draw me one with a lip and a handle when I was a little kid. But they said I got my drawing from my father: he used to be always drawing and writing poetry before he died.

I won lilac certificates from the *Sunday Mail* Sunshine Club for drawing 'A Typical Youth', 'The Moon Cleaners', and 'The Flame of Peace' – my pen-name was Rambling Rose because it was romantic. And I won first prize from West's Theatre for my drawing of Svengali, and two lounge tickets for the Regent in the Maurice Chevalier Smile Competition. One day I went to one of the big stores in Rundle Street and showed the Advertising Manager the book that had my certificates and drawings stuck in it and he gave me a job. That's how I got away from working at the egg factory, where I'd hated it because the girls were common.

There were long queues of people on North Terrace trying to get work. It was the Depression. There were soup kitchens everywhere, and so many out of work, and humpies along the Torrens where people lived who didn't have money to afford a house. But I had a new red pleated skirt and a red jumper; and I wore a suspender belt and rayon stockings and a stiff straw hat. You had to wear a hat to work because it was creating employment in the hat factories – if you didn't wear a hat you'd get the sack.

When I started in the Advertising Department I never got up from my desk all day. I thought I was lucky to have a job like that, and I didn't want to lose it. I worried that if I went to lunch or to the lavatory there might be someone else sitting at my desk when I got back. In the paper you'd read about hundreds of people who'd line up for one job, and I was glad it wasn't me.

All I did that first week was sit and look at the drawings in *Vogue* and *Harper's Bazaar*. For morning tea they came down from the restaurant with big silver trays loaded up with cream cakes and silver pots of coffee and tea. With my first pay I bought a wooden vase with bulgy sides, burnt with a red-hot poker in a flower pattern. I took it home and gave it to Granma. She was a funny woman: she threw it at me. Afterwards she picked it up and it was on the window-sill for ages.

The head artist gave me drawings to copy, and I went to the Art School at night to do Drawing for Reproduction. I'd stay in town after work and have my tea at Balfour's – usually mince on toast and a pot of coffee (once when I was pouring the coffee some spiders came out, so they had to bring me a new pot). The Art School teacher was a fat old man who'd come up and put his arm round you. I hated him. Everybody in the class thought I was a bit flash because I was the only one working in an Advertising Department, and at the end of the year I got Honours.

The first thing I ever drew for the newspaper was a pair of gloves that turned out like monkey's fingers, so after that they made me draw crockery. I drew the pansy design milk jug, the wicker-handle teapot; the Bargain Basement cheese dish, jam dish, butter dish, sweets dish. I was completely surrounded by cups and saucers and plates – the whole floor was covered in sets and sets of crockery: twenty-one piece teasets, thirty-three piece dinner sets. I drew cups and saucers and plates by the millions. Mum was always putting Golden eye ointment in the corners of my eyes because they were sore from so much drawing.

I'd get up early every morning and hurry to get the *Advertiser* from the front garden and look at my drawings. I'd cut them out and stick them in my book – I even stuck in the awful gloves. If a drawing didn't look right I'd say it was the printer's fault.

What I really wanted to draw were fashions, but fashions were the highest thing you could draw, so you didn't get to draw them for ages. The head artist did most of the fashions, and she was a plain woman from the country who dressed like a great-aunt. She had buck teeth, a big nose, and hair tied back in a bun, but she was very nice.

One artist thought he was arty and went to theatrical parties and was a member of the Artists and Authors Club. He said many of the girls who went there didn't wear pants, and you often got slugs in your cold collation.

Another artist had greasy hair because she said she'd only wash it when it would make the water dirty enough. Sometimes if she did wash it, she'd make me brush it and put it up in a roll. I didn't know how to do it and was scared stiff of her: if I didn't do it properly she'd throw the brush at me. She was a real bitch who liked to throw things. When she threw ink over the head artist they transferred her somewhere upstairs.

The Advertising Manager started taking out the artist who drew shoes, and everybody in the office was disgusted because he was giving her double her normal wages. The Advertising Manager's wife found out and came into the office in a dress that had just been drawn and started yelling and screaming and putting on a big act. And then this artist who drew shoes left to marry a little man, and we heard she was always hitting him and trying to knock him out – she was an Italian type and about three times bigger than he was. Once her husband came in while she was ironing, so she hit him with the hot iron and burnt his face.

The ticket-writers were next door. They had a sink and a tap in their room and we had to go in to fill up our water jars and wash our dirty saucers. There was a big dark ticket-writer who thought he was lovely, and all the girls that came up for tickets thought he was lovely, and I thought he was lovely, too. I'd look at him sideways as I walked in with my water jar and dirty saucer, and he'd roll his eyes at me.

The window-dressers were down the passage, and people reckoned they furnished their homes beautifully with the stuff they took home from the windows. One window-dresser was a bit of a queer type, though he had a name that was quite well-known in Adelaide society. He'd been pinching stuff and they'd found out when they followed him. There was a terrible upset in the Advertising Manager's office when his mother came in and tried to stop them taking him to court. He was quite nice looking, a tallish blond bloke, but they still gave him the sack.

Another window-dresser would get me to draw lots of the things that were sent up for the windows. He was engaged to a girl in Melbourne, and he'd send my drawings over to her. If there was anything she liked he'd pinch it to keep for the house he was going to build for when they got married. But the arty artist said I'd be just as much to blame as he was – if he was found out I'd get the sack, too. When I said I wouldn't draw anything else he smacked my face, so I went and told the Advertising Manager and the window-dresser had to apologise to me.

I caught the tram into work every morning and there was always a man sitting on the tram seat at one of the tram stops exposing himself as the tram went past. Then one morning he wasn't there, so someone must have reported him.

Outside it was still the Depression, but there were beautiful georgettes, embroidered, in the Dress Materials Department; and scissors were used with a flourish to cut silk pongee tussore, crinkle marocain, angel skin lace. At lunchtime I walked through the departments: rock crystal choker, tinsel evening bag, Indian python shoes, ultra-smart Nose Dive hat. And I'd try on other hats with red roses and cherries, but it was such a business trying on gloves you almost felt you had to buy them. You'd put your elbow on a little velvet mat on the glass counter and hold your arm up stiff and they'd shake talcum powder into the glove, and then some over your hand, and then they'd roll back the top and push the glove down, and poke all in between your fingers – it was a nice feeling having gloves fitted on.

Sometimes at lunchtime I'd buy a sandwich from the Sanitarium shop in Rundle Street – always wholemeal bread and cold baked beans, and the first time I'd had one I'd thought

147

it was the most delicious thing I'd ever tasted. But usually I brought my lunch from home in a paper bag and ate it with a cup of tea in the staff dining-room. There was this woman on the cash register, and all the time she was working she was smoking and I couldn't understand where the smoke went. She took such a big long draw both her cheeks went in, but no smoke ever came out: it must have stayed down in her lungs. She had black hair and thought she was flash. She'd stand there and take your money with one hand and be smoking away with the other.

One girl was too frightened to go into the staff dining-room, so she ate her lunch sitting on the lavatory. People reckoned it was her who'd had a baby in there (the workmen had found one blocking up the lavatories).

Every pay-day I'd buy walnut creams from Haigh's – that was my pay-day treat. They had half a walnut on the top, and Haigh's chocolate over the creamy stuff in the centre. They were fat and heavy so I'd only buy six. I'd take them home and Granma and Granpa and Mum and my mongol aunty would have one, and I'd keep two for myself.

Granma was great on making you wear a flannel singlet, even in summer, but she didn't like lipstick so I'd have to put it on each morning when I got round the corner. The first time I put on Black Tulip powder my face came out in a rash.

After the crockery I drew horrible things like knives and forks and xylonite hairbrushes and brass firescreens with historical repoussé designs. Everyone hated drawing toys, especially the wheels with the spokes on the toy bikes. The Ma-ma dolls weren't so bad because you could make them look pretty.

We looked forward to Easter-time when they sent chocolate eggs up to be drawn. If you accidentally dropped one you could eat it, so we'd always be dropping them and eating them. One Easter when the man from the Confectionery Department came up for his eggs we'd smashed the lot and were stuffing them down our throats – we nearly made ourselves sick.

Then I drew gloves (velvet suede with fringes, organdie with Irish lace cuffs; doeskin, white piqué, suede lisle). And I drew Sahara sandals and Hollywood shoes.

I bought a pair of white satin shoes on the Lay-by and blackened them with Raven oil. I wore them when I went out with a cowboy from somewhere up North. He had an outback hat and high-heeled boots and took me to the York pictures (he took all the girls to the pictures). I sat there with the stinking Raven oil on my shoes, stinking the whole theatre out with the smell of them, and he got told to take his hat off.

Then I drew La Basque berets, smart straws, quality felts, Softee turbans, new season's toques. I kept putting hats on the Lay-by and when I'd paid them off I'd take them home and hide them because I was frightened there'd be a row. Once I had the hats for the Melbourne Cup ad in a box down by my desk, and I spilt a bottle of Indian ink on them. I nearly died, I didn't know what to do. I sat there and looked at it and I couldn't believe it. They were big-rimmed Leghorn straws trimmed with silk and velvet handmade roses. My stomach was turning over and I felt sick. I started crying and the Advertising Manager came in and said, 'Bugger the hats,' and took them into his office. I supposed he had them cleaned up so his wife could wear them.

The girls from the Advertising Department had to go to the mannequin parades, and we had to wear our best hats and our gloves. We had to lead the clapping every time a mannequin came on. They slouched along the catwalk with their shoulders forward and stomachs out. There was a bride at the end, beautifully dressed – the winter-wedding bride was usually in parchment-toned ring velvet with an orange-blossom muff. We'd get morning and afternoon tea free, and there were delicious cakes and sandwiches. Afterwards we'd go through the dresses and see how they were made. Some had dirt round the hem, and they were from Paris.

At last I graduated to drawing fashions. I liked the summer ones when I first started off, but then I wished the winter ones would come because I thought they'd be nicer. And fashions could even mean maternity corsets that were all straps and laces.

When I drew my ladies I'd put a little white dot in their eyes and a little bit of white on their lips to make them look glossy. Lots of people brought up their portrait photographs for me to colour. It was good to keep in with the assistants, because then you'd get something cheaper.

Fur coats were the hardest thing to draw – you had to have the paper wet and let the ink run into it so it looked soft, and then highlight out just a few hairs. The woman in the Fur Department was a real old devil, and whatever you did was wrong. One day I'd had to draw a rabbit coat, and everyone thought it was all right, but when they took the drawing down to her to be checked, she said, 'It's a fox, it's not a rabbit, it's a fox! – I can't pass it.' They waited for an hour, and then took the drawing down again, and she said it was exactly what she wanted.

The man in Fashions was a fanatic. One day I'd had to draw a white dress with black spots, and he counted the spots on the dress and the spots on the drawing. There weren't the same number so I had to draw the dress and the spots all over again.

After I'd been married two years I left work to have a baby. But when the baby was a year old my husband died so I went back to the Advertising Department.

When I was a kid I was scared of the Japanese and I said my prayers every night, and the last thing I'd say would be, 'Don't let the Japs come.' When it was the War and people in cake shops and bread shops and fish-and-chip shops, and even Mr Rodighiero across the road, got put in a detention camp I never felt scared – I never ever thought the Japanese would want to come down as far as Adelaide. Though the man next door came in to help us make an air-raid shelter in the back yard, and we all had a dig at it. It was just a tunnel in the nasturtium patch. Granma said she wouldn't go in it, she didn't fancy sitting in the ground with dirt over the top of her head.

There were hundreds of things you couldn't get during the War, like bobbypins and peanuts and chocolates. They only had a few silk stockings for their special customers in the Hosiery, but I knew one of the assistants and she saved me a pair under the counter. Everyone wore rayon stockings and even they were expensive. If I got a run in mine I wouldn't throw them away, I'd take them to two sisters who did fancy-work and mending in a shop on the Beach Road. In summer you could go bare-legged, as long as it didn't look like it, so you'd paint your legs with some awful brown stuff out of a bottle. You drew seams up the back of your fake stockings with an eyebrow pencil, and more often than not they were crooked.

Because you couldn't buy things, Mum got a how-to-do-it book. We each made a raffia basket and a raffia hat – you plaited the raffia and then sewed it round and round to make the crown and brim, and then worked flowers on it and lined it with cretonne. And we'd make flower brooches out of bread by working a fresh slice till it was like dough, then rolling out little petals and colouring them with food dye and sticking them together and baking the flowers in the oven.

Because the men had gone to the War, there were only young boys and women in the Advertising Department. As well as drawing I read the proofs for the ads and did layouts – things a man would have done if he'd been there. Paper was rationed so there weren't many pages in the newspapers and they didn't have a lot of advertising. You had to use your drawing paper both sides and you didn't use wash, you had to draw in black line because they couldn't make expensive blocks. I drew a book of handy household hints for women because they were the ones who were mending things and doing men's jobs.

You thought twice before spending your precious coupons. They kept telling you to do your best towards the War Effort by not spending money. They said thoughtless extravagant buying would be letting your country down.

There were Americans everywhere round Adelaide, and all the girls were out after them for what they could get. The Yanks were all right, they were just like anyone else, and after a while you never took much notice of them.

After the War finished the men started coming back and the new Advertising Manager thought he was big deal because he'd been in the Secret Service in Hollywood. He'd walk up and down smacking a ruler against his leg and say, 'Get on with your work... Don't you turn round... I'll have no speaking in this office while work is in progress.' He was a religious maniac who didn't drink or smoke or bet on the Melbourne Cup. He'd leave religious messages on people's desks, and when he left one on the Managing Director's desk he got the sack.

The next Advertising Manager had lips that were thick with blood like balloon lips, and he prowled about looking for kisses. His lips were red and swollen and soft, and he kept touching you and trying to kiss you, and he had spots all over his fly. Every time a girl came into the Advertising Department he'd pinch her bottom, and once when one smacked his face he spun round like a top. In the end the girls revolted and told him off and he didn't last long after that.

Then we had an Advertising Manager with false teeth who always had a pipe in his mouth that dropped ashes down on to his tie. Once he went swimming and lost his teeth in the sea and came to work all gummy and peculiar.

The head artist had something wrong with his head from the War and would go to sleep at his desk. He hardly ever did any work because he was usually asleep. He fell asleep riding his motorbike and crashed into a stobie pole and killed himself and then they make me the head artist.

The artist who drew the shoes thought she was hot stuff. She'd come in to work after she'd had a session the night before and she'd be stretching herself and being voluptuous and pulling her arms back and pushing her chest out. Every time she got herself into trouble she'd go off for a rough ride on a motorbike over potholes.

The artist who drew the crockery was so dumb she reckoned if you dipped a puppy in gin it would stay a puppy, and would never grow up to be a dog. She was a Catholic, engaged to a man in the Menswear, and she started worrying because she didn't want to muck up the sheets on her honeymoon. Then she told us she'd talked it over with the priest who'd said they should do it the night before and that would be all right because they'd be getting married next day.

One of the typists had teeth that absolutely crossed over in the front. She was round shouldered and covered in freckles and smelt like a dozen pasties, but she dressed quite nicely. She went out with one of the ticket-writers a couple of times. She said they sat in the back seat of the car and talked for a long time about doing it, and then decided not to do it after all.

The office boy was red headed with a baby face. He looked as if he was worn out most of the time and he'd often lie down

under his desk to have a sleep. Girls kept coming up to the
office, crying like anything, because he'd got them into trouble.
He got two sisters into trouble and he paid one of them to go
to Melbourne and married the other, and she turned into a
nervous person who shook and trembled and had a mania for
scrubbing the floor.

After the War there were 24 000 surplus bachelors in South
Australia and it was suggested to the Government it should
be arranged for every girl to have two husbands. I was continually being proposed to and I would have liked Gregory
Peck's smile or Tyrone Power's teeth or Clark Gable's devilish
dimples, but in the end I married a man from Gardening. I had
a wedding dress of grey silk sewn with crystal beads and my
bridesmaid, the window-dresser whose face went like a Pekin-
ese dog's when she smiled, wore nylon in a raisin-pink shade.
The office gave me a silver tray as a wedding present and we
came back from our honeymoon with a teaspoon that had the
Harbour Bridge on its handle.

People at the tram stop talked about me because I wore the
smartest clothes. I'd been the first one in our street to wear
the New Look; I wore all the new looks and I drew them, too:
the Dirndle Look, the Sheath Look, the Trumpet Look, the Sack
Look, the Harem Look, the Trapeze Look, the Shaggy Look.

The Shaggy Look was mohair, and one day I had so many
mohair dresses to draw I didn't move out of my chair all afternoon. I was still drawing mohair dresses when everyone else,
except the artist who drew the crockery, had gone home. When
I stood up there was an awful swoosh and suddenly there was
blood over my dress and over the chair and over the floor. The
other artist called out, 'My God, what's happened to you?' I
was having a miscarriage and I was sort of not there, I was
only looking on and blood was running out of me like a
river – there was blood everywhere. She ran and got some
towels from the wash room and wrapped them under me and
round me, but still the blood was running out. I was so thickly
padded up I could hardly walk, but I knew my husband was
waiting in the car by the staff door and if I could only get down
there I'd be all right. So we wrapped more towels and some
plastic round me and she helped me down the stairs, and when
my husband saw the blood he thought someone had tried to

murder me. On the way to the doctor the bottom of the car was filling up with blood. I didn't know I had so much blood in me and it was a wonder I didn't die.

When I went back to work after a fortnight there were still blood spots all down the stairs. But nobody ever said anything to me about what had happened. They knew, but they didn't say anything – they had manners.

GAIL JONES

Gail Jones was born in Harvey, a dairying town in the south west of Western Australia. She grew up mainly in the Kimberlys and on the Western Australian goldfields.

She graduated in English from the University of Western Australia and has since worked as a 'freelance' academic, teaching in several tertiary institutions.

Her professional interests are in literature and critical theory and her writing is characteristically concerned with the problems of representing the experience of women. She considers her work political, feminist, and modestly experimental, and cites as her contemporary influences, Marion Campbell and Angela Carter.

Gail Jones has written many short stories, a volume of which will be published by Fremantle Arts Centre Press in 1992. She is currently working on longer fiction.

Modernity

(I)

In the history of film there is this poignant tale. A young girl, visiting Moscow from her home in Siberia, goes to the cinema to see her very first movie. She is absolutely terror-stricken. Human beings are visually torn to pieces, the heads thrown one way, the bodies another. Faces loom large or contract to tiny circles. There are severed heads, multiple dismemberments and horrible discontinuities. The girl flees from the cinema, and as an incidental service to the history of representation writes a letter to her father describing in detail the shocking phenomenon she had witnessed.

The movie showing in that terror-causing Moscow cinema, in, let us say, the bleak winter of 1920, was a comedy.

Imagine this girl. Imagine Siberia.

(II)

Integrity

In Siberia one knows one's body to be whole because the elements assail it with a totalising force. The air is scintillatingly cold and algebraically precise; there is a mathematical quality to its cutting of angles, its calculable degrees of effect upon the skin, its common-denominative power, its below-zero vital-statistics. In the Siberian cold one feels every extremity, is equated instantaneously to the exactitude of each limb. Even in her favourite bearskin hat, her sealskin coat and her fluffy muff of mink (a gift from the requisite doting Babushka who, in order to buy it, pawned an old grandfather clock from the time of the Tsars), the girl is still rudely recalled to her body. Decked in dead animals she remains feelingly human.

Space

She will push, this girl, through the virgin snow. She will push with her snowboots and her inadequate animal vestments through the all new hectares of still-astonishing white, hectares which, with the sun, will surely bedazzle. She will pass large larch trees hung ornamentally with serrations of ice. Wolf prints sprinkle a pocked track to somewhere. And, looking backwards, she confirms absolutely her own foot-printing pathway.

Space is the lack of conclusion to her horizons. It is the perspectival extensiveness of the trans-Siberian railway, metallically trailing. It is the ample dimensions of snow on snow, so emphatically brilliant that she must squint to discern her journey through every single step of its immaculate empire.

Time

She knows, as we think we all do, time's unamenable incessancy. The clock that used to stand in her grandmother's bedroom ticked in totalitarian and purposive circles. Its hands were definitive, its face as indisputable and blandly commanding as a uniformed apparatchik.

Her grandmother's voice is another aspect of time. Since the death of her mother (a premature extinction in an unromantic snowstorm), this voice is to the girl a regular and reliable instatment of order. Next summer, says Babushka. Last winter, says Babushka. When I was a child of six or seven... She manages the continuum. There is never any doubting the steady progress to next summer. The larch trees await. The very landscape is bound to perpetual and carefully demarcated mobility. And history itself – by government decree – will later submit to subsections of Five Year Plans.

Setting

Of her home nothing is left to the risks of fiction. It is completely actual and labelled everywhere. The town the girl lives in is called Turukhansk and it sits, in a smug and geographical certainty, at the fork of the Yenisey and Nizhnyaya rivers. The girl knows this place as she knows her own body; that is to say, with coy particularity. There are parts of the town intimate as her hands, the cobbled alleyway to school, a handsome bowed bridge, the cavities of the market place; specifically a small bakery that, apart from the usual and all-too-familiar black bread, sells light and dainty pastries displayed with memorable panache in its gas-luminous window. There are also unmentionable places and habitations, but she knows these exist as surely as she knows of her own definite but impossibly unregardable heart.

Density

Solid, so solid, is the world of Turukhansk. Once, just once, the girl rode on a speeding troika right out of the town and to the furthest, ice-burdened limits of the world. There were three snorting horses of massive rotundity – flanks, bellies, the head's bulbous cheeks – and they strove through snow that stirred up in wild eddies and stung incisively. She could feel the muscular energy and rhythm of their gallop; she could see the long heads bobbing and the rim of broad rumps shifting and moving in concert. The breath of the horses was powerfully visible, their odour profound. Bells were atinkle on leather harnesses. And her father, who seemed himself suddenly newly substantial and corporeal, expanded, upholstered, assuming the impressiveness of horse-flesh, reached over and clasped her in an exhilarated embrace.

Narrative

Do not think that this girl from Siberia is uneducated. Each winter–starless night she follows Cyrillic intricacies stretching in long lines into the mythological soul-land of her Mother Russia. There is the omnipresent bible (Russian in tone), there are the national novels of great solemnity, and there are numerous folktales, all enchanting and instructive. Hers is a country both – contradictorily – filled up with stories and sensationally material. And from her Babushka comes the knowledge of other realms: that she is superintended by the unquiet ghost of her mother, by the never-ending story of family melodramas, by plots of kin. Sometimes this girl will weep in the dark, not for the banal complications of adolescence, but for the burden of narratives she is compelled to bear, for inner insurgencies clashing with no less force than the Red Armies with the White.

Identity

You will have seen the wooden dolls for which Siberia is famous, dolls which sit, one inside the other, in a series of smaller and smaller otherwise identical versions. These dolls give the girl an image of self: she may be different with, say, Babushka and Father, but these selves are all uniform, and neatly composed and contained. She has the conservative's assurance of inner conformity. She knows her self-sameness. Symmetries abound. In the mirror, unquestionably, is her exact equation.

As she lies awake in the early morning, watching the crystals of snowflakes alight and dispose themselves dawn-lit and lace-wise upon the glass of her window, the girl thinks often of the dolls, one inside the other. She likes to imagine that her absent mother was also, in some way, a kind of replica of herself, that she is constant in image and form even through the passage of generations. By this means she staves off the fracturing power of grief.

Voices

Apart from the management of time and the deployment of story the girl loves the act of voice for its invisible tendernesses.

As Babushka rakes charcoal beneath the samovar she sings in sweet inflections so sonorous and pathetic that her grand-daughter, enthralled, feels brimful of emotions. The songs seem to invade her; she swells at their presence. There are neatly rhymed couplets and poetic descriptions of perfect Romances and yearning Love. Language carries within it an irresistible tangibility.

Occasionally, by yellow candlelight, her father takes up a book and reads aloud from the works in translation of his favourite English poet. Once he read of a mad king caught foolishly in a storm and the girl realised, in a moment of vision, that the entire world was Russian, that its rhetorics and its extremity had somehow mysteriously extended to the four corners of the globe. From her father's voice came universality. From the movements of his tongue world-wide concordance.

Bodies

There is a man in Turukhansk so large in circumference that he is reputed to have cut a semi-circle in his mahogany dining table, simply to accommodate his ungainly girth. Babushka loves this story. She is interested in bodies and talks of them continuously. Illnesses. Births. Deaths. Copulations. The girl touches her own shape with concupiscent affection. She enjoys her baby-fat and her enlargening breasts. She imagines kisses on the bowed bridge and embraces beneath the larch trees. And once every year, when she has a chance to partake of dainty pastries, she recalls the man so large that he must cut out the world in the pattern of his belly.

When the girl leaves to go outside her grandmother offers, customarily, an ancient folk saying: *Rug yourself well or the wind will enter your body and blow away your soul.* This is a disturbing thought. The girl steps into the cold, into its white-blue squalls, hugging her own garments as if they could provide an adhesive to hold her together. In the cold she knows her body better than anywhere else.

Faces

These are indubitable. She studies faces. To see them together you would say that the girl was in love with her father. She gazes up at his face as he reads the latest broadsheet on the trouble in the Stanovoy and Ozhugdzhur mountains. She regards with lover-propinquity his Semitic nose and his brown hooded eyes. She dwells on the crinkles of his balding hair, is captivated by the peaked configuration of his lips. The grandmother, nearby, is of distinctly unsemitic and peasantish visage, but as utterly intimate.

One can kiss these faces. These faces can be clasped between two cradling hands. These faces come with the ponderous and heavy-weighted import of presence.

(III)

In the especially harsh winter of 1920 our heroine visited for the first time her father's family in Moscow. She descended from the world-famous trans-Siberian railway and fell into the arms of a second, unknown and much wealthier Babushka, a woman who wore about the neck an entire flattened fox, depending sadly nose-downwards.

There was the speed of a slow car, unfathomable chatter, and then the girl realised, incontrovertibly, that she was surrounded by the city. It was a place in which a palpable post-revolutionary unease was contested, again palpably, by a more inveterate aura of historical stolidity. It was a place, that is, in which one might expect dissimilarities and dissimulations.

Faces blurred past. Tall buildings loomed. Red flags, in their hundreds, gestured and stirred.

The visit to the cinema came in the second week. This is what happened. The new grandmother unwisely sent her charge in alone. She equipped her with a handful of roubles and copecks and left her there at the entrance, a mere babe, as it were, in technological woods.

The girl entered a little late and was perplexed by the darkness. There were straight rows of people – somewhat like those assembled for the pantomime at home – but ahead, inexplicably, was not the space for dramatic action but a rectangle of snowy screen. It stretched across the wall, pure and auspicious. The girl took her modest place among the rows of spectators, of whom she knew not one, and patiently waited. Somewhere to the left a man began slowly playing an inconspicuous piano. Then there was a soft whirring sound behind, like the wind in the eaves, or the wing-beat of cabbage-moths, and a long cone of white light shot instantly above her head. This was a bright enlightenment, newfangled, stunning, a distillation of incandescence too shiningly imperious to appear in any way artificial. It might almost have been some kind of Divine Revelation, the trajectory, perhaps, of a passing angel, a signal through space, the pointing finger of God. The girl felt her girl's body tense up intolerably. There was a sensation in her chest of flight and flutter. And then, before another single second had a chance to pass by, there were Russian-letter titles (mysteriously writ), displayed broadly and boldly upon the screen. So that was it. A type of large book. A system of pages. Communal reading.

The piano player pounded a crass fortissimo.

What followed was devastating. The titles gave way to a regime at once human and strikingly inhuman. By some dreadful magic the players appeared to have been robbed of both colour and regularity. Their faces and clothes were crepuscular grey, and their sizes expanded and diminished with awful elasticity. Moreover, they moved wholly within the frame of the rectangle; they did not seem to inhabit any ordinary space. It was some condition of suspension within which bodies were dangled upon the screen in a peculiar coalition of living-semblance and deathly, wraith-like abstraction. Thus transfixed these victims were rendered mute; they cavorted in dumbshow, mouthed words ineffectually, produced verbal nothings.

(And rising above the piano was the almost deafening sound of a battering heart-beat.)

It was at the point when the very first close-up occurred, presenting, in the blink of an eye, a gargantuan decapitation, that the girl suddenly comprehended what it was she saw. It was her mother's death. As the cruel Siberian wind cuts and slices, so too this dissection of the human body. This was how, in her imaginings, she had figured the long-ago maternal dissolution; that a woman, snow-bleached and lacking in the gust-resisting weight of the living, lacking the heaviness of fat men who create the world in their own shape, lacking the cosy enclosure of animal garments, the density of horses, the authority of Babushka, the accessible face, had submitted to execution by the Tundra winds. Bits of her body had exploded into the tempest, disassembled, sundered. Bits of her body had become indivisible from the blurring snow; her inner warmth was ransacked and replaced by cold, her face obliterated, her cry silenced, her soul blown away. In the terrible pelting of the pitiless storm her house-less head was blasted, rendered hollow and windowed as the carcass of a doll. Wracked. Wrecked. Breathtakingly undone.

The girl from Siberia sitting, bolt upright, in the fourth row from the front, was completely terror-stricken. There, caught uncannily on the unreal screen, with its distortions of scale and time, its slow dissolves and its clever montage, she had faced in chimerical vision her own perilous vulnerability.

She fled from the cinema, her screams piano-accompanied.

(IV)

This was a moment of modernity. All that had been solid melted into air. Not electricity or the revolution, not plane travel or radio, but the cinema had inaugurated a new order of perception. The girl of the story was not, as it happened, called Anna Akhmatova or Marina Tsvetaeva, but like the poets she had experienced the metaphysics of fragments. She ran screaming into the winter light of the city of Moscow, carrying in her head an unprecedented multiplicity.

Yet when the girl returned home, when she arrived in the arms of her real Babushka – expecting at last to retell the dreadful vision, to collapse, to cry, to blubberingly divulge – it was not cinematic disintegration she described. She did not tell of the deranged and incoherent bodies of the players, nor of how these recalled to her a personal haunting. Instead she dwelled, in concentration, on single detail: there

had been a cone of bright light, a white passageway of floating
motes, delicate, enchanting, apparently transcendental, which
might, after all, have somehow mystically signified the transit
of angels.

❧GEORGIA SAVAGE

Georgia Savage was born in Launceston, Tasmania, to Iris Wood, school teacher and Hedley Gunton, beekeeper/army pensioner. She grew up in West Launceston, where schooldays were less a matter of study and more of fun; after fourteen years of schooling, Georgia Savage left without passing any exams but with many positive memories of her teachers.

'The women who taught me, feminists, in graduate gowns and silk stockings, were rich in humour and forbearance. They had a love of literature and it rubbed off on me.'

Throughout her life, reading and writing have been a major interest; as has the environment, which is a current concern. 'These days, gardening is my passion,' she says. 'And world politics. I despair of male-dominated governments which instigate wars and encourage the rape of my home planet so I have become a member of Greenpeace. I'm also a supporter of the Gaia theory which means I believe the Earth will find ways to protect itself against us, even to the point of destroying the species.'

Since 1980 Georgia Savage has been a full time writer with a clear agenda:

'In my writing I try to deal with issues that are contemporary. For a novelist to do otherwise seems to me a kind of cop-out. If I have any aim in writing, it is to help women see the world and themselves through their own eyes and not those of men; it is to help them see themselves as winners – for in spite of a couple of double-bunger tragedies in my life, and in spite of being comparatively poor, I've never seen myself any other way.

'Like everyone else in this business, I am aware of the local backlash against women writers. The heady days of the late seventies and early eighties have gone, and women's work is again being trivialised. The literary pages of many newspapers and journals are full of photographs of men and histories of battles from long ago. Reviews of the work of women are kept for the bottom of the page. It seems that the more you threaten men, the further down the page they put your work. Some of it apparently slides right off and disappears.'

But Georgia Savage is still optimistic. 'In the long run,' she says, 'I doubt this will matter. Women everywhere are beginning to see there is strength to be found in learning what is going on in other women's minds. Books are a means to this end. Whether widely reviewed or not, I believe women will go on buying them, borrowing them and discussing them...'

In the short story included here, Georgia Savage insists she has made her positively last appearance as an adolescent; she has been very successful in using the voice of the young as for example in her last highly acclaimed novel, *The House Tibet*.

Among her publications are:

1983 *The Tournament*. Hale & Iremonger, Sydney.

1983 *Slate and Me and Blanche McBride*. McPhee Gribble/Penguin, Melbourne.

1987 *The Estuary*. University of Queensland Press, St Lucia.

1989 *The House Tibet*. McPhee Gribble, Melbourne.

She has also written short stories and book reviews. *The House Tibet* has been published in the United States in 1991, by Graywolf Press, Saint Paul, Minn. *The Estuary* will be published by Graywolf in 1992.

Photographs in Black and White

My nanna, Cicely, admires women like her friend Mrs McGann who had a miscarriage on the beach at Mornington and put her hat on it until her husband came from the pub to pick her up. *Kay* says, long suffering lunatics like Mrs McGann have helped keep women in the dark ages. Kay's my mum. She works on the trams but next year she's going back to uni to do honours. She says if she doesn't, she'll be driving the tram down Whitehorse Road when she's sixty.

I started with that stuff about Mrs McGann and her day at the beach because I'm supposed to be doing this essay on a woman I *admire*. It's worth twenty per cent of my sociology mark so I need to come up with something that'll knock Miss Vandenberg out. The worst part is that I know she'll expect us to choose someone like Alma Bassey, who's got a hearing aid and this jacket with leather patches on the elbows and beetles around on a two-stroke motorbike helping with Meals on Wheels. I *hate* Alma Bassey because I saw her grab a piece of paling off Morses' fence and whomp their dog with it when it barked at her stupid set of wheels.

Miss Vandenberg, who set the essay, carries on about being a feminist but the day Kleo Papageorgiou told her some girl in a book we were using was a whore because she had sex with a bloke while she was *single*, she let go at him with this great stuff about some ward at the Royal Melbourne being full of Greek girls getting their hymen sewn up because their father had been at them, then blew it by bursting into tears and rushing from the room, leaving Kleo to give a loud Greek 'Huh', and go back to his work without a feather out of place.

Kleo got *his* though the day he swore at Miss Forringham who takes us for maths. She's about a metre tall and looks seventy with this horsey dye in her hair. The boys at the back of the room give her hell and I guess this day she'd had enough because when Kleo came out with a stream of Greek shit, she lifted right off – marched to his desk, picked up this pair of dividers lying there and whomped one of the points through his hand, pinning it to the desk. Then, although she was shaking and everything, she went back to the blackboard as if none of it had happened.

It was Jimmy Copolous who got the dividers out of Kleo's hand. When he did, Kleo, who was already the colour of a Christmas lily, folded both his lips in and bit on them but didn't make a sound. After that, still without making a sound he left the room.

Kleo is Papageorgious' only son. They've got these three daughters and they all treat him like a *prince*. Because of that the rest of us kids thought there'd be a stu*pend*ous row with it being in the papers and everything. We even thought Miss Forringham would be sacked or at least pensioned-off. But it turned out that Kleo told his dad he'd *fallen* on the dividers, so Miss Forringham stayed on. Kay said being Greek and everything, he'd be ashamed to let anyone know that a woman and an old one at that had fastened his hand to the desk with his own set of dividers. I guess she's right but a funny thing is that from then on Kleo and Miss Forringham got along together. They didn't *say* much to each other but when they did, it was as if they were sort of equals. In any case, Kleo came top in maths but he'd have done it anyway because although he's such a bastard and everything, he's the smartest kid in the class. He's not bad-looking either if you go in for Genghis Khan eyes and spiked hair with tails hanging down the back.

One thing I *do* like about Kleo is his walk. I know that's a weird thing to say, but you know how Greek kids prowl around the quad with their knees sort of bent so they can stick their crotch out, well Kleo doesn't do that. Instead he rolls a little when he walks as if he's come from a long line of sailors or something. And he walks slowly, so that unlike the rest of him, there's a sort of *patience* in it. Don't get me wrong, I think he's the pits and I only told you about his walk because I'm into walks. I could just as easily have said the Head, Mr O'Brien, gets along on the balls of his feet as if he's about to take off over the hurdles. Or that Miss Vandenberg slides her left foot a bit instead of stepping out with it the way she does with the right. I just notice this stuff, that's all.

To get back to the essay, I want to tell you about this photograph I saw in a copy of the *National Geographic* Cicely brought home from work. It was of a woman I wouldn't mind writing about but I know that if I did Miss Vandenberg would raise an eyebrow at me and say, 'Nice try, Nora, but we were slightly off target, weren't we?' She says that sort of thing a lot, but I'll tell you about the woman in the photograph anyway. She's American and black and about six hundred years old with these swollen ankles and an embroidered cap like one of those old tea-cosy things on her head. Her name's Eva Jessye and she's a famous musician and if you want to know, I admire her because of the way she's *sitting*. Her humped old back is turned to a piano and she's leaning her chin on her hand with her eyes closed. You can tell by the look on her face that she's either listening to music or thinking about it. What's more she doesn't give a stuff if the rest of the world explodes while she's doing it. Another thing you can tell is that she's tired.

Cicely comes home from work some nights too tired to do anything but sit like that. She's a book-keeper for a firm of solicitors in the city. She's also a pianist and quite a good one. In the sixties and that, she was always being asked to play with bands but Mum was young then and Nanna didn't want to leave her with a sitter or something. Just the same she did do *some* playing but says she missed the buzz of the era because all the fun went on behind her back. All she did was smell the dope and look at the sheet music while someone asked her to play *Mr Tambourine Man* one more time. What I'm getting around to saying is that when Cicely comes home tired from work, the first thing she does is put on this tape she's got of Keith Jarrett's *Köln Concert*. Then she sits with her eyes closed like the woman in the photograph, listening, and when what she calls her *poppy* field of music is over, she opens her eyes, gives this big contented sigh and is ready to start preparing the vegetables and stuff for our tea.

When Kay listens to music she lifts her knee and bangs her heel down in time to it. Being so skinny and with short hair and everything, she's like a hillbilly boy and it breaks me up, but I don't say anything. Sometimes she comes home tired too. *Her* method of getting back to *Go* is to lie flat-out on the floor – sometimes still in her green *Met* overcoat. In winter she lies in the sitting room with her feet practically in the gas fire. In summer she lies anywhere that's cool while Cher, our labrador, tries to lick her face. Occasionally Mum grabs Cher and wrestles her to the ground and when she gets away, chases her through the rooms. As they go they knock things over and scuff up the rugs which makes Cicely steam but I think it's great to see my mother letting go like that.

One night Nanna came home disgusted because the spunk in the bottle shop told her she had a great smile and must have been fun when she was young. Telling Kay about it, she said how a woman becomes a big nothing when she's past having kids and stuff. 'An old man, even one of eighty, still has his dignity, his place in society. An old woman has neither.'

'Come off it, Cic,' said Kay, 'your wit and music will always get *you* by.'

Cicely, eyes open to the limit, stared at my mother. 'Thanks a bunch. The one thing I long for is to be known around as an entertaining old *trick*.'

After that the two of them went on looking at each other. Then they began to laugh – shrieked in fact until their faces were red and their eyelashes wet. And if one stopped the other would start her off again. I don't know why they laughed like that and when I asked, Cicely, her face still lit up, said, 'Darling, we laughed because we both saw at the same moment that everything in life's rotten and that *nothing* is.' That didn't make sense to me either but it's all I got out of them.

Cicely, who's been a widow since my mother was a baby, has lived with us as long as I can remember. My dad used to live with us as well but two years ago he went off with one of his students at Chisholm – a tiny blond with this wimpy voice and two little kids of her own. He told Mum this woman, Jenni, *needed* him but four months later he was wanting to come back. Kay didn't let him. She told him she could understand how a man might like a change of women now and then but she was fucked if she could see how a father would want a change of kids. She used the word *fucked* and everything. I know because I listened.

Dad lives in a flat in Malvern now. Every so often he takes me to a movie or the football or something. I guess he's okay but I don't think he's too rapt in me because when we're together all he does is moan about the big mistake he made in leaving home. Then he asks twenty thousand questions about Kay's boy friend, Rob.

Rob's a poet – a real one I mean, who's had collections of his work published and everything. He's a Scot with this long fair hair and what I call far-away eyes and he was once married to an athletics coach called April. When Mum and Rob met, April, a Pro-Lifer and Catholic and all that stuff, had left Rob to live with a girl who holds a sprint record. It turned out though that she was accidentally pregnant – April, I mean, and after some fairly over-the-top scenes, Rob agreed to care for the baby at his place one week out of every two. I can't make up my mind if that was a really *noble* thing to do or just plain wimpy because, you see, he's not even sure the baby's *his*. It certainly doesn't look it. At four months, it's twice the size of any other kid that age and has these enormous Ve*nutian*-looking eyes. It's also one of those babies that only sleeps about half an hour in every twenty-four. Kay says its father was probably a Romanian weightlifter popped out on steroids at the time. In spite of all that, Rob, who works part-time now making fake antique furniture with a friend in a shed in Bruns-wick, stays home every second week writing poetry and doing the nappy routine. The funny part is that in spite of all that he's about the only genuinely adj*usted* person I know.

Rob and Kay met at this party and somehow the conver-sation got around to the subject of dogs. Discovering they each *had* one, Rob suggested they take them walking one evening in what he called his favourite hide. When they finally *got* there, the hide turned out to be Wattle Park out on Riversdale Road. That was okay but at the end of the walk Rob invited Mum into one of the old trams dumped there for kids to play in. Kay agreed and they sat having a joint in what Rob thought were these totally romantic circumstances. Cher and Rob's dog, Mac, went in and sat too while the dusk came down through the trees and everything.

At that stage, Rob knew Mum worked for the Met but he didn't know what she did there. Sitting in the tram at Wattle Park, she told him and when she did, he grabbed his head. Then, rolling the 'r's' and clipping off the consonants, said, 'Jesus. That'd be reet. If I fancied some woman who worked in a fish cannery, I'd go to *infinite* trouble to take her to the Grea' Barrier Reef in a glass-bottomed boat.' Later Kay told us that the way he said, 'Grree' Barrrier Rrreef,' killed her and she knew that the next time he asked her to sit somewhere in a stationary tram with him, she'd hear herself accepting.

As things turned out they both got sort of hooked on those old trams at Wattle Park and still go there now and then. On Kay's birthday, Rob took along these plastic cocktail glasses and a thermos flask of what he called *Mary's breath*. I guess they had a good time because when they got home, they came in laughing like parrots.

At Christmas he gave her a poem she didn't show the rest of us. He also gave her this mobile he'd made from sheet metal. It's shaped like an *otter* and hangs in her bedroom where it changes colour as the sun slides past the window.

I like Rob and look forward to his visits but Cicely worries about him not working much and never having money for petrol and stuff. 'It's your strength he's after,' she says to Kay. 'That's all he wants.'

'That's all any man wants,' Kay tells her. 'We grow up believing some bloke will prance along on a white horse, pick us up and take us to his tent at the oasis where we'll live with exotic rugs and some hand-picked slaves. What really happens is that he comes along all right but we're expected to pick up not just the bloke but the horse as well and carry the pair of them all the way across the desert.' She gave a bit of a laugh. 'So as far as I can see you might as well carry someone who entertains you while you're doing it.'

Nanna and Kay talk a lot about men. Listening to them I get the feeling they *like* them but sort of despise them at the same time. In any case I hear some quite interesting stuff when they talk. For instance, Cicely says it's practically criminal for women to be endangering their health by taking the pill when they're not even *fertile* all the time, whereas men are.

'Sure,' Kay will say, 'And not only that, because they do take the bloody thing, they're no longer giving out the right hormonal smells from the armpits, so men are leching after twelve-year-old girls instead.'

Some of this stuff depresses me but at about that stage Cicely and my mum will go into one of their laughing fits. Maybe that's their way of telling me not to die worrying about it all. And if it comes down to it, I can't see either of them giving up men in the near future – not even Nanna, because the day Rob's gorgeous friend, Smith, came to put up the insect screens he called her his *heart* and when he did, she dropped the fruit and nut biscuits and broke the plate.

In that *National Geographic* I spoke about earlier, there's this photo of Angela Davis who used to be Kay's big hero. I'm sure you know all this stuff but she's the person who was mixed up with the Soledad Brothers and everyone. These days she teaches at the San Francisco University. Or at least that's what it says in the magazine. But back in 1970, when seventeen-year-old Jonathon Jackson slid into the San Rafael courthouse and kidnapped the judge and half the people in the place, the guns he took with him were supposed to belong to her. I should put in here somewhere that when Jonathon Jackson did all that stuff he was only trying to bargain for the life of his brother, George, a black activist who'd been charged with murdering one of the guards at Soledad on what Kay says was decidedly dodgy evidence.

I guess you know too that young Jonathon and the judge were both shot a few minutes after the kidnapping scene, and that *Free the Soledad Brothers* became a famous battle cry among American Blacks.

Kay's got this book of letters by George Jackson. They were written in prison because he was in prison practically all his life. He even died there when he was shot during a riot at Attica. His picture's on the front of the book. He's got his eyes closed and his face looks, well, noble and sort of beautiful too. Kay says the photograph was probably taken after his death which gives you a pretty freaky feeling when you look at it because he was only young and everything.

Anyway, in the *National Geographic*, Angela Davis is sitting up in this tree which I think is a really nice idea. *Her* face is sad and *fearless*-looking but her hair's screwed into those long sausage curls which hang way down past her shoulders. I'm sure if you saw her you'd agree that on someone who hung around with all those black spunks who were trying to get justice for themselves and each other, it looks pretty wimpy. Of course her hairdo's her business, not mine. And that brings me to the point that being white and Australian and everything, I haven't got the right to come out in an essay and say I admire her. I mean, no matter how you look at it, she wouldn't want to know about it if I did.

There are other people who'd go down really well with Miss

Vandenberg. There's Nora Barnacle, for instance, who married old James Joyce. As it happens, I'm named after her though I don't go around advertising the fact. She used to be Cicely's great hero. If you want to know, my nan guessed about five hundred years before anyone else that Joyce used everything Nora said in his writing and a heap of her ideas as well.

Cicely gave Kay this biography of Nora for her birthday. I read it in my holidays and was flattened by the way she ponced around in pricey shoes and things while those women who admired her husband paid the bills. I mean you'd expect *him* to do it because he was such a turd. I just wish she'd been different, that's all. Cicely says that's an unfair attitude; that Nora couldn't just go out and get a job the way you'd do today. She says that back then unless you were trained to make *hats* or something, you practically had to be a prostitute to survive. All I can say is, where's the difference in what the Joyces did? And if Nora had wanted to, she'd have found something. As far as I know, she didn't even try.

Another of Nanna's heroes is that old-time film star Ingrid Bergman. I think what she really likes about her is the way she had the guts to nick off with the Italian film director when everyone told her not to. She says she had *style*. I thought so too when I saw her standing around saying, 'Play it,' in that heartbreak voice of hers. Another thing I don't tell people is that for two months last year I tried to teach myself to speak the same way. I gave it up though because all that happened was people started asking if there was something wrong with my sinuses.

I must say that I think Ingrid was pretty wimpish in her films. As far as I'm concerned she should've rescued Gary Cooper somehow in *For Whom the Bell Tolls*. Even if his leg *was* broken in eighteen places. And if she couldn't, then she should've grabbed a gun and stayed to fight beside him. I'll bet that's what Ingrid would have wanted if anyone had taken the trouble to ask her what she thought of the script.

If I did my essay on old Germaine Greer, Miss Vandenberg would probably give me a hundred and fifty-three per cent, and if two-thirds of the kids in the class weren't already sliding through *The Female Eunuch*, I might be tempted. Just the same, it wouldn't be easy saying you admire someone who keeps appearing on *Aspel and Co* along with people like Joan Collins and Dolly Parton.

My friend Barbara has chosen Simone de Beauvoir. I thought that a pretty smooth idea but when I mentioned it here at lunch today, Kay said, 'Forget it. That ape Sartre treated her like shit and she let him.'

'Hang on a minute,' said Cicely, 'de Beauvoir made an *enormous* contribution. When *The Second Sex* came out it was as if a brilliant light had been shone into corners where there'd never been light before. Suddenly we weren't ashamed of being women. You're not old enough to remember that but I do.'

'She still let Sartre colonise her.'

Passing the bean salad, Cicely said, 'She loved him and in that department he simply had nothing to give. That makes him the lesser person, not her. In any case, instead of negating the legacy she left, what happened in her private life merely shows that like the rest of us she was driven by the need to mother someone.'

Nanna was still wearing her dressing gown. She'd just showered and you could smell the sandalwood soap right across the table. After lunch she'd do her face and hair and everything because at three she was playing at a wedding. A couple of months ago she played at the wedding of this Jugoslavian girl who works at the same place as she does. Anna was marrying against her family's wishes and her brothers had threatened to bomb the church. All the time Cicely was playing what she calls the *get ready* music, she was waiting to be hit by a piece of flying pulpit. To calm herself, she kept saying it would be as good a way to go as any but I guess the bomb was on her mind because when she was given the signal to let go with What's-his-name's Wedding March, she found she was banging out the opening chords of the Funeral March instead. Luckily she was cool enough to repeat them in a really jazzy manner before sliding into the right piece. 'I hope it wasn't prophetic,' she said when she got home.

Kay, who'd been wearing this pained look all the time Nanna was saying her bit about Simone de Beauvoir, turned to me and said, 'If it's sociology Miss V wants, then give it to her. Write about that Turkish woman who was taken to hospital when in labour and, because neither she nor her husband could speak English, died after being turned away by some cretin at reception.'

While I was still staring at her, she added, 'Call the essay, "The Warrior Woman Who Died Just Fighting the Battle of Life".'

'You could do a piece on my friend Mena McGann.'

When Cicely said that, Kay and I began to laugh. I don't think either of us wanted to but once we'd started, we went on and on while Nanna kept asking what the joke was.

In the end, Kay said, 'You're the joke, you old dugong.'

The words were pretty gross but when she said them there was so much love in my mother's voice – on her face too – that Cicely's own face sort of re-assembled itself with pleasure so that for a few moments she and Kay seemed the same age.

Then, from nowhere, the thought came into my head that the person I really wanted to write about was Roberta Sykes. I'd seen her over at the Adelaide Festival when Kay took me there on her holidays. She was sitting up on a platform with some other people in this big tent. I'm not sure who the others were, but Mum said an old bloke waving his feelers in the air was Manning Clark. Anyway, each one made a speech about the first two hundred years of white settlement in Australia. (The topic was probably chosen by Miss Vandenberg.) Roberta Sykes was the last one to speak and the bloke who introduced her said he'd been told she was black, beautiful and dangerous.

She probably felt *extremely* dangerous when he came out with that but let it pass and gave this great speech, finishing up inviting white people to go and call on blacks to *talk*. I don't remember the words or anything but I know she was saying that after two hundred years it was time we all got to know each other.

I can tell you that after listening to her, if she'd asked me to follow her barefoot across the Nullabor, I'd have done it. So at lunch today I turned to Kay and said, 'If things were different, I'd do my essay on Bobbi Sykes.'

'What do you mean – if things were different?'

'I mean I want to but don't feel I've got the *right*.'

'Why not, for heaven's sake?'

'Because we've taken everything from her people and it'd be the *pits* to expect to take their heroes too.'

'You've got a point there but there're a hell of a lot of other things to take into consideration.'

'Such as?'

'Well, in the first place, who does the deciding about who's black and who's white? We'd all be black, wouldn't we, if we looked far enough into the family tree. And if it came to that, Roberta Sykes has a white *mother*.'

'Then why is she called black?'

'You tell me, but it was enough to get her turfed out of school at fourteen. In spite of that she ended up getting a Doctorate at Harvard and coming back to lecture at the New South Wales uni.' Kay leaned over and put her hand on top of mine. 'Why not just write about her as a woman who's lit a beacon for oppressed people *every*where.'

'You think I should?'

'If you don't, you're practising your own little brand of apartheid, aren't you.'

'I suppose so.'

'Anyway, over in Adelaide, I thought she was telling us that since we're all here together, we might as well accept the fact and get on with making a go of it.'

I'll do it, I told myself and after thinking about it for a while, said, 'When we saw her, d'you know what she reminded me of?'

'No, tell me.'

'Remember the flower Emma took her father in *The Edge of Darkness*? The one that was black and fragile-looking but capable of saving the planet? That's what Bobbi Sykes reminded me of. We saw more black flowers – remember – when the credits were rolling. They were growing in the snow and they were so beautiful they broke your heart the way Ingrid Bergman could do with her voice.'

Kay, who'd let go of my hand, gave me the kind of look she'd given Cicely when she called her an old dugong. 'Sometimes, Norrie, you surprise me,' she said, then spoilt it all by telling me to do the dishes after lunch while she went out to put in her tomato plants.

There's one other thing I want to tell you. I wasn't going to but I've told you everything else, so I might as well. About half an hour ago the doorbell rang. Kay sang out for me to answer it and when I did, I found Kleo Papageorgiou standing there. He was wearing this white skivvy and his good bomber jacket and after giving me a smile which lasted for about one thousandth of a second, he fixed his eyes somewhere above my head and asked if I wanted to go to the end-of-term social with him. When he said it, his face was expressionless. That told me that if I said yes, I'd get no favours from *him* but I said yes, anyway, because listening to Nanna and Kay at lunch, I'd worked out that if you say yes to life, things'll go wrong and you'll wish you hadn't. But if you say no, things will still go wrong and you'll have learnt nothing. *Felt* nothing either. Besides, if he gives me a hard time, and I'll bet he does, I'll think of Angela Davis and Roberta Sykes; I'll even think of old Miss Forringham and her dividers. After that I'll cope with anything Kleo Papageorgiou serves up. I know I will.

When I told him I'd go with him, Kleo looked back at my face and gave a stunner of a smile which lasted this time for one *hundredth* of a second. Then he turned and went back to the gate with that walk of his which is different from the rest of him because it's got this sort of patience in it.

ROBERTA B. SYKES

Roberta Sykes was born in Townsville, in 1943; she received a primary education at St Joseph's School and one year of secondary education at St Patrick's College.

'In line with the prevailing policies towards the few Black children who were permitted in to educational institutions at the time,' she comments, 'I was asked to leave the school at age fourteen. When I refused to leave voluntarily, I was expelled.'

Roberta Sykes spent her young adult life in mainly menial work (when she could get it), operating machinery in factories, washing dishes or floors, and working in commercial laundries. She also worked as a trainee nurse at Charter's Towers District Hospital. But that was not all she did:

'As a form of escapism, I read constantly and widely, as well as scribbling down my own thoughts and feelings in countless notebooks in an effort to deal with the anger and frustration which stemmed from my life as a Black woman in an extremely racist society.'

A leader and activist within the Black community, Roberta Sykes became the first executive secretary of the famous Aboriginal Embassy on the lawns of Parliament House, Canberra, in 1972.

'My interest in politics grew out of my oppression,' says Roberta Sykes. 'My writing followed my interests. As one of the few scribes in the Black community, I was charged with a wide range of responsibilities, generating literature and raising public awareness and operating funds for the fledgling Black movement of the 1970s.'

In 1981 Roberta Sykes received the Patricia Weickhardt Award, along with academic qualifications. 'Despite no further formal education after the age of fourteen, on the basis of my already published work I was accepted into post-graduate study at the Graduate School of Education, Harvard University; I received my Master's Degree in 1981 which won the Peter B. Livingston Fellowship from the Harvard School of Medicine, Department of Psychiatry, in 1983 and I was awarded a doctorate in 1984.'

The author of books, government publications, chapters and many journal and newspaper articles, Roberta Sykes has made a considerable contribution to Australian literature. Among her publications are:

1975 (with Senator N. Bonner) *Black Power in Australia*, On Trial Series. Heinemann Educational, Melbourne.

1979 *Love Poems and Other Revolutionary Actions*. Saturday Centre Press, Sydney; 1988, University of Queensland Press, St Lucia.

1981 *MumShirl*. Heinemann, Melbourne.

1986 *Incentive, Achievement and Community; An Analysis of Black Viewpoints on Issues Relating to Black Australian Education*. (Harvard University Doctoral Thesis), Sydney University Press.

1989 *Black Majority*. Hudson Publications, Melbourne.

Black Women and the Continuing Struggle for Resources

Black women have come a long way since the referendum[1] of 1967. Across the nation, Black women now form a powerful chain for the Black community, and operate in almost every subject area. Black women are community health experts, legal, education and community development experts, administrators and more. There are Black women graduates in medicine, law, anthropology, accountancy, linguistics and education, as well as Black women in the upper echelons of all facets of the arts – including literature as well as the visual and performing arts.

In every community there are Black women leaders and negotiators to whom people, Black and white,[2] and particularly police and welfare officers, turn for a solution when there's trouble afoot. Some are very prominent, such as MumShirl (Smith with Sykes, 1981) and Essie Coffey,[3] but there are thousands of others around the country who perform similar invaluable service and remain virtually invisible. Invariably poor, these women and their services are unvalued or undervalued by the institutions and white community, though not by the equally poor Black community members whom they serve. A few of these women have written of their lives, or collaborated in auto/biographical publications, such as Ruby Langford (1988), Marnie Kennedy (1985), Ella Simon (1978), and Patsy Cohen (1990). They pay tribute to the women, mothers, grandmothers, etc., who came before them, establishing role models for them to follow. Those who do not were usually, earlier in their lives, victims of the assimilation policy of Australia, under which these women, as small children and babies, were removed from the care, custody, company and culture of their mothers and placed in institutions to be brought up 'white'. That these policies and practices – carried out against both male and female Aboriginal children – were ultimately ineffective in relation to the government's goals is evidenced by the position many of these women went on to achieve within the Black community. However, merely because the government did not succeed with its efforts to culturally demolish the Black community does not mean the policies were harmless. The forced removal of children from the Black community, fracturing the bonds between parents and their offspring, and between siblings, constitutes a major crime against Aboriginal people and humanity generally, and is arguably the most despicable white activity of the past century. Coral Edwards (Bowden and Bunbury, 1990) says:

'I was taken from my mother, my mother was taken from her mother, and my daughter was taken from me.'

The situation and history of Black women raises important questions about another seriously endangered species – Black men. While I have written on this subject elsewhere (Sykes, 1989), a great deal more expository research is required. I consider, for instance, that different modes of oppression operate against Black men and women, with different outcomes, but that the result of this dual situation, urgently requiring examination, will reveal ongoing genocidal practice.

Meanwhile, Black women are often encouraged to analyse their situation in isolation from the effect on the whole, and it is vital that, while we indeed have, and will continue to do so, we must bear in mind how this activity may fit in the pattern which threatens to destroy our community. We must take the necessary steps to counter that possibility by being aware of, and including in our research, the effects of the social and political environment on Black men.

A major factor in the creation and maintenance of the situation *vis-à-vis* Black women is that we have little, if any, control over resources. In my previous work (Sykes, 1989), I have detailed a social hierarchy which has implications for the analysis of resources distribution. This hierarchy identifies specific white males as social controllers, and the benefits which flow to them from the maintenance of the hierarchy, as well as specific white women whose complaint is that the power and control located at the top of this hierarchy is not equally shared between white women and white men in that group.

In 1984, when I had just started to develop this thesis (Sykes in Rowland, 1984), I wrote that white women expected support for the feminist struggle from Black women, and that Black women were acutely aware that feminism offered no strategy for the re-distribution of resources to enable the Black community to participate in the rewards of such struggle.

Since then, while Black women have made some progress, white women have, in most areas, made really major advances. Naturally, this is a generalisation – not *all* Black women nor all white women have shared in these changes, nor have all the women who have shared benefited equally.

From the perspective of Black women, white women, while not yet in large numbers controlling major resources, have in many instances been delegated the responsibility of managing resources. Certainly they have largely taken over managing those resources which are allocated specifically for women's projects, and they also have a visible hand in managing mainstream resources too. While the size of budgets and the guidelines for fiscal management are still mainly controlled by white men, white women are often the front-person for distribution. This places white women in positions of power over resources for which other white women, as well as ethnic and Black women, must compete.

White women who are not so highly placed as the white female managers still have advantages over ethnic and Black women in relation to the competition for funds. For example, they share the same cultural perspective as their manager-sisters and hence find it easier to put their case for funding in terms they understand in common. As well, they often hold similar views on priorities, which, for example, might manifest in greater priority and more adequate funding being made available for women's refuges than for English as a Second Language centres, though English as a Second Language centres are vital if migrant women are to be assisted to fully participate in Australian society.

Black women, who see their struggle in terms of the community's struggle, are disadvantaged in the competition for resources for women because they often do not exclude Black men from their projects. Indeed, many Black community groups which consist mainly of women do not even consider applying for women's funding for their projects for this reason.

There is a hierarchy of white women managers, and we have observed that the higher the manager, the more likely it is that at some time she will, in fact, make an effort to assist, and perhaps include, Black women. This will not, however, be the top item on her agenda – even though she may privately admit that Black women labour under the worst deprivations. Some of these efforts by white women, unfortunately, have amounted to little more than tokenism.

Many Black women high achievers in a range of areas have remarked on the fact that, increasingly over the past ten years, they have found they are interviewed for jobs by white women and, when employed, become answerable to white women. Rarely, despite their achievements, do Black women have white women employed under them, outside Black community institutions. While most acknowledge that white women are more likely than white men to give consideration to the skills and abilities of Black women, making their initial employment decisions in a less racist manner, many still find that on vital questions such as promotions once they are employed, white women feel more comfortable promoting other white women into supervisory positions when such promotion would lead to a Black woman being placed over a white employee.

Black women also feel that white women managers are promoting a second tier of white women at community level who are to 'manage' resources at that level, even where Black community needs are obviously greater. Refuges for battered and/or homeless women, for instance, are usually established and operated by white women who may occasionally advertise for a Black woman to work in their establishment and provide a service to the Black women in the area. This means that Black women refuge workers operate within guidelines and cultural norms dictated by white women – a situation about which most Black refuge workers complain.

There is also an increasing number of grievances being discussed by Black refuge workers about hostility which they feel is being surreptitiously aimed at them by white lesbian workers. In one instance this has taken the form of a demand that lesbianism be acknowledged as a culture, so that it can be given the same status as Aboriginality, and training on the theme of lesbianism increased to the level of Aboriginal culture, where such training is available.

The situation of competition by white women against the small gains being made by Black women is so common that some white readers may have difficulty discerning what it is we are raising objections about. For the sake of clarity, let me give a few examples. There are remarkably few instances where Black women are perceived, even by white women, as merely 'women'. Black women are not employed as refuge workers unless a position is designated for a 'Black worker' and, in all instances to my knowledge, funded separately through either the Department of Aboriginal Affairs or the Department of Employment, Education and Training. Black women do not receive funding to establish the only refuge or women's service in an area, and are therefore never in the position to advertise for or employ a 'white worker'.

The cumulative effect is that, as in days of old, Black women's energies are largely spent in the search for resources. Black women's resource-seeking efforts are often necessary to finance whole families, organisations and communities, and in these roles they are frequently the sole resource-winner with large numbers dependent upon them.

Black women increasingly find themselves in positions requiring them to turn towards white women as the distributors of government funding. Very few of these white women managers have an understanding of the dynamics of the Black community, preferring to apply a white community political analysis to the Black community and overlook significant cultural differences which would more positively inform their policy decisions.

It also seems that some white women in these positions are in danger of becoming the new masters instead of managers, replacing the white male in the former master/slave relationship between the white and the Black community.

The consequences of their attitudes and actions are to the detriment of Black women and the Black community generally, causing Black women to further question the fruit of the *women*'s (as opposed to Black) liberation struggle.

---

1. A referendum held in Australia in 1967 removed the constitutional barrier which had previously prevented Aborigines from being acknowledged as citizens of Australia and excluded them from the census.

2. Throughout this essay, the words 'Black' and 'Blacks' (when used of people) will be capitalised, as they refer to specific and identifiable groups of people. Other specific racial groups will also be capitalised. The words 'white' and 'whites' are not capitalised because they are generic terms. Black and Blacks

are used to refer to Black Australians, both Aboriginal and Islander, as is the common practice.

3. See *My Survival as an Aborigine,* a film by Martha Ansara (and Alex Morgan).

Bibliography

Ansara, Martha (and Alex Morgan) *My Survival as an Aborigine,* a film.

Bowden, Ros and Bunbury, Bill 1990, *Being Aboriginal.* Australian Broadcasting Corporation Enterprises Press, Sydney.

Cohen, Patsy and Somerville, Margaret 1990, *Ingelba and the Five Black Matriarchs.* Allen & Unwin, Sydney.

Edwards, Coral 1990, 'Raised to Think White' in *Being Aboriginal,* (eds) Ros Bowden and Bill Bunbury.

Edwards, Coral and Read, Peter 1989, *The Lost Children.* Doubleday, Sydney.

Kennedy, Marnie 1985, *Born a Half-Caste.* Australian Institute of Aboriginal Studies, Canberra.

Langford, Ruby 1988, *Don't Take Your Love to Town.* Penguin, Melbourne.

Rowland, Robyn (ed.) 1984, *Women Who Do and Women Who Don't Join the Women's Movement.* Routledge & Kegan Paul, Melbourne.

Simon, Ella 1978, *Through My Eyes.* Dove, Melbourne.

Smith, Shirley and Sykes, Bobbi 1981, *MumShirl.* Heinemann, Melbourne.

Sykes, Roberta 1989, *Black Majority.* Hudson Publications, Melbourne.

— 1984 'Bobbi Sykes', in *Women Who Do and Women Who Don't,* (ed.) Robyn Rowland.

ADELE HORIN

Adele Horin was born in 1951 in Perth; she grew up in a typical baby-boom suburb – new homes, young families, lower middle class with aspirations. She attended the local primary school and high school, where the sound 'no-frills' education steered many towards university. But she wanted to be a writer, virtually from the time she learnt the alphabet. One or two gifted English teachers encouraged her ambitions, and her parents – though not literary types – expected top marks, particularly in 'composition'.

As her interest in current affairs and politics grew, stimulated by the social ferment of the late 60s, so too did her creative writing talents dwindle. She set her sights on journalism instead of authorship, and was offered a coveted cadetship on the *West Australian* newspaper when she left school.

While mastering the art of compiling the weather page, the television columns, the court reports – and eventually the women's features – she attended the University of Western Australia part time to complete a Bachelor of Arts degree.

As it turns out, she did find her niche in journalism; 'It allows you, like a magpie, to pick at this and that interesting morsel, and to flit to far-off places as well if you're lucky.'

She earnt her living for many years in Sydney writing for the now sadly defunct *National Times*; she was also its New York, Washington and London correspondent. 'Through its doors passed many of Australia's best editors, journalists – and libel lawyers,' she comments.

Despite the unfashionable label of 'bleeding heart' which attaches to those who write on social issues, she has continued to chart the social trends and economic consequences of a changing Australia. Most recently she has written a column, *My Generation* for the *Sydney Morning Herald* and the *Sunday Age* in Melbourne, on social justice issues, women and the family; the latter interest has been reinforced by the birth of her son in 1989. She currently lives at Bondi Beach.

'Murder in Adelaide' was first published in the *National Times*, July 26, 1980; 'Obsessive Love' was also published in the *National Times*, November 29, 1981.

Murder in Adelaide

On July 16, 1980 the South Australian Supreme Court sentenced a 47-year-old woman to life imprisonment for the murder of her husband. Adele Horin went to Adelaide to file the following report based on the court proceedings.

On Thursday, April 2, Constable Peter Watson was doing the graveyard shift at police headquarters, Adelaide. At exactly 2.52 a.m. he answered a call on the emergency triple 0 line.

'Police headquarters,' he said.

'I have just murdered my husband,' a woman said.

'You have just murdered your husband?' Watson asked. 'Whereabouts do you live?'

The woman gave him the number of a main street in one of Adelaide's established working-class suburbs.

'I'll leave the lights on for you so you can just walk in,' the woman said. She gave her name.

'How long ago did you murder him?'

'About 10 minutes ago.'

'I'll get somebody down there to see you in a minute, OK?' said Watson.

'OK.'

Constable Trevor McLeod of the CIB was dispatched with his offsider, Constable Healy, to the house. An outside light was on, the front door was open for them.

A woman's voice called: 'The door is open. Come in.'

There was a light on in the passageway. The police officers could see in a lounge room to the left two women sitting on a settee.

The younger woman, in a long white towelling dressing gown, was crying uncontrollably. The older woman, in a floral nylon dressing gown, had her arm around the younger woman's shoulder. She seemed quite calm.

'What's going on here?' said Healy from the doorway.

'I couldn't take any more from my husband,' the older woman said in a soft voice with an English accent, 'so I killed him.'

She stood up, walked past the two constables and walked down the passage to the kitchen. The light was on. She pointed towards an axe leaning against a bureau. There was blood on the blade. She started to open another door, but Healy stopped her.

'Where did the incident take place tonight?'

'In the bedroom where my husband is,' she said.

By this time, 3.20 a.m., the house was full of police. Police Constable Debra Wheatley arrived.

'It was a terrible life that he gave us,' the older woman told her. 'And he treated the girls like that. It's all over with him now and we can lead a peaceful life.

'He had it coming to him. I couldn't let him do that to the girls any longer.'

Janet[1] came to Australia from England in August, 1950. In May, 1954 she married Stan, an Australian professional sportsman who later earned his living as a truck driver.

'The first couple of years of the marriage weren't too bad,' Janet was to tell the Supreme Court 27 years later. 'He was

---

1. All names have been changed to comply with Judge Sangster's order at the trial.

given to fits of violent temper but he always seemed to be able to control them.'

But the court was told that the violence escalated over the years. A family friend was to tell the court: 'If they ever said things out of place, silly little things, he would slam his fist on the table, pick up the nearest cup and slam it on the table and break it or turn the whole table over.

'I have never seen anybody else like that. Janet would sit quiet and say nothing and sometimes she would tremble.'

Every time she fell pregnant – and she had five girls and one boy with him – Stan erupted. He wanted her to have an abortion. When she was in labour with her fifth child, he refused to drive her to hospital.

'All he was concerned about was that I hadn't got his clothes ready for him to go to a ball,' Janet told the court.

When he visited the hospital next day, he brought along a blonde 16-year-old girl – his 'girlfriend', he said.

His wife objected. 'I'll have her there any time I want,' he said. And he brought her on other visits.

He registered the baby in the girlfriend's name. When Janet came out of hospital, she tried to cancel this name but was not allowed.

Janet became adept at ducking knives and cups. Stan would stand over her and make her clean up the mess. He would grab her by the throat, pin her against the wall. The children would grab his fist.

'He would punch us and hit us and he used sticks or straps or anything,' Diane, 22, the second oldest daughter, told the court. 'I have seen him break Mary's (the oldest's) nose. He hit her in the face with his fist.

'He has picked up Sally (the youngest) by the throat ... and hit her across the face.'

He found Diane's contraceptive pills which she took for menstrual troubles and 'went berserk'. He picked her up, threw her against the wall and she passed out.

He would not let his wife take Diane to the doctor though she couldn't see or walk properly after the blow.

'When he was in moods like that he was capable of murder and he just seemed as if he was insane,' Diane told the court.

Her mother said: 'If (these sort of incidents) didn't happen every day we would say we had a good day.'

Friends and relatives, including Stan's own family, stopped coming to the house.

No one knew what lay behind much of the violence. The five girls could not talk about it to each other. They could not tell their brother. They could not tell their mother.

Sexual abuse started on Diane when she was six. She did not understand what it meant. She knew another girl who 'played with her father' and thought it was what fathers and daughters did together.

At nine or 10, Diane told the court, she had intercourse with her father.

Diane knew it happened to her older sister, too. Sometimes she was present. From 12 on, the two girls could not talk to each other about it.

It happened when their mother was away from the house. She worked for many years on permanent night shift at a hospital; in the last four years, the 3 p.m. to 11 p.m. shift.

Stan had been unemployed for the last four years and made no attempt to find work.

Once he was behind a locked bedroom door with Mary, the oldest daughter, when Janet came home and went to walk into the bedroom. There were arguments later about the locked door. The father said that he was 'just rubbing (Mary's) back because she had complained of a backache,' the court was told.

If he couldn't use the bedroom because his wife was home sick, he would take a daughter out 'for a ride' in the car.

He would say goodnight to them in their bedrooms and that would be an occasion for fondling them.

School reinforced Diane's terrible situation. Girls would talk about their weekends, their boyfriends.

Diane's girlfriend told her how she was nervous about sex. 'I felt terrible,' Diane told the court. 'I had to clam up. My experience was so different.'

She was too scared to let boys touch her. She would freeze up.

She said she was close to her mother. She tried to tell her about the incest but couldn't find the words. Her mother held down three jobs at one stage and wasn't home much.

Five years ago, two of the younger daughters, Beth and Rose, then aged 13 and 15, ran away. The father had been having sex with them. They told a welfare officer who contacted Janet. The welfare officer said she would see that both Stan and Janet went to court.

Janet told the Supreme Court how she confronted her husband on this occasion. 'They are making charges of incest. Isn't that sexual relations between father and daughter?'

He said: 'What tommy rot. No way is it true. I love my kids, I love them.'

Janet was distraught that her daughters had said she was implicated. 'I absolutely adored by children – to think that they could even think about things like that. I was so hurt, I just cut myself off from them.'

She saw Beth from a distance, hitchhiking, then once more before Beth and Rose were made wards of the State.

'The first thing I asked Beth was why on earth did she go and thumb a lift. "Don't you realise how dangerous it is?"'

They were the last words she said to her daughter in five years. The three older girls missed this chance to be saved.

They were afraid to tell their mother the truth because she had had a stroke six weeks before. 'We were scared in case she had another one,' Diane told the court.

Janet's eye would twitch and the left side of her face would drop during her husband's violent outbursts.

The three girls left at home were frightened of provoking scenes by resisting or revealing the sexual abuse. A friend of the family sensed what was happening to the daughters but said nothing until the last week.

She said: 'In company Stan used to fondle his daughters, touch them in places and laugh about it. And he would kiss them in front of friends. Yes, Janet has been there at times. He used to do it all the time. She has never spoken about things like that (incest) and I didn't think it was my business to raise it.'

Janet told the court her husband was 'always a long time' when he went to say goodnight to his daughters.

'It used to worry me. If I followed him or went down to see where he was, he abused me and told me I had a dirty mind.'

When she finally learnt the truth, many things fell into place: the locked doors, why her daughters hated her working, why they hated going in the car with their father, and why so much of the violence seemed unprovoked.

A simple event triggered the final week of crisis – the week of truth-telling and of killing: Diane fell in love. She wanted to make her escape.

A trip to Melbourne was the best thing that had ever happened to Diane. She had finished her exams and had taken off in her car with Mary for two weeks of freedom.

It had not been so simple to get away. Her father had flatly refused to let them go. Her mother had written to friends in Victoria asking them to ring Stan and plead with him.

'If they hadn't rung he would never have let them go out of his sight,' Janet had said.

In Melbourne the girls found good prospects for jobs. And Diane had met Michael, a chef.

They fell in love intensely, but Diane could not tell him all about her home life. He sensed, he said later, that she had never had fun. He took her to Tasmania on the Empress and bought her champagne for breakfast. When it was time for Diane to go back to Adelaide, Michael said he would be over in a week.

Falling in love, 'being treated as a lady', stiffened Diane's resolve to run away from home. Mary said she would go with her.

They were happy and excited when they arrived home on Friday, March 27. They brought presents for their father. He went very quiet and pushed the presents aside. They mentioned they had prospects for work in Melbourne.

'And the atomic bomb went off,' Janet told the court. 'He just did his block. Nobody was going to leave him: he would kill the lot of us if we thought about it. "What did I need a big house for if there's only you and me here" ... he went on and on.'

That was how it started. On Sunday Diane and Mary visited a friend, Roberta, and asked if they could leave their clothes with her. They were going to Melbourne: would she help them leave quietly; their father would be nasty if he found out.

Roberta decided to say what she had wanted to say for a long time. She knew it was not a normal father's sadness at losing his daughters.

'I suggested to Diane (their) Dad had been interfering with them, and the girls told me yes, it was true, but what could they do, they couldn't tell anybody: he would deny it anyway or he would turn on them,' Roberta told the court.

The girls raced home. Their father always wanted to know their whereabouts, how long they would be away. He would get upset if they were late.

That weekend, 'You could have cut (the atmosphere) with a knife,' Janet later said. 'Nobody dared to speak. We daren't walk around properly; everybody walked about on their tiptoes.'

On Monday the girls took clothes around to Roberta's place.

Tuesday was a calamitous day, the start of the end. Arguments about leaving for Melbourne filled the day. Diane told the court that her father had said he would track them down and kill them. He had nothing better to do all day, he said.

Towards evening, with her mother at work, Diane confronted her father about the incest. She told him she 'didn't want it to continue.'

He said he couldn't be in the house if he couldn't touch Diane. He couldn't stand being with her mother by himself and 'if he couldn't interfere with us all the time it wouldn't be worth staying,' Diane reported him as saying.

'Either you have to leave or I have to,' he said.

'I will leave,' Diane said. He gave her one week. Then he changed his mind and ordered the three daughters out that minute in what they stood up in, 'or there will be murder here tonight,' Diane reported him saying.

The girls drove to Roberta's house. Diane hid the car. They were crying; Mary was too upset to speak, Roberta told the court.

They rang their mother at work. They told her he had thrown them out but not the real reason for his outburst – Diane's rebellion against the sexual abuse.

The scenes since the girls' return had taken their toll on Janet. That Tuesday night at work, she was at the end of her tether. 'I couldn't take his violence any more,' she told the court.

Then about 9.30 p.m. Stan banged on her office door and entered shouting.

'I hope you're happy now. I've chucked them all out,' he said. 'I have thrown the bitches out.'

She tried to calm him but he slammed the door and left. She spoke to her daughters on the phone, said she would draw money out of the bank to finance their escape. Then her husband rang her.

'I've got over my temper now. I want them home. I want to finish my talk with Diane,' she reported him saying.

The girls were afraid to come home but she told them, 'I'm scared of him but if we all keep together we are stronger than what he is, but if you don't back me up I can't do anything.'

Mary and Diane asked Roberta's husband and his friend to go with them and wait in the street. They saw two policemen and asked them to help but the police said all they could do was keep an eye on the house. Then with their 14-year-old sister Sally they went in.

They stood at the doorway to the loungeroom. Their parents were drinking port.

Stan told them to sit down. He sent the youngest daughter out. Then he turned to Mary and said, 'My argument is not with you,' and told her to go.

'Diane and I are going out,' he told his wife.

'What for?' she said.

'I am going to finish this conversation.'

'You don't have to go out for that,' Janet said.

'I give you my word of honour I won't lay a finger on her,' he said.

'There's no way you are taking this girl out of the house,' she said. 'Go into a room, lock the door, nobody will go in.' Diane said, 'I will be all right,'

Stan promised again he would bring her back in the same condition as he took her. They left the house after midnight. Diane drove her father down towards the railway station and parked under a tree. 'No, this is not quiet enough,' he said. 'There's too many coppers that hang around here.'

They stopped. They argued. Then he hit her across the eye and pulled her by the hair.

'That's when he stuck the knife in my throat,' she later told the court.

'I just got scared. He said, "Can you feel it?" He kept digging it in me.'

She forced the knife away, cutting her hands. Her neck

and her fingers and thumbs of both hands were cut.

Then Stan raped her.

At the house Janet was pacing back and forth. She drank endless cups of tea. She smoked.

'Where have they gone? Why have they gone out of the house? Why is it so important that they can't be in the house?'

At about 2.30 a.m. they arrived home. Stan walked straight into the bedroom. Diane sat down at the kitchen table.

Her eye looked red and swollen and her nose was red. Her hands were folded across her chest and when she opened them and untied the handkerchief, her mother saw they were covered in blood.

'He attacked me with a knife,' Diane said.

'The bastard, I will kill him,' Janet said. She knew nothing of the rape.

'Don't say anything,' Diane said. 'I will deny it if you do. I will leave on the weekend.'

Then Stan came into the kitchen. There was to be no more talk of moving to Melbourne, he told her. They were going to be 'one big happy family.'

Diane went to bed and lay awake all night. Her mother went to bed and lay awake all night, 'staring at the ceiling.'

Wednesday 6.30 a.m. Diane went to Mary's bedroom and woke her. She told her briefly of the night's events. Janet drove Mary to work, then came in and sat on Diane's bed.

'We can't live normal lives,' she told Diane. 'Its gone far enough.' She would get money so they could run away. She looked at Diane's hands again and thought, 'I could kill him.'

Janet rang Roberta and spoke to her husband. Roberta, getting the gist of the conversation, came on the phone.

'I told her not to be silly, that there were other things to do rather than get a gun. She said no, there was no other way; if she didn't do what she had got to do, she would be looking over her shoulder for the rest of her days. He would only get a few years' imprisonment and then he would be out and he would get them no matter where they went.'

Janet told Diane she was going to the chemist. 'I bought some bullets at a gunshop,' she later told the court.

She had the key to her next door neighbour's house. She knew he owned a rifle and searched till she found it. It was the first time she had handled a gun and she couldn't load it.

In her absence, the police arrived at the house in response to a call from Roberta. Diane let them in. The police woke Stan and told him someone had called about a plan to murder him.

The police and Stan joked that it was probably an April Fool's prank, that he should mind his friends. Then the police left.

Stan got out of bed. Diane had to help him destroy some old furniture in the yard. At noon he left for an appointment and Diane was free to ring Roberta about the police visit. Janet was home, took the receiver and Diane moved away.

'Roberta said something funny to me,' Janet said when she got off the phone. ' "You ask Diane what goes on while you're at work," What did Roberta mean when she asked me that?'

Diane started to cry.

'Mum,' she said 'while you are at work, he interferes with us.'

'What do you mean?' her mother said.

'Well, what Beth and Rose said five years ago is true. He has been having sexual relations with us all this time.'

'Oh my God,' Janet said.

'I went cold,' she told the court later. 'I remember taking her in my arms. I don't remember anything after that. I just went cold, seemed like I was dead.'

About half an hour later, about 2 p.m. Stan returned to the house, but Janet said nothing to him. She went to work.

In court Janet said she remembered nothing of the day except at the end saying goodbye to three old ladies she worked with. 'You're not coming back, are you?' one said to her as she left for home.

Diane and her father were out when Janet arrived home. She remembered they had an arrangement to see an uncle.

'Oh my God, she is out with him on her own,' she thought. She smoked and drank tea while she waited.

They came in after midnight. Stan went to the toilet. Diane sat at the table. 'Mum, he tried to rape me. I told him I had my periods so he left me alone.'

Janet told her to go to bed.

'I asked her was she all right,' Diane later told the court. 'She seemed a bit strange. She said, "Yes".'

Her father came into the room. He sat at one side of the

kitchen table and drank a cup of coffee. Janet was at the other side of the table.

Diane started to leave and Stan said he would say goodnight later. The last words Diane heard was her father saying they were 'going to be one big happy family.'

He told his wife he would take her to England.

'All of a sudden I felt something red hot on my arm and I flinched away,' she said, 'for it was him touching me. He was stroking my arm.'

She told the court, 'All I could feel was this hatred.'

Then they went to bed. It had been months since they had had sex. She used to think it was because of middle age or because of his vasectomy. 'He could come up with more excuses than the man in the moon. It was always me that made the advance and it was always him with a headache or a backache...'

This night, he moved towards her. He put his arm across her chest and said, 'I love you.' She pushed him away; she just lay there. Then she sat on the edge of the bed and smoked one cigarette after another.

'I just thought about all them kids and what they must have gone through and what a sucker I was. How stupid I had been...'

She told the court she went to the shed and got the axe.

'I pulled the bedclothes back and said, "You bastard, what have you done all these years." I hit him and the blow glanced off the top of his head... he tried to get up in bed. I kept on hitting him after that and he kept trying to get up. I got scared. I thought, "If he turns the axe on me these kids are at his mercy. They will never be free..." I kept saying, "Damn you, you bastard, die."'

She struck him 11 times at the back of the neck and head, then she had a cigarette and dialled the police.

'I have just murdered my husband,' she said.

Diane and Michael sat hand-in-hand in a friend's house a few doors down from the family home, which will be sold. Michael who had been overseas arrived in Adelaide to be with the woman he had known for a week in March.

He still doesn't know all the details of her life, and sat in on the interview to learn more.

'You wonder at first was it love-making or was it rape,' he said. 'But I know now that she was an innocent girl. To me, she is pure.'

Diane has made her escape. She lives in Melbourne now. The 14-year-old sister, who was also raped by her father, will live with her.

The rest of the family lives in Adelaide. One daughter has just learned that it may be impossible for her to fall pregnant because she was interfered with at such an early age.

The daughters say they are talking about their life to help their mother, and to help other women and children caught in violent and/or incestuous relationships.

The previous night they had attended a public meeting which called upon the South Australian Government to change the law on provocation, so that when a defence lawyer raises facts which suggest provocation they would be put to the jury.

In this case, the husband's cruelty was irrelevant. In his summing-up the trial judge, Mr Justice Sangster, said: 'If there was this long harsh cruel experience suffered by the accused and her family... that is not some kind of defence. Indeed it supports one aspect of the prosecution...'

The meeting also called on the Government to abolish mandatory life sentences in murder cases; it expressed its concern that the Crown, in this case, chose to proceed with a charge of murder when it could have charged the woman with manslaughter as has happened in similar cases in other states.

And it urged that, if all legal avenues failed, the Government should release the woman from prison as an act of executive clemency.

Obsessive Love

She has bright blue eyes and short brown hair and a regular, freckled face. She is tall and attractive but not a beauty who would stand out in a crowd. She has a friendly but unassertive personality. At 23, she must live with her brothers for protection, cling to her friends for safety. She freezes if strangers look at her and when she is asked what she does, she feels like answering, 'I just go crazy.'

She remembers that before he started following her, she was a sane, happy person, rarely moody. But she has become the unwilling victim of a man's obsession. Recently, several women have taken court action against men who have followed and harassed them. This is what it was like for one of them. She spoke to Adele Horin.

It goes back to mid '79. I first noticed that he would be watching me all the time.

There were glass partitions in the office and he would stand up to look at me when I went past to unload a tape for the computer. It was unnerving, having someone constantly watching you.

He had been working in the building for some time before I noticed him. Then they brought him down to the section where I was working. He was a trainee computer programmer – he was still going to college part-time – and at that stage, I was a computer operator.

It started off as a joke. People said, 'Craig has the hots for you, what are you going to do?' I thought then it was serious. He was always a bit funny. I didn't want anything to do with him. As close as we ever really got was, 'Hello, how are you? How was your weekend?'

At first I was not really sure what was happening. I didn't know whether he was keen on me or whether he just liked talking to girls.

I first really noticed something was wrong when I went to work in another office and Craig would come in and sit down. He would not say anything. He would just sit on the desk, watching me.

I felt sorry for him because he was a bit funny. He has these horrible, dark, beady eyes and blond hair. He is so skinny, about six stone, and about 6 feet tall. He walks around sort of hunched over, with his arms folded. He often wore baggy checked shorts, 1960s style, and orange or fawn shirts.

I would say, 'Craig, are you all right?' He would say, 'I have just come in to say hello.' The only news I ever learnt from him, the only thing he ever told me that made sense was that some 'larrikins' had let down his car tyres one weekend.

It was really horrible having someone not saying anything, just sitting on a desk watching you. I told the guy I was working with not to let him into the office, and I asked people to walk past my office to check. Not that he would have done anything. I'm sure he won't.

Finally, he asked me to go out with him, to see Pam Ayres (the English light poet and entertainer) and I said, 'No thank you very much.' I told him I had a boyfriend, even though I didn't. He started to cry.

I would go to the happy hour after work and he would go, too, though he doesn't drink or smoke. I would walk from one group to another and he would follow and stand beside me with his arms crossed in the front or at the back. It was as if I had a string on him and I was winding him in. As long as I was next to him, he didn't mind.

Then he started watching me outside work. I would go to the library to meet Mum for lunch and he would hide behind the bushes. We would be sitting on the steps to the library, and he would be on the balcony above, watching. If I started on the 7 a.m. shift, he would be in the car park waiting for me. If I worked the late shift and left at 11 p.m. he would follow me home.

I was living with a girlfriend and her parents then. I would try to work out different ways of driving home. I was always driving with my eyes on the rear vision mirror. He would follow me right to the house and then drive backwards and forwards but he never came in.

In November, 1979, I went on a holiday to Europe. There was an office barbecue. Craig went and people were under the impression that he thought I would be there. He climbed up a gum tree and sat there all day and looked down on everyone.

He was always alone at work. He never really talked to anyone. I still don't know much about him. I know he is 31, his parents live in Adelaide and a sister lives in Sydney. I know he is religious.

When I came back from Europe, there was a letter in my locker from him, a really sick, gushy love letter. He kept saying,

'I want to show you how I feel. I like you a lot, I trust you a lot.' He was buying a house at the time and he said that he imagined me sitting on the back door step watching the orange sun behind the silvery grey clouds. He imagined me sitting next to him in church listening to a sermon. He finished off the letter with a paragraph from the Bible: 'Love is patient, love is understanding and kind.'

'There were even times I thought I would forget her. But forgetting's not something you do, it happens to you. Only it didn't happen to me.'
– from *The Collector* by John Fowles

I felt, 'Oh God.' He rang me up once or twice and said our relationship was not getting anywhere. I told him we did not have a relationship. He began writing me letters and would send them to my parents' address. Some of the big, padded letters I never opened. He would send me messages over the computer terminal, and would leave notes under my car windscreen wipers. Always it was how much he loved me and trusted me but our relationship was not going the way he planned.

Once he'd rung me up and I had said, 'I've got enough problems without you hanging around.' So in the next letter it was, 'I really appreciated talking to you over the phone. I would like to spend more time with you. It sounds as though you have *big* problems and I would like to help you in any way possible. I have big problems, too. I trust you and I hope you can trust me, too.'

In June, 1980, I got a promotion, and I also started a part-time computer course at college. He would be following me around then. For a long time I thought, this must be coincidental, accidental. He was probably around at the time I was around.

I worked out from his college timetable that in a five-day week our paths should cross once but he was always there, outside lecture theatres, the library. He would hide behind bushes. There were times when he tried to talk to me when I was by myself.

Once he said, 'I've got to talk to you. I like you a lot.' I said, 'You don't know anything about me.' He said, 'You have every quality I like in a girl: pretty, outgoing, flamboyant.' He never said or wrote anything sexual. Once he told me he liked me because I was 'respectable.'

But mostly he never came up to me. He was always at a distance, but it is as if he was saying, 'look, I am here.' Some days I would really pray and hope he would come up and hit me or grab me so I could hit back. He was like a shadow, there all the time, but I could never touch him.

He was sending me around the bend. I was scared to be by myself. When I drove I didn't really concentrate, I was looking into the rear vision mirror. I became paranoid about people walking behind me.

I was in conflict with myself one day. It was a really nice day. I was thinking: 'Well, you have a really nice day to be shot.' I was looking behind bushes, over my shoulder. Then I heard these footsteps behind me. I saw this long shadow. I threw down my books and screamed: 'Keep away from me.' It was this poor guy running late for a lecture.

I was getting so upset. I just wanted to know why he would not leave me alone. I had told him he was weird. Any normal guy would have pissed off when you told him to go. My girl-friend told me she would come with me for a meeting with him. I arranged it for four o'clock on a Saturday.

He was all dressed up. It was the first time I had seen him in a tie. He came out from the bushes, just his style. We sat in the restaurant and I said: 'Say everything you have to say, now.'

He said that it was very hard when I put it that way. Then he said he loved and trusted me. We were there for two hours. I was ready to strangle him. 'I really hate you,' I told him. But he had this smile on his face and a really vacant look as if every-thing I was saying was going over his head. My girlfriend said to him at the end to talk his problems over with friends. I was thinking: 'Kill him, kill him.'

He tried to make a deal with me, that he would leave me alone for a month if I would meet him at the end of every month. I told him I couldn't handle that. 'What happens if I move away?' I said. 'I don't know,' he said. 'I might find you.'

After that, there were still notes on my car. 'I've got to talk to you.' I got paranoid about my car. I thought he had put a homing device in it. On days off work I'd go shopping, and he'd be around. I bought a new car.

Just before Christmas 1980, I went to the police. I had tried being understanding: I told him he was not the right person. I'd tried using every swearword so he would think I was disgusting but that was part of how he could help me. I didn't know what to do next.

The police were really helpful and they put a tail on me for a week. But it's as if he had a sixth sense. When there's someone to help me he is not there. It was as if I was making it up.

About a week after this I got the Bible. It was wrapped in brown paper and my mother thought it might be a bomb, so I took the parcel to the police. I was upset and crying. They told me it was a Bible and there was a fairly sick letter with it. They went around to see him, but it was as if he was expecting them.

They tried to bluff him and say they would arrest him but he said, 'You can't.' It is true. He had not laid a finger on me.

Male friends and my two brothers wanted to punch him but I didn't want them to get into trouble because he might bring charges against them.

I was getting really upset at work. I told his boss. Craig went to counselling at work three times. Finally his boss told him it would affect his work if he didn't stop following me. Last December he resigned and he hasn't worked since. He has so much time by himself, he can think of ways and means of seeing me.

People said, pretend he is not there. I thought I would look at the ground when he was coming. For three weeks I did that. That was when he touched me on the arm. I went off my brain. Sometimes I have thought: 'I want to punch him, really hurt him,' but at the same time, I don't want to touch him. It's as if he is a leper. The time he touched me, he said: 'Don't you see me any more? Can't you notice me? I am not invisible.' That was the only time I ever got back at him. I have tried doing it since, building my strength to really hurt him, but it is very hard.

It had been going on for two years. A male friend of mine, a really big guy, said he would come with me to frighten him.

We met in a bar. My friend pretended to be my boyfriend. He told Craig: 'You leave my girlfriend alone.' He was slamming his fists, laying it on. Craig just said: 'I have come to talk to Merril.'

It was this time he asked me my religion. 'What do you want to know for?' I said. He said it was important for everyone to be a Christian, to know they go somewhere after death. He said something like if he couldn't have me in this life, he would have me in the afterlife.

This was too much for me. My friend yelled at him to leave. But this did not worry Craig at all. He sat there, smiling, hunched over. My friend yelled again. He said: 'I have not finished talking to Merril yet.' That is what really scared me. The next week, in August of this year, I went to the solicitor.

I had to get from the court an order to keep the peace. I rang the court. 'Has he threatened your life?' they asked. 'Your property? Has he touched you? Well,' they said, 'he hasn't done anything. You can't prove anything.'

'But he is haunting me,' I told them. Finally I got to see the clerk of the court and got the necessary piece of paper so that I could proceed with taking Craig to court.

He didn't turn up the first two times. But he went to see my solicitor. He told the solicitor that my taking him to court only proved my love for him.

On October 2, he turned up at court, unrepresented. The magistrate asked him right from the beginning would he stay away from me.

He said: 'I'm sorry, I can't give any agreement like that. This is a small place.' We had to go through the whole proceedings.

I can understand what girls have to go through in rape cases. Trying to make someone believe you. You feel as if you are making it up. The way they ask the questions: Yes, no. Have you been out with him? Are you sure you haven't?

There were so many things I wanted to say. I didn't know where to start. It had been going on for so long. But it sounded like a story to me that day: 'He's been following me around, making me go mad.'

I went blank. My barrister tried to help me but the magistrate excluded her from the proceedings. He said she was feeding me the questions. Before she was excluded, the barrister tended evidence, letters, and print-outs from the computer, but the magistrate wouldn't accept the computer print-outs: How did I know it was from Craig? It could have come from anyone. I thought: 'Oh, no, the magistrate doesn't believe me.'

I got so shaky I burst into tears. 'I can't handle him being around.' I said. 'He is always around.' All I could hear was Craig sighing: 'Oh, Merril, Oh, Merril.'

The only time the magistrate seemed to listen was when I told about the Bible and the business about the afterlife.

He asked Craig about it. Craig said: 'Merril will just have to understand me.' The magistrate fined him $100 and said he would get three months' jail if he followed me around again. Even at the end, Craig was saying: 'This is a small place, I could bump into her.' The magistrate said: 'You won't bump into her if you don't follow her.'

Craig turned to me and smiled: 'I have upset you but I can't help it,' he seemed to say. I left court knowing I had not achieved anything. I knew that if Craig had denied anything, it would have been so hard to prove because it always happened in a public place.

Two weeks after the court case, he started following me again. I have seen him six or seven times.

The first time, I was walking by the bus terminal near work, thinking: 'Am I dreaming he is there? Is it possible he is looking at me?'

I looked down the stairwell and he was there. I raced across to Myer's and hid behind a clothes rack, wondering if he was following me. I thought: 'I can't hide like this every day,' so I started walking through the store. I saw him out of the corner of my eye, walking towards me. He was at my shoulder: 'You have to talk to me Merril, please talk to me.'

I don't want him to go to jail. He won't survive in there. I asked my solicitor: 'Can't we get him psychiatric treatment?' The solicitor said the law wants to punish, not rehabilitate.

I once rang a mental health crisis centre to see if I could get him to a psychiatrist but he has to agree to go. I just wish they could give him some help.

Some nights I can't sleep because I am thinking of every possible way I am leaving myself open; I plan where I'm going, how to get around things.

I try to think along his lines. If he really wanted to get me he can. I think he is going to get a gun and shoot me. It's a silly thought. I know he won't. But I am not giving him the time he wants and he might try and get me some way.

I am thinking I will have to leave town. I am so sick of it. It has taken over my life to a great extent. For a whole 2½ years I have not gone a day without thinking: 'Is he going to be there?'

❧ FINOLA MOORHEAD

Finola Moorhead was born in Victoria in 1947, and in her own words says: 'I was brought up wandering about the coast of Port Philip Bay at Mornington by a single mother who worked and went to meetings. Then I went to boarding school for a couple of years. A B.A. from the University of Tasmania in 1968 and I have been a full time writer since 1973.'

In her writing life there is a before and after feminist stage. In the before period, and as a full time teacher, Finola Moorhead wrote *The Dreamer* (1970) and adapted for the stage several short stories of Henry Lawson's. She also wrote *Staff*, a one act play, which had a reading at Monash University in 1972; in the same year she wrote and directed *The Blood and the Birth* (a Christmas play) and in 1973, *Horses*, one of the plays workshopped at the first Australian National Playwright's Conference. *It Might as Well be Loneliness* followed, and some work in the Theatre-in-Education, in the Old Nick Company of the University of Tasmania, and on the University Review.

It was after her first Adelaide Writers' Festival that Finola Moorhead decided to become a full time writer: 'I came into the sitting room and announced it and my mother's friend who was there said – "There's a girl who knows her mind." – And my mum went pale. "How are you going to support yourself?" But when she complimented my work – once – it gave me more confidence than any other person doing so.'

From 1974 to 1976, Finola Moorhead worked as an

editorial assistant at *Meanjin*, received a half year
fellowship from the Literature Board, and wrote
short stories and plays. She was also a member of
the Women's Theatre Group in Melbourne.

And then there was women's liberation: 'For years
and years the difference between writing writing,
and *women's* writing, was too broad for me to breach;
what you said, how you said it – they were big
thinking times when I tried to work out that one.'
This was the period when her first novel was
written; '*Lots of Potential*, is still unpublished. I haven't
read it for fifteen years.'

During the 1980s Finola Moorhead continued to
write and from 1980 to 1987 she worked on her big
novel, *Remember the Tarantella*. She has had assistance
from the Australia Council (1988–90) and her short
stories appear in fifteen anthologies; her novel, *Still
Murder*, was published by Penguin in 1991.

In 1986 she wrote *Miss Marple Goes to Ayers Rock*
as part of a play, *Lindy and the Dingo*. She is currently
working on experimental drama and prefers to
'retreat' to live and write.

Miss Marple Goes to Ayers Rock

A Performed Reading

SLIDES OF CENTRAL AUSTRALIA SHOWING TWO GREY-
HAIRED WOMEN ON HOLIDAY. MUSIC.
SLIDES OF PRESS CUTTINGS OF LINDY CHAMBERLAIN
1980–85. TAPED CHANT:

There is a tent. There is a tracksuit. There is a
blood stain on the tracksuit. There is no baby in the crib. There
is a sleeping bag. There is a barbeque. There is a camera. There
is a man at the barbeque fire. There is a can of baked beans.
There is a bus of tourists. There is a red road. There is the Rock.
There is a camera case. There are two boys. There are the folks

from Tasmania. There is a hurricane lamp. There are as many Gideon Bibles as there are rooms in the motel. There is a huge night sky. There are suddenly hundreds of Free The Dingo T-shirts. There is fear. There is a dark-haired woman with fastidiously feminine taste in clothes. There are many photographs. There is an article which claimed the Rock did it because Rocks can, as Hanging Rock did it to some young girls on St Valentine's Day, 1900. There is something to be desired in the way the mother conducts herself. She didn't cry at the right time. There is a tall fair husband. There are religious beliefs. There are accusations against the particular religion itself. There is a massive campaign of self-defence on its part. There is a supposition that the baby's name was 'Sacrifice in the Desert'. There are young mothers who know what it feels like to want to kill their kids. There is no charge of infanticide in the Northern Territory. There is, however, a murder charge. There is a new pregnancy. There is separation of mother and new daughter. There is a change in the mother's clothes. There is an unexplained fear. There is an appeal to the High Court. There is no corpse. There is the Aboriginal tracker. There are half-tame half-shepherd dingos. There was a bull terrier in Carlton, Victoria, which ate a baby. There are the Northern Territory Police. There are four-wheel drives galore. There is adult blood on the upholstery. There is a tracksuit at the dry cleaners. There is a forensic expert from Adelaide. There is an English one, or two. There is a female forensic expert from New South Wales who now works for the Northern Territory. There is a pair of scissors. There is only a mean time eleven minutes for her to have done it. There are drag marks in the sand. There are magical caves in the huge red Rock. There is a hanging-on-to rope on Uluru. There is a baby gone. There is a snipped baby singlet. There is no canine saliva. There is mystery in the air. There is a trial of forensic science. There is a dark-coloured baby dress. There is mythology in the press. There is no matinee jacket. There is baby's blood in the camera case. There is a question whether the reagent solution could conclusively prove it is foetal haemoglobin. There are horrific imaginings of how and why she did it. There is a widespread religious campaign to free Lindy. There was a dingo destroyed. There is the private eye team. There is no defence of insanity. There is an expensive forensic campaign finding in four other Holden Toranas out of forty a spray of the substance called Dufix HN 1081 which looks like spurted blood. There is no mention of a third person. There is a woman in jail. There are hundreds of people giving money to prove her innocence. There is a new tourist development at Ayers Rock. There is also a piece of paper which says this national park now belongs to three tribes of the Dreamtime people. There is a woman in jail who makes her own clothes.

Journey of Madge,
A Poetry Reading

A hot coming we had of it,
Celia Marple and I
Just at that time of year
Hot days, bitter nights and the winds
Moaning through the sands and desert oaks.
The bus broke down and the coach captain
Swore foul oaths as the vehicle lay deep in the bulldust.
The outback stations like sore thumbs
On the sandscape, the spindly windmills,
And the dusty blacks guzzling beer
The white men filthy and cursing
And pissing off in old Holdens, and wanting their liquor
And women, though few were to be seen.
They must have taken gins beside embers of bushfires
In the night. And the locals unfriendly and charging high
    prices:
A hard time we had of it
On the Centralian coach tour.
We preferred travelling by day,
Sleeping in snatches,
With the voices of the willywag women
Singing in our ears, at night, saying
That this was all folly. Go home whites.

Then we saw the dawn across the Olgas,
Such beauty rendered Celia and I speechless for a day

As we sat apart from the others under three low trees.
We swore we saw a wild camel for a moment
But it disappeared.
Then we came to the motel at Ayers Rock
A few blokes were playing poker at the bar door
And there were empty stubbie bottles everywhere
Pathetic ignorant and boozed were the conversations inside
But we slaked our thirst
And pitched our tent at evening in the caravan park
Finally there; it was (you may say) satisfactory.
There's been such a hullaballoo about that time and place,
Since, yet, I remember
Our supper, and we would do it again, but set down
This set down
This: were we led (we felt led as if fate dictated
Our decision) all that way for
Birth or Death? There seems to have been a Death,
Certainly, but as Celia said we have evidence only
Of a Disappearance, an absence of the baby and no doubt.
Celia and I thought different theories; like Birth for me,
Really. I am not the same. I don't bemoan the hard and bitter
    agony
Nor the sympathy I felt for both beast and beauty
(For the mother had such pretty dresses)
I am reborn in an ancient dispensation
With an alien people clutching their desecrated gods.
I should be glad to die as Celia died,
Convinced of the power and truth of the Dreamtime.

Miss Celia Marple's Narrative

PERFORMED AS A LECTURE WITH A POINTER AND A LARGE BOARD
DISPLAYING CELIA MARPLE'S DRAWING OF THE CARAVAN PARK, BUSH
AND AYERS ROCK.

There is one culprit in this whole case and it is Evil. I chose
a place outside the caravan park to scribble and sketch my
thoughts and observations of the whole affair. I know it is my
last case, now. When Madge first suggested the trip my

trepidation was tinged with excitement. Premonition was it? I couldn't refuse to come for it would have meant I lacked the courage to pursue my fate. I, with my pendulum, have been at the scene of many deaths, murders most of them, for it seems to have been my lot to have Detection as my main passion and commitment in life. The Holy Spirit has guided me to arrive at just and true conclusions and it has provided me one simple singular aid – my tiny crystal pendulum. With this I detect the flow of good and bad energy through the living being of creation.

In detection, it is necessary to believe in the endless battle between the light and the dark forces of the universe(s). Then in deed and effort to fight on the side of good. The genre would be nothing at all without the overall intention of the detective to do good – to seek not financial rewards, not honour and re-spect from the world or the media but, rather, justice – to see the real culprit sent to whatever punishment justice has to offer. Sadly, many sentences and judgements are ill-advised, either inadequate or too harsh. However, it is not a part of my passion or talent to fight on that front. It is beyond my control.

All through my long life I have felt that in this land of the Holy Spirit, Terra Incognita, I would be led into the Centre and there I would take my life. Or, more accurately, It, the land, the Holy Spirit, would finally relieve me of the burden of constantly doing for others with little gratitude, misunder-standing mainly being my reward. But belief is belief and we carry on.

It was to be our holiday. Biannually we take a bus trip to-gether, a couple of old spinsters with time on our hands. We had been everywhere else so I suppose we had to come here, yet some strange eerie feeling commenced immediately on our booking the seats. I was afraid and yet I knew we must go on. I think Madge, in her way, also felt somehow grasped by fate and sent in a certain direction for I saw in her frown a queer determination as if she saw something I did not. I called it her 'star in the West'.

Anyway, we came and the events of August the seventeenth occurred. It seemed quite simple at first. The magistrate, later, said the native dog had done the deed. There were, however, little problems, loose ends which didn't seem to tally. Grasping these loose ends, the prosecution tied them into a case and had the first inquest's findings reversed by the second.

My hand is useless as an artist's tool but you will see on my scribbling a view of the caravan park and the Rock. There are a few vehicles and tents, caravan and the toilet block. Between the park and the Rock there is a distance of about five miles; no, it is not that far, but it's a reasonable walk. It was in this bush that I made my most interesting discoveries. The caves in the Rock's face are another story in terms of negative and positive power. The entire region is immensely powerful, my pendulum could hardly contain itself. I have gone over the whole area sifting and making assessments.

Much of my life has been spent considering Evil. It is not rational yet it appears rational. It defies generalisation while inviting it. For example, in the first case it appears rational because it is materialistic and, in the second, it invites a generalisation such as all dogs are bad or all blondes are goodies and dark-haired women are to be feared, and defies an equivalent generalisation of itself, such as all men with a mean and nasty demeanour are rapists with the truth that some quite handsome men and pleasant social types have hearts (or souls) as black as soot. It takes such a thing as the pendulum operated with humility to the divine and good purpose to actually decide one way or the other; sometimes.

Let us suppose that the drawing I've done is as the caravan park was on the evening of the seventeenth. Only two of the many tents conveyed to the pendulum good vibrations. These are the Lowes' and the Chamberlains'. The Holden Torana and the landrover also sent the pendulum on the clockwise course. The Falcon station-wagon and the caravan gave negative vibrations and the toilet block positive. Because there was such an overwhelming predominance of anti-clockwise motion, I was forced to check the trees and the bush, because there is always the possibility the deeds occur because the place itself is Evil and likely to cause human beings to act uncharacteristically. In such a powerful place as this, dominated by the huge sandstone monolith of Ayers Rock considered by the original peoples to be a god and by scientific Western geologists to be quite a phenomenon, it is highly probable that at some time or another a horrific

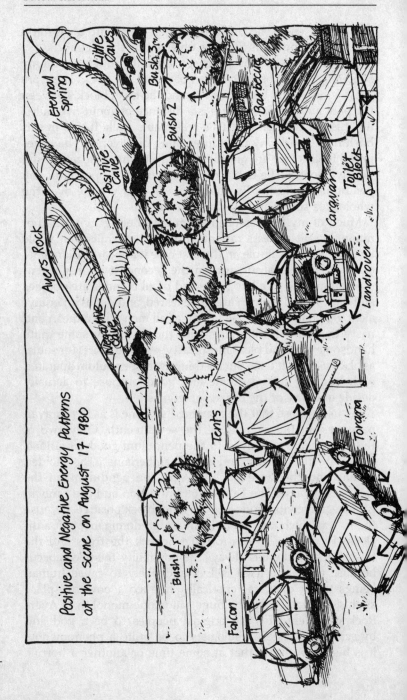

Positive and Negative Energy Patterns at the scene on August 17 1980

blasphemy or many little blasphemies could have taken place to turn it into a place to be avoided.

I found, however, that this was not so. The power of the Rock was extraordinarily balanced and well left as a sacred place by the Aborigines. Any punishment this particular god dealt to those who believed in its divinity would be quick and fair. So the culprit was mankind, not the spirit world.

My suspicions that a ghastly injustice was about to occur were aroused by just such accusations towards the spirit world. We were there. We heard the gossip and so did every interested Australian because the media was here with its huge inquisitive nose to the ground. A miniature coffin had been found in the home at Mt Isa and a Bible underlined in a way that one interpretation might have indicated some Satanic motive and the baby had had its last medical examination in a black dress and someone had dredged up biblical proof that Azaria, an odd name to the Australian tongue, really meant 'Sacrifice in the Desert'. I deduced that mischief was afoot in just this stirring up of superstitious feelings in a public so usually indifferent and apathetic about such immaterial things.

In fact, their very materialism gave weight to these weird and wonderful coincidences that they in themselves did not deserve. They could only be explained with imagination and compassion and these qualities – virtues – seem less delectable to a mass than the inexplicable, the mysterious. So, in my little investigations, I dismissed these 'proofs' as useless and purely psychological and relevant only to a parallel phenomenon; the extreme, nay, universal interest this incident aroused.

My attention turned to what really had happened. The loose ends. I kept in mind the incredible desire of the Territorians to exonerate the semi-native dog, the so-called dingo, when, on their stations, they would have no qualms at all about shooting a marauding canine beast. There is to the south the dingo fence which these same types consider a necessity. Madge and I on our trip to Western Australia stared into the eyes of a suffering emu stuck in that inhumane wire barrier. We watched it die.

An insane fever grew in the community around here. Nurse Downs was nearly hysterical with it – such excitement she'd never had.

My pendulum had told me that there was little human sympathy to be milked. It is necessary to have some kind of moral geiger counter lest one spend too much time with the wrong type.

I sought the owner or driver of the landrover – the ranger. This man had shot the half-tame half-shepherd dingo within hours of the disappearance of Azaria. He, unfortunately, could not hear my questions. He thought me a silly old maid. Still, I knew his vibrations were fundamentally all right.

The Aboriginal tracker, Daisy, was taken with my trinket. She saw me squatting on the ground in the bush I've marked bush '2', fascinated by the huge rightwise circles the little crystal on the string was making. She showed me where she had tracked the drag marks to – stones. The dog walks lightly on stone – no more marks. There we were both mystified. I brought out my diviner. It hurled itself in the opposite direction. By this time, Daisy was nodding sagely at its antics. There was some quite conscious human Evil here. Not far away, eventually, they found the tot's clothes apparently snipped by scissors.

This was, indeed, a loose end if one were to consider the mother herself innocent, as my pendulum indicated I must. My friend left me quite suddenly and she did not walk back toward the settlement.

Real Evil. It is one thing to murder directly in person with passion or malice aforethought. It is quite another, having found some savaged clothes, having not murdered anyone yourself, to tamper with the evidence in such a way as to imply a murder had taken place and point the finger at an innocent being. Quite peculiar motives came to my mind for this was the most bizarre aspect of the whole affair. Let me be cautious and say – hypothetically – somebody or bodies had found the baby clothes in the sand and deliberately taken scissors to them and strewn them about or left them under a rock. If this were so, did it mean, therefore, things had come to such a pass for the Territorians that, maybe without a body for evidence, they would not succeed in getting a conviction? A body they possibly knew to be consumed – a murdered baby's body? And why did they need a conviction so badly? Or perhaps it was the work of a mischievous imp. There is a strain of madness in the white men in this area. One need only be around for a while, even a short while, to notice an accepted level of insanity. As Madge would say, we – whites – should not be here.

The forces of Evil were already generalising: the dark-haired lady, the inscrutable, the witch must be burnt and tried on any evidence at all; all dogs are good. Indian wolf-boy stories are, no doubt, true, and Romulus and Remus drank hound's milk. The truly wild canine is more likely to suckle a defenceless human babe than eat it. But all dogs are not good. There are mad dogs and sane dogs; bad dogs and good ones. Half-wild feral beasts having learnt no lore in the native pack or the indigenous environment, having an innate distrust and knowledge of human beings who have cast them out and fed them irregularly, are likely to scavenge where they can. What disturbed me most was this unknown human element that would disguise the evidence of the animal's destruction and create evidence of a human's, and yet I grew convinced that this had happened.

I began to doubt my own sanity, as we had spent many weeks in this uncomfortable atmosphere of suspicion, of speculation.

My despair becomes impossible to bear as I hear the progress of the trials. Justice has given way to spurious science and prejudice. The legalistic gymnastics of the Queen's Counsels are a damnable indictment of their profession where such scurrilous tactics of persuasion are left free to whip the innocent and the just pedants with scorn and sarcasm.

So many courts of law indulge themselves getting huge salaries to puff and pant and pander to legalities and technicalities and inhuman practices that I find myself in an invidious position. All my arts and talents of inspired detection are absolutely worthless if their results are always to be thrown into the sausage machine of the legal profession – which, even if it retains some good intentions, is so structured as to be time-wasting, ridiculously expensive, awfully circuitous and, in the end, relatively toothless as far as worthwhile and fair punishment goes. There is no point in my going on.

I gaze at my crystal. I must follow the Holy Spirit now and walk west until I drop and die as I lived, just another old bag of bones. Maybe out there I'll meet a strange fair wolf-girl – but now I am being fanciful. I am old and have no use for hospitals with their life-support systems. If I have any choice at all in the illusion of my own freedom it is to refuse. In this case, now, to refuse to continue living.

DARKNESS

Notes in Retrospect

Miss Marple Goes to Ayers Rock was performed at Belvoir Street Downstairs Theatre over three Monday nights in January 1986 as a part of a whole evening called 'Lindy and the Dingo'. Players, photographers, musicians, other writers and contributors to the evening included: Louise Fanos (photo-slides of Central Australia); Glenys Page (original music and song); Margaret McLaughlin and Silva (slides from press cuttings compiled by Sydney Rape Crisis Centre); Joanne Burns (Madge); Chris Sharpe (Celia Marple); Mary Fallon (solo piece, Lindy in Berrimah); Miranda Mills, solo clown piece with songs; Anu (song) and technical assistance by staff at Belvoir Street. The audience were equally important on these three occasions for their intense concentration on the innocence of Lindy Chamberlain.

The story of the short life of Lindy Chamberlain's baby, Azaria, played itself through the media of Australia. I remember the instinctual reaction to hearing about that cry in the dark: 'The dingo's got my baby.' We could not believe a dingo would do that, take a baby from a tent. Between August 17, 1980, and February 20, 1981, when Stipendiary Magistrate Denis Barritt had his findings of the first inquest televised live, arguments among my own friends generally favoured the view that the dingo was innocent. Barritt and one friend I recall found the dingo the culprit. Everybody enjoyed making up or retelling dingo/baby jokes. We were hungry for any details we could consume about Mrs Chamberlain and the discoveries of the Northern Territory Police. And the press favoured us with every rumour and speculation possible: the more biblical and superstitious the better.

November 20, 1981, the Northern Territory Supreme Court quashed the findings of the first inquest and ordered a second. February 2, 1982, NT Chief Magistrate, Gerry Galvin, committed Lindy and Michael Chamberlain for trial. September 13, 1982, the trial opened in Darwin. As superstitious and religious speculation was not admissible in court, the case was almost exclusively forensic. Pictures of Lindy appeared daily on television and in the newspapers. She began to look fat and pregnant, grumpy and bitter. No-one had sympathy for her manner of dealing with the tragedy. She learnt about the behaviour of dingos and how they tear off skin carefully before devouring their prey. She described this on the popular Sixty Minutes program. She and Michael provided the *Australian Women's Weekly* with numerous photographs of Azaria, for which it was assumed they were paid. She got pregnant with Kahlia.

October 29, 1982, Lindy Chamberlain was found guilty of murder and Michael, her husband, guilty of accessory to murder. She was sentenced to life imprisonment and his sentence was suspended as someone had to look after the sons, Regan and Aidan. She was taken to Berrimah Jail, Darwin. November 17, Kahlia was born in Darwin Hospital. The Chamberlains appealed to the Federal Court and Lindy was granted bail. The prosecution had proved that Lindy grabbed her child from her bed, ran to their car, a yellow Holden Torana, stabbed her quickly with a pair of scissors and stowed her in Michael's empty camera case, in the space of eleven minutes, on the forensic evidence of Mrs Joy Kuhl and others saying that the spray marks in the Torana were foetal blood. The Defence maintained that, if that were so, where was the matinee jacket that Azaria was wearing? The Northern Territory Police had overturned everything belonging to the Chamberlains both at the site and at their home in Mount Isa.

April 29, 1983. The Federal Court rejected the Chamberlains' appeal and Lindy was taken to Mulawa Women's Prison at Silverwater, New South Wales. A bail application was lodged pending appeal to the High Court of Australia. This was refused on May 2, 1983. Lindy Chamberlain was transferred to Berrimah Jail in the Northern Territory. On February 22, 1984, the High Court rejected their appeal, three to two. The dissenting judges were Justice Lionel Murphy and Justice Deane. Murphy, I remember, said if there wasn't a body, there wasn't a case, bringing the only bit of common sense into the whole discussion. While some women may have been saying 'I'm sick of the sight and sound of Lindy Chamberlain,' others were now really worried about the extent of injustice done to her and many turned their attacks on the media-fest made of her plight.

Lindy was still in Berrimah when we did our little performance at Belvoir Street. Mary Fallon portrayed a victimised woman in jail with down-to-earth inmates, a victimised woman going mad on the one-track of a yellow-trimmed matinee jacket. Theatre and religion have the same prehis/storic roots, the ritual, the reverence, the concentration on one subject by a number of people in one place.

On February 2, 1986, an English tourist fell off Ayers Rock and, when they discovered his body, they found little Azaria's yellow-trimmed matinee jacket.

On February 7, the Northern Territory Government remitted Lindy's life sentence and released her from jail on licence. Still loyal to Sixty Minutes and the *Australian Women's Weekly*, Lindy showed that she had been far from victim in Berrimah and suggested that she had had to slap a few girls around to become top dog. Her haircut was smart and her tongue sharp. But it still wasn't over, they were not officially 'innocent'.

On May 8 1986, a Commission of Inquiry was formally opened. It went on forever here at the Supreme Court of New South Wales. Once I shared a lift with Lindy and a flock of black-plumed barristers, wondering if our little bit of theatre helped or if she'd even like to know about it. She and Michael had grown pale from being inside day after day during the dry, boring, still forensic-burdened legal proceedings of the Commission. Eventually, in June 1987, the Northern Territory Government pardoned Lindy and Michael Chamberlain after the Commission found that they would not have been convicted if the jury had been given all the evidence. On September 15, 1988, NT Court of Criminal Appeal quashed convictions and entered verdicts of acquittal.

THEA ASTLEY

Thea Astley was born in Brisbane in 1925 and was educated at Queensland University; she was a primary school teacher, a secondary school teacher, and until her retirement in 1980, a Fellow in Australian Literature at Macquarie University.

She consistently combined writing with her teaching career but now lives in the hills of the New South Wales South Coast and writes full time.

The winner of many literary prizes she has on three occasions won the Miles Franklin Award; she was the winner of the *Age* Book of the Year Award, the James Cook Australian Studies Award, and in 1986 she received the Australian Literary Society's Gold Medal. She is also the winner of the Steele Rudd Award and the 1988 Fellowship of Australian Writers ANA Literature Award for *It's Raining in Mango*.

Much of her writing is concerned with an exploration of some of the peculiarities and contradictions of life in Northern Queensland. The disintegration of the individual, and the desperation that is involved, is a theme which she repeatedly returns to; it is at the centre of 'Northern Belle', the work included here, taken from the book of short stories, *Hunting the Wild Pineapple*, first published by Nelson, Melbourne, in 1979 and in 1981 by Penguin. Her latest novel, *Reaching Tin River*, won the NSW Premier's Award in 1990. She has also published uncollected verse and short stories, and a critical study *The Australian Writer* (Foundation for *Australian Literary Studies* Monograph, No 5, 1979) as well as numerous scholarly and popular articles.

Among her novels are:

1958 *Girl with a Monkey*. Angus & Robertson, Sydney.
1987, Penguin, Melbourne.

1960 *A Descant for Gossips*. Angus & Robertson,
Sydney.

1962 *The Well Dressed Explorer*. Angus & Robertson,
Sydney. 1988, Penguin Books, Melbourne.

1965 *The Slow Natives*. Angus & Robertson, Sydney.
1990, Penguin, Melbourne.

1968 *A Boatload of Home Folk*. Angus & Robertson,
Sydney. 1983, Penguin, Melbourne.

1972 *The Acolyte*. Angus & Robertson, Sydney.
1980 University of Queensland Press, St Lucia.

1974 *A Kindness Cup*. Nelson, Melbourne.
1989, Penguin, Melbourne.

1982 *An Item from the Late News*. University of
Queensland Press, St Lucia. 1984, Penguin,
Melbourne.

1985 *Beachmasters*. Penguin, Melbourne.

1988 *It's Raining in Mango*. Penguin, Melbourne.

1990 *Reaching Tin River*. Heinemann, Melbourne.

A Northern Belle

The night Willy Fourcorners sat with me, awk-
ward in his Christian clothing, he told me, between the club-
bing blocks of rain, what it was like sometimes to be black in
these parts. He's sat with me other nights as well and what
he told me of this one or that, this place or that, was like taking
a view from the wrong side of the fence. Wrong's not the word.
Photographing in shadow, the object that is? No. I'm still
hunting the wild simile. It was... it was like inspecting the
negative, framing and hanging its reversals, standing back to
admire, then crying in despair, 'But it's all different!'

People I knew, he knew, but he knew them some other-
how – as if he saw Lawyer Galipo and Father Rassini from the
lee side of the banks of heaven. I asked him once why he'd ever

left his little house on the outskirts of Tobaccotown, and he was silent a long time. I coddled his silence and at last he told me. I put his story onto their stories and still I get one story.

This is Willy's story, my words.

She was born in one of those exhausted, fleetingly timbered places that sprang up round the tin mines of the north. Not in the poverty of a digger's shack, let it be understood, but in the more impressive veranda'd sprawl of one of those cedar houses that loiter in heavy country gardens. How capture the flavour of those years? Horse-rumps, sweat, hard liquor, crippled shanties, all forgotten in the spacious hours after lunch and before tea when baking fragrance settled as gently as the shadows across and into the passion-vined trellis.

A porky child with a fine cap of almost white dead-straight hair, her body gave no indication of the handsome bones that were to emerge in late adolescence. Skip some years. Now we have her at fourteen bounding confidently across the town hard-court, shimmering with sweat, her hair longer now, darkening now, still fine and unmanageable; but it's still no pointer to the strong-minded Clarice of nineteen who, despite a profile of pleasing symmetry, still boyishly racquet-scooped balls, served low and hard, and later dispensed lemon squash in the tin side-line shed where other acceptables of the town gathered each Saturday afternoon.

She had early the confidence of her class. Her father was a mine manager and owner. 'AG' they called him, and he knew to a nicety what line of familiarity to draw with the blacks who still hung about the perimeters of town, even instigating a curfew for them, but was less certain when it came to men of his own colour. Which was either bright red or mottled white. In snapshots from the period he, heavily moustached and mutton-chopped beside his wife, dominated rows of sawney after-picnic guests. She always appeared formidably silked and hatted and her bust was frightening. 'Breasts' is somehow too pretty, too delicate a word to describe that shelf of righteousness on which many a local upstart had foundered. Along with the bust was a condescending familiarity with the town's priest, two ministers of other religions, and four members of parliament whom she had seen come and helped go. Clarice was an only child, not as much of a son as the father had hoped for and something less of a daughter; but with the years her looks fined and softened; and if she was not in fact a beauty privilege made her just as desirable in a country where a fine bank account is as good for launching a thousand ships as a face: it's even better.

Her mother was determined Clarice would marry well, but no-one was ever quite well enough.

Motor-cars and Clarice's teens created small tensions. There were various young men; but the town had little to offer beyond bank- and railway-clerks, or the sons of Italian tobacco farmers whose morals the mother suspected to be doubtful. Should too long a time elapse between the drawing-up of a young man's car and Clarice's flushed entry to the house, her mother would tighten her mouth, draw up that juridical bust, and struggle to find words that were at once proper and admonitory. She was rarely able to draw that nice balance and one afternoon, as she worked with her daughter in the kitchen crumbling butter and flour for scones, she said without preamble and quite formally:

'I was once attacked by a sexually maddened blackfellow.'

Clarice was startled.

'That is why.' Her mother shut her lips tightly and a little line was ruled.

'Why what?'

'Why you must keep men – all men – at a distance.'

'All men?' inquired Clarice. 'Or just sexually maddened blackfellows?'

'You are too young, Clarice,' her mother said sharply, 'to use such words. Girls of sixteen should not even know such words.'

'But I don't understand,' Clarice persisted. 'Were you – ?' she hesitated. 'Harmed' seemed not an exact enough word. 'Were you carnally known?'

Her mother fainted.

'I do not know where,' she later gabbled to Clarice's father, 'where this – this child – could pick up such ... I have done all ... appalling knowledge ... how the good nuns ... wherever ... she must be protected from ...'

She spoke at length to her daughter on the necessity of virtue, the rigours of beauty, of chastity, the clean mind, and the need to expunge lust. She went so far as to summon Father Rassini to give spiritual advice. She read her daughter an improving poem. Clarice listened to all this with an expression on her face as if she were trying to remember a knitting pattern. Young men were discouraged from calling. Her current bank-clerk went away in the army and Clarice, after dreadful scenes in which she finally proved herself her father's daughter, took a little branch train to the coast, caught the main line south, and burrowed into essential war industry.

The city was only partly strange to her, for she had been educated at a southern convent where her only achievements had been to stagger the nuns by the ferocity with which she played badminton and Mendelssohn's *Rondo Capriccioso*. She revealed no other talents. They taught her a little refined typing and book-keeping, insufficient to addle or misdirect any feminine drives; enough French to cope with a wine list in the better restaurants; and some basic techniques in water-colours. She had a full and vigorous voice that dominated, off-key, the contralto section of the school choir for three years, but even this mellowed into suitable nuances before the onslaught of the mistress in charge of boarders.

'My dear Clarice,' she would reprove icily, 'you are not a man.'

'*Non, ma mère*,' Clarice would reply dutifully, giving the little curtsey this particular order required.

'And further, you seem to forget that men do not... oh, never mind!' Mother Sulpice rolled her fine brown eyes upwards, a kind of ecstatic St Teresa, and swished off with her beads rattling.

The boarders pondered Mother Sulpice.

'You can see she was quite beautiful,' Clarice's best friend, a thumping girl, commented doubtfully. 'Quite Renaissance.'

'Do you think she was jilted in love?' The students spent much time in these speculations.

'Oh, I heard. I heard.'

'What? What did you hear?'

'I shouldn't say.'

'Oh, come on! What?'

'My mother told me something.'

'Told you what?'

'I shouldn't really say.'

'Oh, yes you should,' Clarice insisted. She kicked quite savagely at the iron railing of the terrace that looked out over Brisbane hills. 'By not telling me you are creating an occasion of sin.'

Thumper went pink. 'I'm not. How could I be?'

'Who knows what I shall think,' Clarice said cunningly. 'I could think almost anything. In fact, I do think almost anything.'

She looked slyly at her friend and observed the moral contortion with interest.

'You've got to promise,' Thumper said, 'that you won't tell.'

'Well?'

'Do you promise?'

'Of course.'

'Well,' Thumper said with a pretty play of hesitancy, 'well, she was engaged. Before she entered.'

'And what then?'

'He died. He was killed in France. It wasn't,' she said, lowering her voice in horror, 'a true vocation.'

'Oh, stuff that,' Clarice said. 'How did it happen?'

'Mummy said it was quite tragic.' Clarice saw her friend's eyes grow moist and noticed she was getting a new pimple. 'He was running to regain the trenches and he ran the wrong way. He was dreadfully short-sighted.'

Clarice wanted to laugh. Instead, she looked at her friend hard and asked, 'Do you think they'd had sexual intercourse?'

'Now you *will* have to go to confession!' her friend said.

'Poor Mother Sulpice!' Clarice sighed.

But it was for her, perhaps for the wrong reasons, transfiguration.

She studied the nun's graceful walk, imitated the Isadora-like arabesques of her hands, modulated her voice, and began training her hair into expressive curves across her ears.

'How Clarice has changed!' the nuns observed with relief. 'She's growing up at last.'

In class, her mind closed to the finer points of the redundant *ne*, she sought for and thought she discovered the delicate prints of tragedy on Mother Sulpice's completely calm face.

'That will be the way I will bear it,' she said to herself.

After she left home the first job she obtained was as an office assistant in a factory supplying camouflage tents to the troops. She left the day the senior accountant, who was married, suggested they take in dinner and a show. When she leapt offendedly onto a tram, an American serviceman asked could he help with her bag. She had no bag but was so confused by the nature of his offer that before she had gone three blocks she found herself in conversation with him. He told her many lies, but those she most vividly remembered were about a cotton plantation in Georgia, an interrupted semester at Yale, and no engagement of the heart, legal or otherwise. As she dressed in her YMCA cubicle for her third outing with him, she kept telling herself it was Mother Sulpice all over again, and she dropped her firm tanned neck, glanced back into the speckly mirror, and lowered her eyes in unconscious but perfect parody.

On the sixth outing seven days after they had met, he attempted to take her to bed, but she resisted with much charm. On the seventh he told her he had been drafted to the Pacific and they then exchanged deeply emotional letters that she read again and again, all the time thanking God for the good training which had prevented 'that' from happening. 'That' was happening all about her. Thumper was pregnant to a marine who had crossed the horizon without leaving any other memento of his visit. Men were all like that, Thumper assured Clarice between her sobs. Clarice thought it a pity her nose got so red when she cried.

Clarice managed to repress her feelings of righteousness and exultation that she was the one spared, and after she had seen her friend take a sad train back to her stunned parents up country she slid into Thumper's job in an army canteen. She was totally unprepared for a letter some months later from Roy telling her he had married a nurse in Guam because he had to. 'Honey,' he wrote, 'you will always be very special to me. You will always be my one true love, the purest I have ever known.' He was lying again, but she was spared the knowledge of this.

She was not built for pathos. The troubles of others found in her a grotesque response of incomprehension. She kept meeting more and more men, but they all failed to please, were not rich enough or wise enough or poor enough if wise, or were too worldly or unworldly. And through all of this, growing steadily older and handsomer, she bore her singleness like an outrageous pledge of success.

At parties when other girls more nervous than she spilt claret cup or trifle on the hostess's carpet at those endless bring-a-plate kitchen teas she seemed always to be attending, she would say offhandedly, 'Don't worry. It's not *her* trifle,' and go on flirting tangentially and unconsummatedly with this or that. She was moving up the ranks and knew a lot of colonels now.

When the war was over she settled more or less permanently into a cashier's desk at a large hotel where for half a dozen years she was still courted by desperate interstate commercial travellers who, seeing her framed between the stiff geometry of gladioli, found a *quattrocento* (it was the hairstyle) mystique which they did not recognise as such but longed to explore. She accepted their pre-dinner sherries with every symptom of well-bred pleasure, went to films, dog-races, and car-trials with them, but always bade them firm good-nights outside her own apartment.

Then her hair began to show its first grey.

Her father died suddenly shouting at a foreman; and after Clarice had gone home to help out her mother held onto her for quite a while, determined to see her daughter settled. Rallying from grief, she arranged picnics, dances, barbeques, musical evenings, card suppers; yet even she gave up when Clarice returned home far too early from a picnic race-meeting with a *fin de siècle* languor about the eyes.

'Where's that nice Dick Shepworth?' her mother demanded from a veranda spy-post.

'At the races, I suppose.'

'You left him there?'

'Yes. He is suffering from encroaching youth.'

'But, my God!' cried her mother. 'He's the manager of two cane mills with an interest in a third.'

'He holds his knife badly,' Clarice said, picking up a mal-formed piece of knitting.

'You must be mad,' her mother said.

'And he chews with his mouth open.'

'Oh, my God!'

She was dead by the end of the party season. Clarice got Father Rassini to bury her alongside AG, sub-divided the property, sold at a profit and, having invested with comfortable wisdom in an American mining corporation, retired into her parents' house and spent her days in steady gardening. It became a show place. It was as if all her restrained fertility poured out into the welter of trees and shrubs; and if the rare and heady perfumes of some of them made occasional sensual onslaughts she refused to acknowledge them.

The day she turned forty she bought herself a dog.

He was a fine labrador who established his rights at once, learnt smartly to keep away from the seedling beds and to share her baked dinner. They ate together on the long veranda which stared down at the mined-out hills beyond the garden, and the tender antithesis of this transferred the deepest of green shadows into her mind, so that she found herself more and more frequently talking to Bixer as if he had just made some comment that deserved her reply. Her dependence on him became engrafted in her days: he killed several snakes for her, barked at the right people, and slept, twitching sympathetically with her insomnia, by the side of her bed. She only had to reach down to pat Roy, a colonel, a traveller, or even Dick Shepworth, and they would respond with a wag of the tail.

Although so many years had passed since her parents' deaths, Clarice still believed she had a position in the town and consequently gave a couple of duty dinner parties each year – but not willingly – to which she invited old school friends, townsfolk who still remembered her father, and occasionally Father Rassini. He dreaded the summons, for she was a bad cook; but attended, always hopeful of some generous donation. Aware of this, she would keep him sweating on her Christmas contribution till it was almost Easter; and when she finally handed him the envelope they both remembered her stoniness as he had talked to her, thirty years ago now, about the sins of the flesh. He'd been young, too; and whenever he sat down to an especially lavish meal at some wealthy parishioner's home he recalled her cool look as she had asked, 'Are you ever tempted, Father?'

As her muscles shrank the garden acre flexed its own, strengthened and grew more robust than a lover. There were rheumatic twinges that worried her. One day when she went to rise from where she had been weeding a splendid planting of dwarf poinsettia, the pain in her back was so violent she lay on the grass panting. Bixer nosed around, worried and whimpering, and she told him it was nothing at all; but she thought it was time she got a little help.

She was fifty when she took in Willy Fourcorners as gardener. He was an elderly Aborigine, very quiet, very gentle, who had been for a long time a lay preacher with one of the churches. Clarice didn't know which one, but she felt this made him respectable. Willy wore a dark suit on Sundays, even in summer, and a tie. He would trudge back from the station sometimes, lugging a battered suitcase and, passing Clarice's house and seeing her wrenching at an overgrowth of acalypha, would raise his stained grey hat and smile. The gesture convinced Clarice that though he was a lesser species he was worthy, and she would permit herself to smile back, but briefly.

'Willy,' she said one day, emerging from the croton hedge, 'Willy, I wonder could I ask your help?'

Willy set down his bag in the dust and rubbed his yellow-palmed hands together.

'Yeah, Miss Geary. What's the trouble then?'

She came straight to the point.

'I need help with the garden, Willy.' She was still used to command and the words came out as less of a request than she intended. She was devastated by the ochreous quality of his skin so close to hers and a kindliness in the old eyes she refused to admit, for she could not believe in a Christian blackskin, preacher or not. 'It's all getting too much for me.'

Willy's face remained polite, concerned but doubtful. He was getting on himself and still worked as a handyman at the hardware store. On weekends he preached.

'Only got Saturdays,' he said.

'Well, what's wrong with Saturday?'

'I like to keep it for m'self.'

Clarice struggled with outrage.

'But wouldn't you like a little extra money, Willy?'

'Not that little, Miss Geary,' Willy said.

Clarice's irritation riveted at once upon the simple smiling face, and unexpectedly, contrarily, she was delighted with his show of strength.

'I'm a fair woman,' she said. 'You'd get regular wages. What I'd give anyone.'

Willy nodded. He still smiled through the sweat that was running down his face, down his old brown neck and into the elderly serge of his only suit.

'Please,' Clarice heard herself pleading. 'Just occasionally. It would be such a help, Willy. You see, I can't handle the mowing these days.' And she produced for him what she had managed to conceal from almost everyone, a right hand swollen and knobbed with arthritis, the fingers craned painfully away from the thumb into the beginnings of a claw.

Willy looked at her hand steadily and then put out one finger very gently as if he were going to touch it. She tried not to wince.

'That hurts bad, eh?' he said. 'Real bad. I'll pray for you, Miss Geary.'

'Don't pray for me, Willy,' Clarice said impatiently. 'Just mow.'

He grinned at that and looked past her at the thick mat of grass that was starting a choking drive about the base of the trees.

'Saturday,' he said. 'Okay.'

He came every few weeks after that and she paid him well; and after a year, as her right hand became worse and the left developed symptoms, he began to take over other jobs – pruning, weeding, planting out, slapping a coat of paint, fixing a rotted veranda board. She grew to look forward to the clear Saturday mornings when with Bixer, ancient, dilapidated, sniffing behind her, she directed him down side paths as he trimmed and lopped the flashy outbursts of the shrubs. Although at first she tended to treat him and pay him off as she would imagine AG to have done, gradually she became, through her own solitariness, aware of him as a human; so that after a time, instead of returning to the veranda for her cup of tea after taking him his, she got into the habit of joining him at the small table in the side garden.

'Where is it you get to, Willy,' she asked one Saturday

morning as they drank their tea, 'when you take the train down to the coast?'

'Don't go to the coast, Miss Geary.'

'Where do you go then?'

'Jus' down as far as Mango.'

'Mango?' Clarice exclaimed. 'Why would you want to go to Mango?'

'Visit m'folks there,' he said. 'Got a sister there. Visit her kids. She got seven.'

'Seven,' Clarice murmured. 'Seven.' She thought of Thumper. 'That's a large number, I must say.'

'They're good kids,' Willy said. 'My sister, see, she'd like me to go an' live down there now they're gettin' on a bit.'

'She's younger than you, then, Willy?'

'Yeah. Fair bit younger.'

'And have you any, Willy? Any children, I mean?' She knew he lived alone, had done since she had come back to live.

'Two,' he said. 'Two boys. Wife died of the second one. But they been gone a long time now. Real long time.'

'Where to?'

'South,' he said. 'Down south.'

'And what do they do? Do they write?'

'Yeah. Come home sometimes an' stay with m'sister. One's a driver for some big factory place. Drives a truck, see? Other feller, he's in the church. He's trainin' to go teachin' one of them mission places.'

'Well, he's certainly done well,' Clarice said. 'You must be very proud of him.'

'Pretty proud,' old Willy said. 'Teachin' up the mission when he's through. Up Bamaga way he'll be. Might get to see him then, eh?'

'Do you get lonely, Willy?' she asked. But he didn't answer.

Bixer developed a growth. When Clarice noticed the swelling in his belly she summoned the vet from Finecut who took one look and said, 'I'll give him a shot if you like.'

'Get out!' Clarice said.

She cared for him as far as she was able, but he could only shamble from bedroom to veranda where he'd lie listless most of the day in the hot northern sun, not even bothering to snap at the flies. He lost control of his bladder and whimpered the first time he disgraced himself on the bedroom floor. Clarice whimpered herself as she mopped up.

Willy found her crying over the dog one Saturday morning. Bixer could hardly move now, but his eyes looked their recognition as Willy bent over him.

'Best you get him put away, Miss Geary,' Willy advised, touching the dog with his gentle fingers. 'Pretty old feller now.'

'Help me, Willy,' she said. 'I can't do that.'

He brought along an old tin of ointment he'd used for eczema on a dog of his own, and though he knew it wouldn't help he rubbed it in carefully, if only to help her.

'There y'are, Miss Geary,' he said looking up from where he knelt by the panting dog. 'That might do the trick.'

She was still tearful but she managed a smile at him.

'Thank you, Willy. You're a good man.'

It didn't do the trick; and when finally on one of the endless bland mornings of that week she found he had dragged away to die under the back garden bushes she could hardly bear it. She sat for a little on the veranda, which became populous with the ghosts of the endless summer parties of her youth. The smack of tennis balls came from a hard-court. The blurred voices of bank-clerks and railway-clerks and service men and travellers, and even the sound of Dick Shepworth eating, hummed and babbled along the empty spaces where her mother still sat in her righteous silks.

She put on her sun-hat and walked down town to the hardware store, where she found Willy sweeping out the yard.

'You've got to come, Willy,' she said. 'He's dead.'

'Strewth, Miss Geary. I'm real sorry. Real sorry.'

'You'll have to help me bury him, Willy. I can't dig the hole.'

'Strewth, Miss Geary,' Willy said. 'Don't know whether I kin leave.'

He propped himself on his broom handle and regarded her awkwardly. She was trying hard not to cry. He felt all his age, too, leaning there in the hot sun thinking about death.

'I'll fix that,' she said. She was still AG's daughter.

After it was over she made some tea and took it out to the garden. Willy looked hopelessly at her with his older wisdom.

'Don't you worry none, Miss Geary,' he kept saying. 'I'll get you a new little pup. A new one. Me sister, she got plenty. Jus' don' worry, eh?'

But she was sobbing aloud now, frightful gulping sounds coming from her as she laid her head on her arms along the table.

'Please, Miss Geary,' Willy said. 'Please.'

He touched her hand with his worn one, just a flicker, but she did not notice, did not look up, and he rubbed his hand helplessly across his forehead.

'Look,' he said, 'I got to be goin' soon. But true, me sister she's got these two dogs an' they jus' had pups. I'll get you one of theirs, eh? You'd like that. There's this little brown feller, see, with a white patch. He's a great little dog. You'd like that, eh?'

Slowly she lifted her head, her face ruined with weeping, and saw the old black man and the concern scribbled all over his face.

'Oh, Willy,' she said, 'that's so kind of you. It really is. But it won't make any difference.'

'But it will,' Willy argued, human to human. 'Nex' time I come to mow I'll bring him back. You see. You'll love him.'

He pushed his chair back, came round the table and stood beside her, wanting to cry himself a bit, she looked that old an' lost. She looked up at him, messy with grief, and Willy put his old arm round her shoulders and gave her a consoling pat.

'There,' he said. 'Don' you mind none.'

He'd never seen a face distort so.

She began to scream and scream.

EVA JOHNSON

Eva Johnson was born at Daly River in the Northern Territory. At the age of two she was removed from her mother and placed on a Methodist Mission where she remained until transferred to an orphanage in Adelaide at the age of ten. She holds an Associate Diploma in Community Development.

She has been actively involved in Aboriginal Land Rights, Black women's issues, Black theatre and the struggle against racism.

Eva Johnson has made a remarkable contribution to the representation of Black women; she is a writer of reality and vision and a consummate performer of her own work. At the Fourth International Feminist Book Fair in Barcelona, 1990, she received a standing ovation for her powerful and painfully poignant portrayal of Aboriginal life.

An Aboriginal drama teacher (at 'Worriapindi'), the writer/director of the first Aboriginal Women's Art Festival in Adelaide (1984), the writer and co-director of *Onward to Glory* – a look at the effects of the Australian education system on women (Adelaide Women's Theatre, 1985), the 1985 recipient of the Aboriginal Artist of the Year Award, and the writer/director of the First National Black Playwrights Conference (Canberra, 1987), she is one of the outstanding practitioners of the day.

She is the author and co-director of the play, *Tjindarella*, which had its debut peformance at the first Aboriginal Women's Arts Festival in Adelaide in 1984. It examines Aboriginal oppression and highlights the effects of government policy of enforced removal of Aboriginal children from their parents and culture; these concerns are also expressed in *What Do They Call Me?* She is also the author of the play 'Murras', which explores the theme of the loss of identity and 'Mimini's Voices', produced and directed by Magpie Theatre Company in Adelaide and performed overseas at the Hiroshima Festival in 1989.

Her performances have been many and much applauded; she has appeared at the first women writers' festival to be held in Melbourne in 1985, and the Adelaide Arts Festival (1990). Her work has been included in anthologies such as Susan Hawthorne (ed), *Difference* (1985), Cathie Dunsford and Susan Hawthorne (eds), *The Exploding Frangipani* (1990) and *Plays from Black Australia* (1991).

Eva now lives in the Flinders Ranges in South Australia where she is completing her book, *In Search of My Mother's Dreaming*. Aside from this she is also studying for a degree in Aboriginal Studies through the University of Adelaide.

What Do They Call Me?

The play *What Do They Call Me?* is in three inter-related parts – each with a different view of how the legislation of the *Aborigines Act* of the 1940s–1970 affected Aboriginal people.

Performed as three monologues, each character gives a personal revelation of her experiences as an Aboriginal woman, delivered optimistically, in minimalist setting, based on incisive observation and a reservoir of Aboriginal secrecy.

CONNIE BRUMBIE: A 58-year-old Aboriginal woman. We first meet her huddled beneath a blanket in jail, recovering from a night of cards, drink and false arrest.

Connie reveals her story to another Aboriginal woman across the cell from her, who listens as Connie unveils and relives the trauma of her daughter's removal from her care, her hostile existence with her de facto husband, and the continual harassment from the police in search of her son, Billy.

REGINA BRUMBIE (also known as REGINA PENROSE HILL):   A conservative 38 year-old woman, married to a business man, she has two children and has adopted the values of a conservative middle-class family.

Believing she was Eurasian, Regina responds with extreme anger when she confronts her adoptive mother, and then unfolds the search for her Aboriginal mother, her family, and her own Aboriginal identity.

ALISON BRUMBIE: A 35-year-old radical feminist. She is a strong, aware and politically conscious woman.

Ali lives with her lesbian lover of six years and the scene takes place on the night of their anniversary. Both Ali and her lover Sara, discover the strength of their own personal relationship, their feminist ideology, separatism, homophobia and feelings of deceit and false sisterhood.

The dialogue is thought provoking, analytical with the power of Aboriginality and womanhood.

Connie

Connie is in jail.

She has been arrested and charged with assault, abusive language and for being drunk and disorderly.

She lies still under a blanket, she coughs and the light slowly lights up. She moves slowly, mumbling to herself, raising herself. She is confused and slightly disorientated, she fixes her eyes on the screw at the desk...

   ...you got no right I tell you, no right
   ...what am I doing here?

Phew! this place stinks, like stale piss.
Makes me wanna throw up.
HEY! what you fuckin charge me for this time?
HUH? abusive language?

what did I fuckin' say? can't even swear in my own country.
everybody likes a charge,
I wasn't drunk, just happy, that's all, just happy.
We was just playin cards, that's all,
havin a bit of fun, no harm in that
you had no right, no right I tell you
bargin into my place like that.
I told you before, Billy don't live with me
I don't know where he lives.
What you want him for anyway? you got nothing on him.
I'm sick of you mob pickin on us all the time,
you had no right frightening the kids like that
linin them all up, friskin them
searching the place, smashin everything.
YOU don't go bargin into Gubba homes like that.

   'you got the right to remain silent
   you got the right to call your solicitor'

Huh, we got no rights, that's all bullshit.
What about my rights to privacy?
mob of racist bastards.
I'm gettin out of here, gettin out of here
Ha, I gave it to em, put up a good fight,
tryin boss me around, I'm not scared of them
Huh, Disorderly? Grievous bodily harm?
throwin' a fryin pan ain't disorderly
I was just protectin my family
Wheeee... I never seen fried rice fly like that before.
should have seen you mob scatter...
   [*Connie hears someone laughing,*
   she sees Maud in the cell opposite]
Who's that? who's that laughing?
What? O, hullo, my name's Connie, Connie Brumbie
you probably heard me come in aye?
I'm from top end, where you from?
what you in for Maud?
well, you gotta feed your family aye?
but, how come you all bashed up like that?

who done that to you?

Bastards, you seen a doctor? or someone?
Bastards, they real bastards, true as God...
abusive language, grievous bodily harm
ha, I even made up my own swear words to make me
sound real wild
they must have thought I was swearin at them in language.
Na, I'm used to them, it's nothing for me
I just get sick of it all the time.
Well, they broke into my house
nearly knocked the door down
we was playin cards,
heard a knock and Gladyse opened the door
they barged through, knocked her over.
I knew, I knew it was them.
I shut Gladyse's kids in my bedroom
they dragged the kids out, lined them up in the passage
started asking them questions about Billy, my son.
That's when I got real mad.
I grabbed the frying pan from the stove,
it was still hot too.
They wouldn't let the kids go
so I threw the pan at one of them,
hit him, he didn't even duck, stupid bastard
you should have seen him Maud
fried rice everywhere, kids took off pissin themselves laughin
threw me in the back of the van.
I asked to see their warrant
'don't need no special licence to break into a coon's home'
... bastards... real bastards...
God I'm sick of it Maud
them fullas looking for Billy all the time.
why don't they just leave me alone?
they reckon Billy killed his stepfather
it happened six years ago.
... I know that Billy must have seen some terrible things
my old man treatin me that way
he was a real bastard Maud, a proper mungeral bastard
but Billy got used to it
what could he do? he was just helpless
he was frightened of that bastard too.

Billy just took off all the time.
and he couldn't have been there that day
I know he wasn't there, he couldn't have been
God, that was a terrible, real nightmare
... I remember it clearly.
I can still see that mungeral bastard coming
coming through the front door
staggering down the passage towards me
I headed for the back door, but he took a swing at me
grabbed me by the hair and dragged me outside
over the gravel and the rocks
he held me down, the stink of rum on his breath
his eyes was real white
he was frothing at the mouth just like a mad dog
spitting saliva in my face
he thumped me to the ground so hard
true as God Maud, I thought my neck was broke
my legs was stinging from gravel rash
he rolled me over and over till my head hit the rotary line
I felt dizzy, I was stunned, I saw stars and went numb
I shut my eyes real tight and just lay there
I never cried Maud, I never cried
just then I heard a thump, or a bang, something
and all of a sudden he went completely still.
He went real heavy, wasn't moving, wasn't breathing
I couldn't work out what happened.
Then I felt something warm running down my neck
I dragged myself out from under him
I was covered in blood, I almost fainted
then I heard someone running down the side of the house
heavy footsteps, everything was blurred, I couldn't see
so I called out ... but nothing, they took off.
I felt sick, sick in my stomach, I wanted to throw up
I grabbed the hose and turned it on full pelt
just stood under it, tryin to come to my senses
the neighbour came to the fence
told us to keep the noise down, his wife had a migraine
then he saw what happened, and called the police
I was charged with manslaughter.
242
But they got it wrong Maud, they was wrong

so they had to let me go
that was six years ago
they had to charge someone
they been tryin to nail my Billy for it ever since
but they got no proof
Huh, 'we don't need no warrant to break into a coon's home'
Well that's what they did.
And what about you Maud, just look at you
don't worry, we gonna get out of here tomorrow
they not gonna kill our spirit Maud
we'll go up the centre tomorrow, they got a doctor there
and we'll have a good feed, there's a soup kitchen too
I work there sometimes, to help out
you got a family Maud?
Yeah, I had two daughters
welfare gave them to Gubba family
took them away from me
and now they tryin to take my Billy.
Yeah, that's what they tryin to do
but they'll never find him
you know that aye?
they'll never find him.
Hey, did you hear that?
You'll never find him, my Billy
so you take me, you hear
come on, come and get me.
I'm Billy Brumbie's mother
come on, what you gonna do to Connie Brumbie
what *can* you do to me now?
HANG ME?
   [blackout]
They turned the fuckin lights off,
gutless bastards.
you got a blanket Maud? Maud? you all right?
We'll get out of here tomorrow.
We'll be all right.
can't wait to play cards,
this time I'll cook spaghetti
yeah ... goodnight Maud.

Regina

Regina has, for some time been questioning her own identity – an incident in the pub confirms her true identity.

This monologue spans both past and present.

Regina reflects on her past and the events that led up to her finally discovering her identity.

We first meet Regina in a fit of rage, questioning her adoptive mother. She then moves into the present and the next tableau is the story of that process of resolving her inner conflict. The final tableau occurs in the present with her adoptive mother once again.

... why? why did you lie to me?
why didn't you tell me
why did you lie to me all these years, Mother?
to protect me?
FROM WHAT?
who am I?
when you adopted me, who gave me to you?
who is my real mother?
what is my REAL name?
NO, nothing's wrong, I just want to know.
things are happening, I don't understand
the other day I walked into a place for a drink
and the man behind the bar leered at me and said
'We don't serve Boongs here'
He was talking to me, Mother
I couldn't believe this was happening to me
'Who me?' I said, 'are you talking to me?
can't you see I'm practically white?' I shouted
'My father is a white man, just like you
that proves I am not a primitive.
I was *not* made in the bush
for your information, my name happens to be
Regina Penrose Hill'
He laughed at me.
For the first time in my life, I felt ashamed
degraded, dirty, ugly, yes, *ugly*, Mother
Why? why did you hide me in this false white skin?
were you ashamed of me? did you hate my black skin?

well, my whiteness has let me down.
No, I'm not over-reacting,
I'm totally confused and I'm angry
you made me believe that I was someone else
you lied to me, you lied to me
so tell me, Mother
am I still a Eurasian?
or is that a fancy name for BOONG?
    [*Pauses, addresses the audience*]
... when I was growing up, my family wrapped me
in a blanket of whiteness.
When I was growing up, I was proud of my English
my grammar, my spelling,
of fitting in ... getting in line ...
belonging to the more intelligent group.
When I was growing up, my friends always got praised
for their beauty.
I wanted to be like them,
I read fashion magazines, attended modelling and
    deportment classes
wore expensive clothes, went to the cinemas
and there, right up there on huge silver screens
were women with beautiful flowing hair, sensuous lips
women elevated, to be desired.
I longed to become that woman,
I began to wear imaginary pale skin,
bleached my hair, and avoided the sun
and when men asked me out, I felt special,
they had special names for me
like – princess, exotic lily, tigress
they loved to show me off to their friends
said I had style, had what it takes
loved the way I moved.
When I was growing up, people always said
I had beautiful eyes, a nice smile, and pearly white teeth
people would ask me if I were Filipino, Maori
or Polynesian – anything but Aboriginal.
O, I was articulate, intelligent and successful
I had money, beauty and virtue
I thought I had everything, I thought I was somebody ...

So, there I was
thriving under the smug illusion that I was not
the stereotype image of the Aboriginal Woman
I have a degree in communications, a major in psychology
and an associate diploma in social work.
For the past twenty years, I had been the busy social worker,
wife of a business man,
and mother of three growing children.
I guess I had created an underground culture of survival
for myself.
My husband and I wanted the best for our children
like any other normal family
Michael gave me all the security I needed.
We eventually talked about our differences
and Michael said that he wasn't too bothered
that I might be part-Aboriginal.
He said I didn't act like them anyway.
He wanted me just the way I was.
He always said I was special, different, perfect.
and my mother, my real mother, Connie Brumbie
says Michael's okay, as long as he treats me right,
I'm not sure what she means,
I think she's a little suspicious of him
anyway, he's offered to paint her house out for her
and fix the fence.
But Alison, my younger sister's already done that
Yes, we're so different.
I'm different.
Alison always knew she was black
I only knew how to be white
I was brought up different.
When I was growing up I was told that being born
of Aboriginal parents,
being Aboriginal, was somehow... limiting
was alien,
was... so... un-Australian.
I had always felt ashamed of other people's blackness
never my own.
I'd felt ashamed of those black men
lying in the parks

their lanky bodies half clad,
their spitting, swearing at strangers
their sucking on flagons, sending their minds into oblivion.
I peeped at them behind dark glasses
from bus windows
I never spoke to any of them
I always avoided them
I was afraid of them.
... one day, I saw two people embrace
I took my dark glasses off
they were laughing, holding each other, kissing
he was black and she was white.
I had this sudden urge to reach out to them
I wanted to ask her
did she have a feeling of blackness?
did this black man make her feel black?
I wondered if I would have a feeling of blackness.
I got out of the bus and walked towards them
they felt me approaching and turned to look at me
she smiled
he reached out his hand to me and said
'Good-day, my name's Billy, I'm from top end where you from?
I squeezed his hand, tears welling in my eyes
I couldn't speak
I panicked and ran back for the bus
I looked back at them through dark glasses
from the bus window.
I had this strange feeling that I should know him
and somehow I had a strong sense of being lost.
It's taken ten years to unlearn the belief instilled
in me, that white is better than black.
   [*Present time*, REGINA *speaks to her adoptive mother*]
... No mother, I don't hate you
I understand why you wanted to protect me
and what it is that you wanted to protect me from
I know now.
No, I'm not going to lose what I have
in fact I'm adding to my life
I'm teaching my children of their Aboriginality; and Michael.
Well, he's had me the way he's wanted me to be

he's going to have to accept me for who I am.
No, I'm not degrading myself, there you go again
I'm claiming my identity Mother,
and if you can't accept that then I can't forgive you,
you're not listening, can't you hear what I'm saying,
I understand,
I know why you wanted me to be accepted in the white world,
but what was best for me?
Yes, of course I felt I belonged
but I didn't know who I was
you don't understand why it's so important for me?
It's about *me*, my whole life, my children, my future
I am claiming my own identity.
Believe me Mother I haven't struck a jackpot out there,
but I belong to that race
I've finally found my real family
we are re-connecting our lives
my mother Connie, my sister Alison and my brother Billy
do you know where I officially met him mother?
in jail, I'm his social worker
he's waiting trial for a crime I believe he didn't commit
six years ago.
Do you know what that could mean?
being in jail, what the consequences might be, do you?
no, of course not.
Alison? she's younger than me,
we're so different.
She's taught me a lot about myself.
I never thought I'd ever have the guts to march in
a land rights rally.
She believes that all women are powerful, are warriors,
    she calls them.
Afraid? no, what's there to be afraid of?
Mother, there are hundreds of Aboriginal people
out there that you would be proud to know
I want you to be proud of me
of who and what I am.
No, I don't hate you
I have loved you as my mother for thirty years
you can't hide me anymore

and I can't run away from who I am.
Who am I?
I am the daughter of Connie Brumbie... yes...
and my name is Regina, Regina Brumbie.

Alison

Alison is an Aboriginal woman who has for many years been the subject of all forms of maltreatment, and through the processes of her learning, through suffering, and at most times having to pay the price, discovered within herself her own preferences in life.

Her honesty has given her strength to live her life without denial, justification, or sense of guilt.

Alison is a true non-conformist, anarchist, radical feminist, lesbian warrior.

She speaks with honesty and pride of her mother, her sister and, most of all, of her lover Sara. Alison begins by remembering their initial meeting. All through the dialogue she addresses Sara.

... Sara, remember when we first met?
We were travelling on that Greyhound bus to Alice
I wasn't aware of you on the bus till it broke down.
God everyone panicked
but you were just magic
you organised everyone, and somehow managed to keep
    the women together in one group.
I was fascinated, I was playing 'spot the dyke'
when the other bus came, you know I sat up the back
and watched you all the way to Alice.
Three weeks later you rang me in Adelaide
remember that revolting, revolving restaurant?
you were nervous? God I could hardly speak
then you started your conversation
on the philosophical, healthy outlook and advantages of
'Unconditional Love'
I had no idea what you were on about
I was just so impressed, you had it all together
... and here we are, six years later...
Happy Anniversary, Sara...

Cheers, here's to us.
O, I have a surprise for you
you have one for me too?
I bags opening mine first, I just love surprises.
Uh huh, *This Bridge Called My Back*
Writings by Radical Women of Color
Edited by Cherié Moraga, Gloria Anzaldúa
Foreword: by Toni Cade Bambara
A book written by Black Women, Black Feminists.
What an anthology!
thank you Sara.
What? you want me to read something from it?
Why not, let's see, uh huh, 'And When You Leave,
Take Your Pictures With You' by Jo Carrillo.

Our white sisters
radical friends
Love to own pictures of us
sitting at a factory machine
wielding a machete
in our bright bandanas
holding brown yellow black red children
reading books from literacy campaigns
holding machine guns bayonets bombs knives
Our white sisters
radical friends
should think
again.

Our white sisters
radical friends
love to own pictures of us
walking to the fields in hot sun
with straw hat on head if brown,
bandana if black
in bright embroidered shirts
holding brown yellow black red children
reading books from literacy campaigns
smiling.
Our white sisters radical friends

should think again.
No one smiles
at the beginning of a day spent
digging for souvenir chunks of uranium
of cleaning up after
our white sisters
radical friends.

And when our white sisters
radical friends see us
in the flesh
not as a picture they own,
they are not quite as sure
if they like us as much.
We're not as happy as we look
on
their
wall.

No, I don't see you like that Sara,
You are my white sister radical lover,
you don't have a stereotype image of me.
Pictures on walls?
Well, some of your friends have.
Well, we've never discussed how I feel about your friends
and yes, I do see some of them that way
I have sat in their kitchens and discussed issues
concerning women, and our differences
and how these issues affect me as a Black Woman
and whenever I ask questions like,
why the feminist movement excludes Black Women's ideology,
particularly in Women's Studies references,
and why I believe there's no such thing as equality.
Your friends call me paranoid, over-sensitive, aggressive,
emotionally hysterical and Racist...
and there, there right there on their walls,
are the symbols of the Aboriginal race
my history, on posters, my flag, my colours, my dignity,
glorifying their walls.
Sara, you are seen as 'the Aboriginal expert', aren't you?

Your relationship with me not only means that you have
married into the whole Aboriginal race,
but you are the liaison agent who can assure
not only the presence of Black Women at conferences,
you also relieve the fears of some who find it difficult
to converse with Black Women.
But just because we sleep together doesn't necessarily
free us of racist thought.
As women we share the same exploiter
we shouldn't be each other's enemy.
I want to believe that you and I HAVE something in common.
God, I love being in your life Sara.
Yes, of course, it's worth the pain Sara,
you and I have to fight harder for our relationship
because there are those out there that want us to fail.
You know, I wanted you to believe that there is
 Black Sisterhood.
I wanted to believe that there was.
But there are those who do not accept a truly radical
practice, who denounce me as a sister, and have resorted
to violence.
I've been at the receiving end of that violence.
God I get pissed off Sara.
pissed off at having to always justify my Aboriginality
to everyone –
because I don't live in the bush,
because I have a relationship with a woman,
because I own my own house,
because I won't be patronised,
because I don't sell out for a well-paid job,
because I look as if I have my shit together,
and I look pretty contented and comfortable living in this
society, and to them I really don't look too Oppressed.
As if I just turned my oppression off.
It's not a matter of just slipping back into it again,
oppression didn't just come to me, I didn't choose it
I was born into my oppression.
I don't just think that, well, today's a good day to be
oppressed, I think I'll look oppressed.

HOW? How do I justify the pain of being taken from my mother

being put into government institutions
being given to white mothers, who got paid
who were subsidised to raise me WHITE?
Institutionalised Kinship, that's what I call it.
GOD! MY GOD! I SHOULD BE INSANE...!!

... and when I finally find my real mother
I'm worried that she'll think I'm too white.

... Hello, are you Connie? Connie Brumbie?
You don't know me, my name is Ali ... Alison Brumbie
I was told you worked here, it's taken me all this time
to pluck up enough courage to come and meet you.
Yes, it's been thirty-two years
I, I don't know what to say
just that I work in a shelter, and, I, I never got married.
and, and I'm glad that I've found you ...

God Sara, I felt so stupid.
I thought that my mother would be so disappointed in me.
All I was thinking of was how I was presenting.
I didn't worry how she felt, I didn't ask her how she felt
after all these years, I wasn't even worried about her pain.
My God, Sara, how can you tell a mother you've never known,
that you're a radical feminist, anarchist, amazon, lesbian warrior?
that you belong to a collective,
that you march for peace, for whales, for land.
that you march to reclaim the night,
and that you live with a woman?
Well, I finally told her,
I wonder what she really thinks.
As for my sister, Regina
I completely freaked her out
all she knows is husband, kids, house, tupperware,
Avon, two cars, dogs, cats and microwaves.
Her role models were Mary Kay and Jenny Craig.
It was a struggle for her to accept that she WAS Aboriginal
let alone the fact that her mother is an alcoholic, her
sister's a radical feminist lesbian, and her brother is
wanted for murder,

she was in total SHOCK!!
Yes, I'd say that she's had a pretty tough identity crisis
… well, it's taken her all this time to come to terms
with her Aboriginality…
And where? where could she go to find her identity?
Who has the magical formula to say what makes you
    Aboriginal?
Where can she go where she can be accepted as an Aboriginal
despite her white orientation? without being called a coconut?
Brown on the outside, white on the inside.
On the one hand she's called a Boong
on the other she's called a coconut.
In a way we are both victims,
our credibility, our identity is at risk.
The irony, my mother, my sister, and I, after all these
years, coming together, as strangers, needing desperately
to reclaim our identity, our Aboriginality.
The very tool that was the source of our separation…

… But Sara, just look, just look how far we've come
just look how far Aboriginal women have come in the
struggle against oppression.
Take my mother, Connie Brumbie for example
she's the most courageous woman I've ever had the pleasure
    to know.
When I was born, the racist rules of the day
gave her every disadvantage.
She never demanded anything
whatever she wanted for herself –
just for her sanity's sake – was denied her.
She was continually bashed, her head permanently scarred,
her physical image criminally assaulted and mutilated,
she was raped and denied the right to cry out in her pain.
She's been sworn at, spat at, rounded up and accused.
She's been called a lubra, gin, slut, whore, black velvet
her children confiscated from her, as if illegal merchandise
and jailed in a government compound.
She's confused, frustrated, hurt, resentful,
she's frightened and angry – and

who dares to brand her now?

what can they do to her now?
what can they do to Connie Brumbie now?

Sorry Sara, I didn't mean to get too heavy.
It's that poem I read.
Thank you for this book Sara.
It's a perfect gift
at last here's an ideology identical to mine.
I love you too, Sara.
By the way, how do your friends feel about you
having a relationship with me?
Oh? they are concerned? some of them are?
Well you tell them Sara, that Ali Brumbie
will make a perfect partner for the future.
That you and I are the perfect partners for the future.
Maybe we can start a new revolution.
Break down the fear between women.
If we're the ones who can imagine it, or dream about it
and we're the ones who need it most, then we're the ones to
do it.
What do they call me?
HAPPY ANNIVERSARY!!!!

JOCELYNNE A. SCUTT

Jocelynne Scutt was born in Perth in 1947; she holds
degrees in law from the Universities of Western
Australia, Sydney, Michigan, Cambridge and in arts
from the University of New South Wales. She has
worked with the University of Sydney Law School,
the Australian Law Reform Commission and the
Australian Institute of Criminology, and was
Associate to the Hon. Lionel Murphy of the
High Court of Australia. From 1983 to 1984 she
was Director of Research with the Victorian
Parliamentary Legal and Constitutional Committee
and, from 1984 to 1986, Commissioner and Deputy
Chairperson of the Law Reform Commission,
Victoria. Since 1986 Jocelynne Scutt has been in
private legal practice.

Even as a child, Jocelynne Scutt was a writer; she
wrote poetry and essays, as well as a 'block buster'
novel and television screenplay starring the Beatles
and a coup in Indonesia. 'It was written in the early
1960s when the situation between Australia and
Indonesia was tense,' she says by way of clarification.
'What the Beatles had to do with it I can't now recall
but I do know it was a lively screenplay even though
it never reached the screen.'

But fiction writing gave way to non-fiction when
Jocelynne Scutt began postgraduate work in law.
'Having articles published in "straight" law journals
is particularly pleasing,' she says as she outlines some
of the politics. 'I ensure that the language is non-
sexist, that women's work is extensively footnoted
(yes, even women with whom I disagree), and the

work of women and women's organisations is mentioned in the body of the writing, whenever appropriate. And I do this not only for contemporary readers, but for future readers as well, who will be relieved to know that there were those of us "back then" who recognised the *substantial* contribution of women.'

She has not always received the same acknowledgement for her own contributions. In commenting on the way in which her own considerable efforts as a research assistant on a book once went completely unacknowledged ('my name didn't even appear in the preface!'), she raises the issue of the disappearance of women from the cultural records. So much of her writing is directed towards making visible the existence of women.

Jocelynne Scutt does not expect to make her living from writing; she writes primarily to document the details of women's lives and believes that this is the motivation for many other women as well. 'Payment is not a major factor in precipitating women into writing,' she says. 'Often, it is not a factor at all. Writing is a means of ensuring that the realities of women's lives be told; otherwise history is both parochial and limiting.'

Having produced a remarkable (and impressively extensive) number of books, academic papers, articles, chapters, addresses and speeches, Jocelynne Scutt has recently returned to fiction writing to make her point; she has thoroughly enjoyed writing two books of short stories on the theme of women imaginatively solving some of the problems of the work place – but 'there have been difficulties finding a publisher.' She has had a science fiction story published and currently has two murder novels in her head – 'as well as one planned on the "novels" file in my computer.'

For her the difficulty is in finding the time to write – fiction, non-fiction, and the 'opinions' which she provides as a professional. 'I like writing,' she says, 'both the paid and the unpaid.'

Her publications are much too numerous to list; among them are:

1980 *Rape Law Reform.* Australian Institute of Criminology, Canberra, ACT.

1980 *Violence in the Family.* Australian Institute of Criminology, Canberra, ACT.

1981 *Women and Crime* (with S. K. Mukherjee). George Allen & Unwin, Sydney, NSW.

1983 *Even in the Best of Homes: Violence in the Family.* Penguin Books Australia, Ringwood, Victoria. 1990, McCulloch Publishing, Carlton, Victoria.

1984 *For Richer, For Poorer: Money, Marriage and Property Rights* (with Di Graham). Penguin Books Australia, Ringwood, Victoria.

1985 *Growing Up Feminist: The New Generation of Australian Women.* Angus & Robertson, Sydney.

1985 *Poor Nation of the Pacific: Australia's Future.* George Allen & Unwin, Sydney.

1987 *Different Lives: Reflections on the Women's Movement and Visions of its Future.* Penguin Books Australia, Melbourne.

1987 *Lionel Murphy: A Radical Judge.* McCulloch Publishing, Carlton, Victoria.

1988 *The Baby Machine: The Commercialisation of Motherhood.* McCulloch Publishing, Melbourne. 1990, Green Press, London.

1990 *Women and the Law: Commentary and Materials.* Law Book Company, Sydney.

1992 *The Sexual Gerrymander.* Spinifex Press, Melbourne.

Fair Shares of Our Heritage:
Women, Men and the Socialist Ideal

Inaugural Peggy Martin Memorial Lecture,
Heidelberg Town Hall – 12 October 1986

*The Labor movement can only be great... by the united efforts of all
those who believe in it, of individuals, who are not in it to get out of
it something personal, but in it because it is a great political party
designed to bring to all the community a fair share of the things the
world is capable of giving them.*

Ben Chifley, Things Worth Fighting For

In the eulogy delivered by the Hon. Brian Howe
at the funeral of Peggy Martin earlier this year, Brian Howe
acknowledged her as one such as those of whom Ben Chifley,
once Australian Labor Party Prime Minister and leader, spoke
as 'not in [the Labor Party] to get out of it something personal,
but in it because it is a great political party designed to bring
to all the community a fair share of the things the world is
capable of giving them.' Brian Howe said of Peggy Martin that
she was such an individual:

Not in the sense only that she gave her all to the Labor Party, but
rather in the sense that she gave everything which was in her to
fighting for the benefit of her fellow human beings.

For those of us who believe in and fight for the socialist
ideal, Peggy Martin's life is a guide to where that ideal stands
in the Labor movement and the Australian Labor Party. Born
in Melbourne in 1922, Peg Martin was a member of the League
of Young Democrats from the age of sixteen to twenty years.
She joined the Coburg Branch of the Australian Labor Party
in 1958, holding virtually every position in the local electorate
in federal, state and municipal committees from 1958 to 1970,
including the presidency of the Wills Campaign Committee for
many years. She worked for the federal branch of the Liquor
Trades Union and for the Moulders Union. Peg Martin was

member of the Trades Hall Council Equal Pay Committee from approximately 1958 to the mid-1960s. She was executive member of the Women's Central Organising Committee of the Victorian Branch of the ALP. She worked for the Italian Union paper, *Il Progresso*, and the trade union paper, *Scope*, for about ten years.

In the 1950s, a time we have been told when women returned in force to the homeground, producing children to the exclusion of all outside activities, it is appropriate to ask why Peg Martin, married to Felix, mother of Paul, Felicity and Peter, should have been leading an apparently double life. Or is the better question to ask, why is our history – the history of women, the history of activism in Australia, the history of socialism, the history of the Australian Labor Party – distorted through the lack, in official writings, of recognition of the work, the presence, the very existence of women like Peg Martin.

In Australia today, real efforts are being made to recapture the lives of women, lives which have been written out of official history, or simply ignored by the pundits. Yet sadly it is at the same time true that even some women historians, writing as feminists, accept the lies of the dominant culture as to the reality of other women's lives. Some feminist historians have fallen into the trap of accepting the 1950s as the dark ages of women, a time of total absence of women from the political scene, the public world. This deception has been practised so that too many of us accept that feminism 'began' in the late 1960s and early 1970s. That if it didn't begin then, that was the time of the 'second wave' of feminism. That women had lain supine, dormant since the early part of this century, until a second awakening in the decade of the seventies.

The dominant ideology has persuaded us that women's efforts to gain a foothold in policy making in political parties, to ensure women's voices should be heard beyond the private sphere, run in cycles. This ideology paints the efforts of women as subject to rises and falls, to pits and troughs, to peaks and shallows. This ideology discounts the consistent and continuing efforts of women – alongside some men – in the cause of women's rights and a recognition of socialism as encompassing not just equal rights and distribution of wealth amongst and between men, but equal rights and distribution of wealth amongst and between all persons – women and men.

There is an equally damning and distorted vision of women's efforts as solely directed at making the tea. In 'Labor Women: Political Housekeepers or Politicians?' the feminist political historian Robin Joyce, seeing through the fallacy of the dominant view, writes (1984: p. 66):

One myth which has been particularly damaging to women involved in party political activity is that perpetuated in relation to women's past role in the parties. The main discussion has centred on the Australian Labor Party which has been seen as particularly male dominated and the effect which this has had on women members' role. It has been described as a housekeeping role which limited women to the areas traditionally described as women's work: tea-making, fund-raising and supporting male activists.

Joyce continues (p. 66):

Although it is true that a number of women undertook these tasks, it is also true that some women were active in areas which have been seen as exclusively male. That this occurred in the labour movement as early as the beginning of this century demands thorough scrutiny of the myth [and possibly] a complete reassessment of women's past political experience, a justification for discarding the myth and [finding] new approaches to old problems.

The fallacy of assuming that the women of the past contributed 'only' through cookery has been repeated up through the 1940s and 1950s. Yet Peg Martin's efforts make clear the mistake. She was a principal in organising catering for ALP conferences. On one occasion, a dinner was arranged by the ALP to be held at Richmond Town Hall. Over six hundred people paid for tickets and were poised to attend. 'Who's doing the catering?' came the cry on the morning of the planned event. No-one had thought to arrange for the food! Peg Martin and three union officials went out to buy, and Peg Brown, Peg McNolty and Peg Martin arranged the smorgasbord dinner. (Peg Martin and Peg McNolty were traditionally known within the Party as 'the two Pegs'. On this day, together with Peg Brown, they became 'the three Pegs'.) At the end of the evening, when everyone had been well fed and entertained, these workers sat upstairs on the floor, spread with tablecloths (chairs and tables had by that time, late into the early morning hours, been removed), and drank in celebration. Yet simultaneously with saving such an event with catering and culinary skills – 'making the sandwiches', and no doubt the punch on this oc- casion – Peg Martin was active as a delegate to conference, and active as a unionist. That role – as political activist in the traditional (seen by some, wrongly, as exclusively male) sense, was not thereby less significant.

The truth is that women have always played a firm role in feminist-socialist development and feminist-socialist thought, on their own terms, or at least fighting for their own terms against less enlightened views of the meaning of socialism. In the early days of the ALP, from the 1890s and onward, women were active in recruiting members, holding conferences and formulating resolutions for action. They were not solely in- volved in making cups of tea, scones and sandwiches. In the various states, women fought for the right to vote and did so through feminist organisations as well as through political parties. A foremother of the women of the 1950s, and of our- selves, involved in the campaign for the vote and other feminist campaigns in the ALP was the Western Australian activist, Jean Beadle. In 1909 she said (Joyce, 1984: p. 148):

We are enthroned in the hearts of men; that is why men use us and pay us half the wages, but we don't want to be enthroned in men's hearts under these conditions.

Jean Beadle was special in the sense that she was outspoken about the rights of women. Like Peg Martin, she was active in a high profile way, within the ALP and the union movement. However, like Peg Martin, she was not alone in any of these aspects; nor was she alone, in the sense that many women backed her, fought alongside her, and lobbied on the issues which were her and their concerns, issues which took the time and energies of Peg Martin and other women active in the 1950s, 1960s and 1970s, and the women of today.

263

It is sometimes wrongly said that women were granted the vote without a fight, throughout Australia. In Victoria the right of women to vote in state elections was not conceded until 1908, and this after much lobbying against, and numerous derogatory remarks about, the women simply demanding their rights, their entitlements to equal political participation and decision-making, and these rights and entitlements for all women. It is also suggested that after gaining the vote women somehow went home, giving up fighting for anything more. Again – the myth that similarly dogs the women of the 1950s: home they supposedly went, to the fireside, the public sphere forgotten. But the public sphere was not forgotten. The women did their fireside chores (as well as those their husbands should rightly have done) but retained a firm foothold in the public world (Joyce, 1984: p. 149):

Many activists realised that the vote was not a panacea for all women's problems. In the following years they established themselves as politically influential pressure groups committed to a general feminist position. Some of the women were radical feminists who attempted to change the low status of women rather than concentrate on the need for amelioration of the consequences of injustice. They attempted to raise the status of female roles in economic terms rather than in myth-making, and sought participation in the roles which were the exclusive property of men.

Labor Women began organising at the turn of the century and before. In 1912 the first women's conference was held by Labor Women, which became an organisation in its own right, within the ALP in Western Australia. In other states, sometimes a similar approach was adopted. A Labor Women's organisation was established in New South Wales, and one in Queensland. Other states took a different route, with women forming policy committees rather than their own organisation within the ALP. In Western Australia, the Labor Women's organisation went further than in any other state, creating women-only branches alongside mixed branches. Thus, women at that time were involved in the same debates we hear and participate in today – on separatism versus assimilation or mainstreaming; whether women have particular ideas and views demanding separate representation; about whether, on the contrary, women are 'the same' as men and should gain recognition through the same channels as men.

The concerns of Labor Women in the early part of this century have a familiar ring. Resolutions from the Labor Women's conference of 1912 included (Joyce, 1984: p. 149):

1. That this first Labor Women's conference urges upon the government to promote legislation that will remove sex disability and grant to women full citizenship, thereby permitting [women] to nominate as candidates for the Legislative Council and Assembly, Municipal Councils, Roads Boards, Licensing Benches, etc.

2. Also, since women find it a great hardship and injustice that [women] should have to plead before men only, and since it is so evident that the interests of women suffer from the want of comprehension or prejudice of the male jury, this conference of women urges upon the government the need in all cases where women and children are concerned that [women] shall be eligible therefore.

3. This conference of Labor Women is of opinion that women magistrates shall be appointed to deal with [all] cases concerning women and children, and that conference further urges that in all government offices (state and federal) men and women shall receive equal pay for equal work.

4. That this conference of Labor Women affirms the desirability of admission of women to Parliament, and considers that when elected they shall be regarded as being eligible to accept and fill any position therein open to members of the opposite sex.

These demands have a contemporary sound, combined with a certain datedness. The contemporary flavour meshes with the realisation that at the same time the demands of women of today have moved on. This movement forward is a direct result of the achievements of women early this century and before, and of the women in the 1940s, 1950s and 1960s.

Taking the first resolution, the aim was 'to remove sex disability'. Today, the demand goes further, to affirmative action, supporting legislation and policies taking into account past discrimination and actively working towards eliminating or overcoming it. With resolution 2. women were concerned to sit as jurors on cases involving women and children. We have now won the appropriate right – to sit on juries, whatever the age or sex of the defendant. Taking the third resolution, women demanded the right to sit as magistrates on cases involving women and children. Today, we demand the right – and are slowly winning it – to sit as judges and magistrates on *all* cases. Finally, resolution 4. saw the need for women to gain the right to enter Parliament and, once there, to participate at all levels equally with men. Today, women are demanding equal opportunity and affirmative action policies be implemented to ensure that women stand for winnable seats rather than the (mostly) unwinnable or swinging seats for which they have run in the past, if at all. Women have achieved the right, now, to hold office as Speaker of the House of Representatives and President of Legislative Councils.

The struggle by women to win these aims did not arise out of the dead ashes of a past women's movement. The present day demand is directly founded upon a live and vigorous tradition of the work of women through this century and before. But within Australia generally, and in the ALP, the lack of recognition of women's efforts and the desire to downgrade or deny women's role in shaping reforms which have given greater substance to the cause of socialism arises out of an inability, on the part of some (male) members of the socialist movement, to embrace fully the socialist ideal, of fair shares for all.

As Gough Whitlam (1985: p. 509) points out in *The Whitlam Government 1972–1975*:

For most of Australia's history, women have lived without visible social power. They have been excluded from almost all levels of government, most forms of corporate management and virtually all modes of trade union activity. The momentous decisions of war and peace, of finance and technology, as well as the everyday decisions which affect how all people live, have been made by a minority of individuals who happen to be born white and male.

But he adds (1985: p. 509):

The dilemma is that women have actively sought representation and social power and have actively fought to have women's issues seriously discussed within all the significant forums of national debate. Yet over the decades success at either of these endeavours has been at best only sporadic.

Whitlam pinpoints the problem: it is not that women have not been active; that women went home, refused to participate, or attempt to participate, in political and trade union activism, and feminist separatist activism. Rather, the so-called 'waves of feminism', the 'retreat of the '50s' arises out of a lack of external recognition of women's efforts, women's work. It arises out of a refusal of public institutions to recognise women's role as significant in the scheme of things, both in the private sphere and the public world of paid work and officialdom. Sadly, it arises too from a blindness on the part of those in power to overcome institutionalised prejudice, to overthrow their own socialised acceptance of women as non-existent in the public world, and to acknowledge women's achievements and brave political stands as real, and really there.

The ALP has at various intervals been driven to recognise – or chosen to ignore – 'the woman problem'. (Women, of course, know that this problem is wrongly named – for women, it's 'the man problem'.) The 'woman' question was relevant to the National Committee of Enquiry established in the ALP after the 1977 federal election. The 1979 report to the National Executive of the ALP stated that the 'ALP's blue collar, male, Anglo–Irish image increasingly handicaps its ability to appeal to emerging forces in contemporary Australia.' (It could have added that the image conceals the reality of women working within the party, with the same energy and commitment, though rarely – most times never – the same rewards.) That report stressed the need to improve the representation of women within the party, to improve the party's performance among female voters (ALP Federal Branch, 1979: p. 59):

The reasons for the relative weakness of female support for the ALP are complex, and they are not peculiar to Australia, since the greater conservatism of women voters has been observed almost everywhere. In the long run, the move by women from a predominantly domestic role is likely to reduce the difference between male and female voters. For the immediate future, however, positive action is imperative, if only for electoral purposes. In this sense, there is an obvious connection between lack of female involvement in ALP affairs and lack of electoral support.

But the women have always been there, in the party. Maybe 30 per cent, not 50 per cent, but the women are not the problem. The problem arises out of the limited meaning given to the socialist ideal, the narrowing of that ideal to male concerns, or world concerns seen through male eyes, from the viewpoint of the masculine ethos.

Today the major party which professes socialism, the Australian Labor Party, prides itself on closing the 'gender gap', the gap between women and men voting for the Labor Party. It prides itself on gaining more votes from women than does the conservative side of politics. Yet it is important to understand why this change has come about, and what the fundamental reasons were for the failure of most women to vote socialist in the past. Any swing of women's votes to Labor will not continue nor be sustained unless the reason for it is recognised and followed through. Women are not easily fooled, and if their legitimate expectations are not met, can withdraw their votes just as easily as they can bestow them.

Women have a tradition of 'fairness' and 'injustice', a sense which is basic to the socialist ideal. In the past, women were socialised into distancing themselves from personal injustices – unfairness directed against themselves as individuals – and developing a strong commitment to fairness derived through the way their husbands and families were treated by the community, by social mores. There have always been women ready to fight for the rights of the whole of humanity, not just on behalf of men. These women have fought against injustices meted out to women themselves, fighting for women as human. These women have seen the fallacy of accepting that woman's role was to stand by and accept that any 'rights' she might have came not to her as a person, but as a by-product of the fact that she was a member of a family, or one of a couple, the male partner of which really had the rights. Yet these women have not traditionally been in the majority. Now, through the unremitting efforts of women such as Peg Martin, whose motto was 'I don't have to *ask* to be equal; I *am* equal,' there is a chance that women in this latter grouping are growing to significant numbers. The chance is that these women's demands for economic equality with men, and redistribution of power and resources amongst women and men as individuals who may simultaneously be part of a couple or family unit, and of the community generally, will have to be met.

But this cannot be done without a sincere recognition amongst men that women's demands are legitimate, and that without their fulfilment, the socialist ideal will never be met. It is not just a problem of the public sphere recognition of women and women's rights. It is a problem of private sphere acknowledgement, too. The issue is not limited to Australia, nor to Australian male chauvinism. In Sweden, where a concept of socialism as including equal rights of and for women as well as of and for men is ostensibly accepted, the executive secretary of one of the women's organisations within a major political party has said (Scott, 1982: p. 52):

We have trouble with our men, although the younger ones are better than the older ones. But people in political life have arranged their own lives in a conservative way, and it is difficult to talk to them because we are challenging their private lives.

It is far more comfortable for men to believe that the status quo is the way the world should be, because it is more favourable to their short-term interests that this be so; longer-term interests will not be met without upheaval which may cause short-term distress for them. For the proponents of socialism and the seekers after the women's vote, it should also be remembered that it is far more comfortable for women to believe that they can find security and economic support through marriage rather than by fighting in a hostile 'male' world of paid work, particularly where working alongside men who are unhappy about women taking non-traditional roles. It is also easy for those who are dependent upon male paid workers (though there are fewer and fewer in this category) to believe that women should not enter the paid workforce after marriage, and should leave, when they marry, to provide

269

jobs for men. A spurious tradition is being reasserted by conservative forces calling for a return to a false past of husband, wife, several children, cat, dog and (today) television set, the mother being full time in the home. Yet there is indeed no way women can in reality be 'sent back to the home' – to which the majority have never really been confined, anyway, being forced throughout the nineteenth and twentieth centuries by economic circumstance to bring some income, however small, however sporadic, into the household. Women's participation is as vital to the operation of the economy as it ever was.

But if socialism does not follow through on its present-day promise of equal rights for women and men and the proposed opportunities and realities going with that equalitarianism, then the voices of conservatism will make more and more sense to women who work in degrading conditions in factories or offices, who have to bear daily the harassment of the boss or fellow workers, or both. Who wouldn't want to give up that eight hour day in the factory or chicken shed, for what might seem like relative bliss at home? Even if the home is inhabited by an abusive husband or worse, to the woman threatened and harassed by a male supervisor or co-worker on the job, eight hours a day, the husband has to be put up with only for the time he is at home, and the times he is abusive – if he is. If she is in paid work under inhuman conditions, her whole day is divided between the harassing supervisor and the possibly abusive husband, or other likely detrimental conditions at home.

It is important to expose the antiwoman nature of conservative philosophy. It is most important to reveal socialism in its positive light, but the negative nature of conservatism is also to be made clear, so that a true assessment can be made of the possible place of women in the political and social structure. This is not difficult. The lack of concern for women in conservative policies and the abject indifference of those policies to the realities of current socio-economic structures and the place of women is patent. Thus a member of the Centre of Policy Studies at Monash University uses the tourist industry as a paradigm for the creation of an economy where growth is the answer, and 'benefits' accrue. Michael Porter (1985: p. 42) says:

Within the tourism sector one finds that where restaurants and other tourist ventures have managed to free themselves of market constraints such as penalty rates, they have proven able to expand quite considerably. A common example is Chinese restaurants – employing family labour. Other examples include fast food chains which are able to expand so long as they are able to employ labour at competitive rates. Rather than employ almost no labour on weekends because of penalty rates, such restaurants and fast food outlets, to the extent they can internalise employment arrangements through family and equity arrangements or avoid penalty structures, can thereby continue to offer full service at the most profitable time – for example, weekends and nights. As a result of this differential capacity to avoid regulation the small restaurant has prospered.[1]

But who prospers? who benefits? Within the family organisation, research shows that the major income is controlled by the husband and father (where one exists). Research into financial arrangements amongst families shows that where a man's wages or salary increases, this increase is not passed on to the person organising the homeground – the wife and mother. Rather, her housekeeping remains set at the level arrived at prior to the raise. Housekeeping money does not keep pace with the consumer price index, despite wage and salary rises. Thus it is false to assert that within family businesses 'the whole family' prospers, as the proponent of conservatism tells us. As well, the right of employees to decline to work long hours for little pay should not be removed simply because a worker is employed in a family business, and is a member of that family. It is wrong to say that within family businesses prosperity and benefits are equally or equitably divided amongst members. Promoting 'prosperity' for one member of a family against the better interests of other members should not stand the scrutiny of a society adhering, at base, to egalitarianism and to a fair return for a fair day's work. 'Benefit' should not be seen to override the regressive nature of 'arrangements' avoiding legislative standards which are set on the basis of preventing exploitation. Exploitation should be outlawed equally in 'family businesses' as in businesses where workers have no blood ties.[2]

There are numerous problems with a sterile conservative

debate that ignores women's very existence, or considers women will be satisfied if only 'their men' are prospering. Yet the attitude of the conservatives to women has parallels apparently crossing party lines, and ideological lines. The idea that the family business prospers because the head of the family makes more money has too often had its place in the ideals of some professing to be socialist. We have accepted as good socialist philosophy the famed Harvester judgment of Henry Bournes Higgins in 1907, the foundation of the 'family wage'. Yet feminists have come to protest about the lack of recognition given to women's existence as independent beings, women's right to financial self-sufficiency, which is evident in that judgment. Higgins established a basic wage for an unskilled adult male labourer, keeping a wife and children. In 1919 in the *Clothing Trades Case*, Higgins subsequently determined that the female basic wage should be 54 per cent of the male basic wage. He referred in passing to an earlier judgment, by Jethro Brown of South Australia, in the *Printing Trades Case*. In that case, it was maintained that (South Australian Industrial Reports, 1919 pp. 42–3):

...the comparative inefficiency of women in a large number of occupations may be attributed to a physiological constitution which involves periods of relative inefficiency... In many industries the value of the employee is largely dependent upon an ability to cope with periods of exceptional stress. This ability in men as distinguished from women is not affected by the physiological condition just referred to... In the case of men, their occupation is their life's vocation; in the case of women, their occupation (beyond the domestic sphere) is, in most cases, transitory...It is not that women are not conscientious; they are often pathetically so. If there is a dreary monotonous task to be performed, which needs minute attention, it is found that a woman's service is unsurpassed. It is not that women are not intelligent, individual women have again and again in various branches proved their worth. It is not that women are physically weak, individually they may be stronger than individual men and, at any rate physical strength is no longer the greatest factor in industry. Women are inferiors in the industrial world because they have not decided (except individually) that they desire to be otherwise, or at least that they desire to pay in training the price of efficiency.

Jethro Brown also deplored the 'serious menace' to Australia of 'the growing sterility of the population'. He was not referring to any lack of ability on the part of men. Rather, he was referring to the deplorable fact, as he saw it, that (SAIR 31, 1919: p. 39):

...so many women would rather work in factories at low wages than assist in domestic service ...

leading to women lacking a desire to enter into motherhood as quickly as he would have wished. 'What would happen', he asked (SAIR, 1919: p. 39):

if the wage for women in factories were doubled ... Women's true apprenticeship for her future career is to be found, not in the work-shop or the salesroom, but in some form of training or apprenticeship directly related to wifehood and motherhood.

Henry Bournes Higgins apparently shared something of that view, in that in the *Harvester Case* one of the items he took into account as relevant in assessing the male basic wage was a component for domestic help. There was no component for domestic help in the female basic wage: for women, the task of doing for themselves their own chores, presumably so they might develop a liking for that form of activity and gracefully retire from the paid workforce.

To be critical of the Harvester judgment is not to repudiate the achievement against 'the bosses' that it represents (though what a greater achievement against them would it have been, had women been seen as equal recipients of the same basic wage as the men!). Nor is it to join other of Henry Bournes Higgins' critics. But one of the major problems facing women (and those few men) fighting for women's autonomy and participation, is that a myth of women's dependence has been founded in law. It has been founded in many areas of law apart from the industrial sphere, and other judges are responsible for that. Yet it cannot be ignored that in the industrial sphere women's dependency has had far reaching effects on women's rights. The dependency myth has succeeded in establishing women who work – hard – in the home, for no monetary

273

reward, as 'dependents'. For a woman who cleans, cooks, washes, vacuums; plays the efficient and charming hostess to business colleagues, family friends, trade unionist mates; uses her energies and resourcefulness in building up a family business or farm; cares lovingly and effectively for the children – often on a twenty-four hour basis, alone; psychologically supports and ministers to her spouse, the idea that she is a 'dependent' must be taken as a wry jest.

In the private realm, this myth of dependency renders assessments of women's contribution as less than those made by men, particularly in the sphere of marital assets. As men are seen as independent beings, it follows naturally in traditional thought that they should be assumed to do all the work on their own; build up the business alone; work the farm without wifely assistance; contribute all the business acumen (which women are seen to be lacking – falsely); survive in the world of paid work – the factory, the shop, the market place – through their own efforts, alone. This ignores two realities: first, the reality that women work hard at home, and often work equally hard in the paid workforce; that men give little assistance at home, mostly expending their energies in the paid workforce alone. And second, the reality that men do not 'do it alone' – do not possess business acumen or political nous in isolation from their discussions about business and politics with their wives; nor do they work in industry in isolation from the psychological support, comfort and care received daily on the home ground, making their life in the paid workforce easier to organise and sustain.

The myth of the dependent woman not only operates against the rightful interests of those few women exerting their energies full time in the home. It operates also against the interests of women engaging in part-time paid work, and against those of women taking on full-time paid employment, and those setting themselves up in businesses into which they put a deal of their energies, whilst simultaneously maintaining marriage and family.[3]

For women in part-time employment, the dependency myth ensures that the part-time work is seen as trivial, of little moment (rather than the hard work it really is, with inadequate return), and thus not worth assessing in real wage terms, or in terms of contribution to marriage and the marital economy.

For women engaged in full-time paid employment, it is not seriously recognised that they are required to carry out two full-time jobs – that in the home, and that in the paid workplace. Judgments in the area of distribution of assets on marital breakdown show that a husband is in legal interpretation entitled to have his contribution seen as exceptional when he engages in business alone, failing to make an equal contribution to the home and family life in the way of housework, homecare, childcare – in most cases doing minimal amounts (if anything) in this regard. With women working full time at building up a career or business, the myth of dependency makes it almost inevitable that in assessing contribution to marital assets, or assessing worth in the paid work world, the assessor will be looking inevitably for the 'brains' behind the woman. How could one of those delicate, dependent creatures known as 'a woman' possible build up a business all alone, from her own skills, energies, acumen, vigour? How could a woman working in a 'woman's profession' possibly be working as hard, and require as much money for it, as a man working in a 'man's profession' who *needs* a full wage? Faced with a dissonant view of womankind when confronted by a real-life woman who exhibits skills usually attributed solely (though wrongly) to men, who is *really* (in the law's eyes) a 'dependent', little wonder that in the family sphere courts cannot cope with placing a realistic measure on her contribution to the marriage. Similarly in the world of industrial arbitration and wages policy, little wonder that it is difficult for women to gain a real recognition of their work's worth.

There is no doubt that in trade unions, as in the Australian Labor Party, women have fought strongly for recognition both of their own skills and for the rights of women generally, and continue to carry on that battle. The fight within the trade union movement, by women, for the passage of and updating of the *Working Women's Charter*[4] has its forerunner in demands of women at the turn of the century for equal pay. It had its origins in the campaigns during the 1950s, by the Peg Martins, the women teachers and others, during those dark years of the 1950s, when we are supposed to accept that women were silently contemplating the family hearth. As we know, those in control were not, and are not, always receptive to these demands. What receptiveness there is, too often relegates the talents of women in the unions and concerns relating to all women workers to the lower reaches of the paid work agenda. The Australian Conciliation and Arbitration Commission[5] compounds the problem: during the 1983 *National Wage Case*, when the Women's Electoral Lobby asked of the Commission that it establish a panel to deal with work value cases relating to 'women's professions', 'women's trades' on a systematic basis, the response was that this was impossible: that the economy could not bear the recognition of women's work as of equal value to men's and equally worthy to be paid at equal rates. The Commission endorsed the long-standing view that women should continue to work equally hard as men, yet simultaneously should continue to forebear from achieving equal pay. The Commission effectively acknowledged that women must continue to be robbed of 35 or 40 cents in the dollar, by their bosses, in the name of keeping the economy afloat.[6]

But whatever the Commission says, if trades unions adopted a consistent and continuous policy of bringing work value cases before the Commission and demanding that they be heard, where women's trades and professions are concerned, this pattern and practice of economic deprivation for women would have to be remedied. At minimum, such a campaign would succeed in exposing at the highest industrial level the anomolous position of women workers who consistently throughout this century have been seen within the industrial relations system as second class citizens, to be paid second class wages.

For socialism to come into its own, indeed to survive, feminism must be seen to be, and accepted fully as, a fundamental tenet. Most important is to map out positive policies and strategies for implementation: if there are positive socialist policies and strategies in the offing, which being truly socialist incorporate feminist principles and concerns, then rights and demands of women will be properly addressed and the principle of fair shares for all be on its way to fulfilment. To ensure that this be so, the Australian Labor Party must recognise more fully women's demands. Otherwise the party professing to be socialist will be exposed to women's rightful anger. And the trades unions must reorientate themselves to the socialist demands of the women's electorate, demands for equal recognition of women's rights to fair pay for 'women's work', whether done in so called traditional women's fields, or in non-traditional areas. Trades unions otherwise expose themselves to attacks not only from conservative forces, but from women who have become angry, and rightly so, at a general ignorance of women's rights in the paid workplace, or a lack of political will to follow through the implementation of those rights.

The current debate on superannuation illustrates this dilemma well. It is not sufficient to classify superannuation for all paid workers as a socialist demand, as covering the entire paid workforce, without simultaneously recognising that it will continue to be those in low paid, part time, casual or broken working life jobs who end with less superannuation benefits at the close of their paid workforce life. The feminist-socialist demand is for a recognition of co-contribution to superannuation and rightful benefits accruing to the co-contributing spouse. Trades unions must not only demand extension of superannuation to all paid workers. They must ensure that the way schemes operate, the rationale upon which superannuation accrual comes about, recognises the nature of the contribution made to the buildup of superannuation, and the benefits which a direct contributor gains from the efforts of a partner outside the paid work relationship. Also to be recognised is the benefit of both parties – direct contributor and co-contributor – foregone through the setting aside of income into the superannuation scheme, or the deferment of employer benefits to a later date. The onus is on trades unions to determine the nature of superannuation and contribution, and the egalitarian operation of the schemes, or to establish such egalitarian operation, if the drive toward recognising superannuation as a socialist measure (aimed at redistribution of wealth) is to be accepted in its entirety.[7]

Sometimes those professing to be socialist lament that women's organisations, or women members, appear to be opposed to a particular measure, or that measures they work toward implementing are 'not socialist' (as defined by men).

The issue here is too often of the formers' making – the making of those 'socialists' themselves, through their failure to acknowledge sexism and discrimination existing within the present system and hindering the road towards the socialist ideal. One such instance arose in the early 1970s in the form of probate laws and their eventual abolition. Another has arisen more recently, with regard to property rights of de facto spouses on breakup of the relationship. If a socialist proposal in the private sphere had been accepted readily before those debates arose, or during discussion on the issues, there would have been no need for differences to arise between socialists and feminists, differences weakening the socialist cause.

In the 1970s, women recognised the discrimination inherent in probate laws operating between spouses. Because all property was seen as belonging to the husband in a marriage, upon his death his surviving spouse was forced to wait for long periods to have the estate admitted to probate and administration wound up. This affected not only those with substantial holdings. Relatively modest holdings were also caught up, particularly with rising inflation. (Take, for example, the case of the war-grants home purchased in the name of the ex-serviceman only.) During this time, after the husband's death, the wife had no access to any finance or property which was in her husband's name. Most property was, although it gradually became the practice for women to be advised to have their names added to the title of the family home. (If a house is owned in joint names, on the death of one, the ownership of the whole transfers automatically to the survivor.) The idea of joint ownership meant that where a woman survived her husband, she would at least be securely housed whilst waiting for probate – but might have difficulty with the mortgage. It is true that the smallest estates are not subject to probate. Yet this does not mean that the plight of women in the survivor situation should be ignored. Indeed, women's groups lobbied to abolish probate between husbands and wives, purely on the ground of sex discrimination. At the same time, capitalist forces were lobbying for abolition of probate on capitalist grounds. In the upshot, probate was abolished between spouses.[8] But then, beginning in Tasmania and Queensland, governments began abolishing probate between parents and children. This is an obviously non-socialist policy.

Certainly the abolition of probate between spouses is also non-socialist. Yet it would have been unnecessary had a socialist-feminist proposal been accepted: namely that of recognising husbands and wives as owning in equal shares any property built up during the course of the marriage. On death of one of the parties, under such a system of equal rights to marital assets, the survivor would own intact 50 per cent of the assets – that is, his or her share. Probate could then be levied against the 50 per cent share of the non-surviving spouse. The surviving wife would, like the surviving husband, have access to the 50 per cent share of the property rightfully hers or his. After probate, the remainder of the deceased's share would pass where it had been willed. The demand that probate be paid on estates of certain value would be met. So, had there been a will to implement the ideal – that women's and men's efforts in contributing to marital property are equal, as are women's and men's efforts in contributing to the outside economy, the abolition of probate laws as sex-discriminatory would not have been necessary. Socialists have, sadly, been slow to recognise the need to extend their equalitarian ideas into the realm of marriage. In this case, such ignorance led to an apparent conjunction between feminist demands and those of capitalists. But this apparent conjunction had no common basis in ideological aim: the essence of the aims of both groups were not contiguous. Yet the force of capitalists was added to by the force of women fighting for equal recognition of women's rights to share in the marital estate.

In New South Wales laws now cover property rights of those living in de facto relationships; a similar proposal came before the parliament of Victoria in 1986. The legislation provides that if the parties to a de facto relationship have lived together for a particular period – say two years – then the surviving spouse, or aggrieved spouse in a separation, can bring an action in the (state) Supreme Court for a share of the property accumulated during the course of the relationship. The spouse would argue that her (it usually would be her) efforts as childcarer, husbandcarer, housecarer contributed to the accumulation of property. She could then be awarded a share of the property on the basis of that contribution. (This effects rights similar to those accruing to married parties under the *Family Law Act* 1975, which operates in the federal sphere.) But what if the man has previously been married and has built up assets in that marriage, together with his former wife, yet property settlement with that former wife has not yet been finalised? What if the settlement has been finalised, but (as is too often the case)[9] the husband retains a greater share of the assets – a share incorporating a portion which rightly should have gone to his former spouse? If under these circumstances the de facto wife brings an action in the Supreme Court, her action will be related to the totality of the property, some of which really belongs to the former wife. (That is, part is attributable to the efforts of that wife, in terms of care of children, husband, house, and likely monetary contribution, whether direct or indirect.)[10] Yet again, if the feminist-socialist proposal of equal rights to marital assets – socialist or equalitarian marriage – were recognised, this problem would not arise, and feminists would not have to agitate against the form of the new de facto property laws on grounds that this pits women against each other, in that whilst recognising one woman's rights, it ignores the rights of another.[11]

There is little point in introducing policies or legislation without regard to the feminist content of that policy or legislation. There is less point in railing against the women who are obliged to lobby against measures which ALP governments wish to implement, if those measures have not been thought through for all their implications and effects on women, for all their implications in accordance with socialist-feminist ideals.

The superannuation and equal rights to marital assets issues illustrate another problem with current socialist debate. Socialism does not begin in the paid workplace and end at the cottage door or garden gate. Socialism is not a recipe for the outside world, whilst the world of the home continues in its medieval way, a hangover from the manorial system. As has too starkly been pointed out (Peattie and Rein, 1983: p. 23):

Every movement for social reform comes up, sooner or later, against the barrier of the natural: that which cannot be changed because it is in the order of things, outside the span of intervention... We may argue about the circumstances under which it is appropriate for women to work, and the kinds of employment they may appropriately enter, and we may argue about the proper allocation of rights and responsibilities between husband and wife in the family, but most people consider it is only natural that the man should be both the main breadwinner and the family head because women naturally are best adapted to rearing children and men are able to earn better in the world of work outside.

Current policies too readily shirk the task of confronting exploitation on the home front, however brave they may be about addressing it in the depersonalised work world outside. Efforts are being made to ensure that girls and women develop skills in the public as well as the private sector. Men and boys continue to see the public sphere as their lone arena for full participation.

Yet the boy and man problem is so much less expensive to correct: having men and boys learn how to participate in the home life of children, cooking and cleaning costs nothing in money terms. Just as girls and women have learned these skills on the homeground during their growing years, boys and men can learn them, with reinforcement from school surrounds. It is far more expensive (though necessary) to ensure that girls have a fair participation in mathematics and science classes, access to computers, equal attention from teachers and career guides. It is far more expensive (though vital) to ensure that all teachers become skilled in non-sexist teaching, and that employers become attuned to the talents and skills of young women. Far more expensive (though essential) to embark upon re-education for employers in terms of equal opportunity programming and the establishment of procedures to deal with – and hopefully eliminate – sexual harassment in educational institutions and on the job; equal opportunity recruitment and promotion programmes; affirmative action training, to ensure that women and men, boys and girls, are equally well trained, equally skilled and have equal experience so that they may equally compete for positions.

The expense involved in ensuring that girls are able to gain access to interesting careers in the public world of paid employment is essential: it means that girls and women develop their intellectual and other abilities, and make good use of those skills; it means that knowledge and skills are increased throughout Australia; it means that more opportunities are created for the development of positive technology, of better ways of working: all members of society would be working together to ensure that the political economy works to its optimum capacity. Yet the lack of expense involved in ensuring that boys gain access to participatory skills in the private world of the home and community is equally worthwhile. Is there a lack of will involved where boys, men and the private world of the home is concerned?

The domestic economy – the world of the home – is suffering because women are participating (as they have a right to do) in paid work and public effort, in combination with work and care of the homeground, but men have less easily recognised the need to combine paid and public work with unpaid, private work and caring in the home. It is time that efforts in the public world were integrated with efforts in the private world, so that each can boost and assist the other. The efforts undertaken for girls and women in the paid work world must be matched by efforts of boys and men in the unpaid world of the home.

An economic debate exists which goes well beyond that reaching the daily financial pages. Economics is seen in limited terms. Economic wellbeing should be measured not just in terms of the level of the dollar, the balance of trade, the size of the deficit, but in terms of the human economy: human needs, the pursuit of happiness, comfort, leisure, and hard, satisfying work – outside and inside the home.

We are faced with a world where women's concerns are as always, at risk, even with Labor governments in power. The opposition to women's rights is based on the idea that the economy cannot afford to recognise in equal terms women's efforts in paid work; nor can it recognise, *vis-à-vis* men, women's efforts in the unpaid world of the home. There is also a danger of malaise: charges are levelled that women have what we want. There is affirmative action legislation and sex discrimination legislation at federal level. All Labor states have implemented equal opportunity or antidiscrimination legislation. Federal offices of human rights, equal opportunity, or women's information services have been opened in Queensland and Tasmania where state governments are inadequate to the task of recognising human rights for women, their governments being wedded to conservative ideologies. Various laws have been amended to eliminate the most obvious injustices of sexism and discrimination. The implication is that we should again shut up, pack bags and baggage and retreat to silence. Or simply cease to speak so loudly, so that it becomes easier for our voices to be ignored.

In *Modern Capitalism and Revolution* Paul Cardan (cited in Altman, 1980: p. 150) has said:

Meaningful action is whatever increases the confidence, the autonomy, the initiative, the participation, the solidarity, the equalitarian tendencies and the self-activity of the masses and whatever acts in demystification. Sterile and harmful action is whatever reinforces the passivity of the masses, their apathy, their cynicism, their differentiation through hierarchy, their alienation, their reliance on others to do things for them and the degree to which they can therefore be manipulated by others – even by those acting allegedly on their behalf.

For women, these words have real meaning. For women like Peg Martin, 'I don't have to *ask* to be equal, I *am* equal', efforts over her lifetime have ensured that women have engaged in meaningful action. The lesson we have to learn is that we have indeed made strides. We must recognise real wins. The passage of affirmative action legislation, the distribution of jobs under various job creation programmes so that women gained an equal footing in that distribution; the increase of women in parliament; the establishment of rape crisis centres, women's health centres and all the other advances which demand recognition, have been won by women, by women's action. (With participation by some men, and their numbers, sometimes, in parliament.) But for the action of women, governments would never have taken up and run with those issues. In order to keep ourselves going, and to continue the work of the women going before, the Peg Martins of this world, we have to acknowledge the advances that they and we have brought about.

For it is certainly true that once an oppressed or deprived group has achieved recognition, however inadequate; has gained some aims, however few; this stirs the group to further advances. The greatest danger facing women is the pressure to see any further advances we might demand as selfish or detrimental to the real cause, when they, in combination with associated demands, *are* the real cause.

As Ben Chifley said, the real cause is socialism. The real cause is to ensure that fair shares of the things the world is capable of giving are dealt around, amongst us all. It is only when women gain fair shares of our Australian heritage, that socialism can be truly recognised. As Peg Martin said, 'I don't have to ask to be equal. I am equal.' Women aren't asking any more. Knowing we are equal, we're demanding a recognition of that equality, demanding our incorporation into the true equation of fair shares.

---

1. For a critical analysis of this position see Legal and Constitutional Committee, 1983, p. 185

2. On the issue of distribution of wealth and income in families see Edwards, 1982 and Scutt and Graham, 1984.

3. See for example the analysis of *Mallett* v. *Mallett*, a decision of the High Court of Australia in April 1984, in Scutt and Graham, 1984.

4. The Working Women's Charter was devised by a group of union-based and union-concerned women in Melbourne, and gained support from women around Australia. It did not originate with the Australian Council of Trade Unions (ACTU).

5. Now the Australian Industrial Relations Commission.

6. For a discussion of the case see Scutt, 1985b.

7. See generally WEL Family Law Action Group, 1982.

8. Di Graham of the Probate Action Group led this campaign. On the campaign see Graham, 1987.

9. See generally Scutt and Graham, *For Richer, For Poorer*, 1984. Work of the Institute of Family Studies based in Melbourne, under the direction of Dr Peter McDonald, bears out the results of the research conducted by Scutt and Graham.

10. See Family Law Act, 1975 and discussion in Scutt and Graham, 1984.

11. On equal rights to marital assets see Scutt and Graham, 1984, and WEL Family Law Action Group, 1980.

Bibliography

Altman, Dennis 1980, *Rehearsals for Change: Politics and Culture in Australia*. Fontana, Sydney.

Australian Labor Party (ALP) Federal Branch 1979, *Report of the National Committee of Enquiry to the Executive*. ALP National Secretariat, Canberra.

Edwards, Meredith 1982, *Report on Income Distribution in Families*. National Women's Advisory Council, Canberra.

Family Law Action Group (convenor Di Graham) 1982, *Submission of the Women's Electoral Lobby on Superannuation*. WEL, Sydney.

— 1980, *Submission to the Australian Government and the Australian Law Reform Commission on Equal Rights to Marital Assets*. WEL, Sydney.

Family Law Act, 1975. Commonwealth.

Graham, Di 1987, 'Through Life in Pursuit of Equality', in *Different Lives: Reflections on the Women's Movement and Visions of its Future*, (ed.) Jocelynne A. Scutt. Penguin, Melbourne.

Joyce, Robin 1984, 'Labor Women: Political Housekeepers or Politicians?', in *Australian Women and the Political System*, (ed.) Marian Simms. Longman Cheshire, Melbourne.

— 1984, 'Feminism: An Early Tradition Amongst Western Australian Labor Women', in *All Her Labors, Vol. 1, Working it Out*, Women and Labour Conference Collective. Hale & Iremonger, Sydney.

Legal and Constitutional Committee 1983, *Report on the Subordinate Legislation (Deregulation) Bill*, Australian Government Printer, Melbourne.

Peattie, Lisa and Rein, Martin 1983, *Women's Claims: A Study in Political Economy*. Oxford University Press, Oxford.

Porter, Michael 1985, 'The Labour of Liberalisation', in *Poor Nation of the Pacific: Australia's Future*, (ed.) Jocelynne A. Scutt.

Scott, Hilda 1982, *Sweden's Right to be Human – Sex-Role Equality: The Goal and the Reality*. Allison & Busby, London.

Scutt, Jocelynne A. (ed.) 1985a, *Poor Nation of the Pacific: Australia's Future*. Allen & Unwin, Sydney.

— and Di Graham 1984, *For Richer, For Poorer: Money, Marriage and Property Rights*. Penguin, Melbourne.

— (ed.) 1985b, *Growing Up Feminist: A New Generation of Australian Women*. Angus & Robertson, Sydney.

— (ed.) 1987, *Different Lives: Reflections on the Women's Movement and Visions of its Future*. Penguin, Melbourne.

Simms, Marian (ed.)   1984, *Australian Women and the Political System*. Longman Cheshire, Melbourne.

South Australian Industrial Reports (SAIR), Vol. 20

Whitlam, Gough   1985, *The Whitlam Government 1972–1975*. Penguin, Melbourne.

Women and Labour Conference Collective 1984, *All Her Labors, Vol. 1. Working it Out*. Hale & Iremonger, Sydney.

ROSALEEN LOVE

Rosaleen Love was born in 1940 and grew up in
Ipswich; her mother was a member of a writing
group which met at her home (and which included
Helen Haenke). A member of a writing family,
Rosaleen Love's mother wrote romantic fiction
(under the name Mary Bishop) while her daughter,
Penny, favours the horror story as her genre.

She was educated at Ipswich Girls' Grammar
and the universities of Queensland, Cambridge
and Melbourne. As an academic (she chairs the
Humanities Department of the Swinburne Institute
of Technology) she finds that, 'office life' is full of
'literary' possibilities.

'The institutional arrangements of a higher
education system undergoing weird and wonderful
changes provide material for the writer of
speculative fiction, though she must set her fictional
scene somewhere off this planet.' She comments:
'My writing takes the following forms: the smart-arse
inter-office memo; essays on science and society;
short stories, mainly speculative fiction; and attempts
at writing a novel.' She is currently turning one of
her short stories, 'The Total Devotion Machine' into
a full length play, with assistance from Thérèse Radic.
When asked how she sees her role as a writer,
'as a feminist and a satirist, a feminist satirist, and
occasionally a satirist of feminists,' she responds.

Changes in the commercial world and personal
experience have suggested to her that it is extremely
difficult to earn a living from writing:

'I can't earn a living from writing. I have published

with too many publishers who have been taken over and my books have been held in more warehouses than I like to think about. My collection of short stories, *The Total Devotion Machine* (The Women's Press, 1989) sat in a Melbourne warehouse for months because of a takeover of the Australian distributors. I published a science anthology with Greenhouse Press back in 1987, *If Atoms Could Talk*, just before Greenhouse was taken over. Nobody pays royalties on time, and with all the takeovers, money may be years late arriving, if ever!'

But writing is still a source of satisfaction. 'What I do is embellish my daily life with writing in order to enjoy myself in my work. I can imagine life after retirement when I can write full time... but I don't know if I really could fill up the day with just putting words on paper. I think I need the social life and stimulation that working at Swinburne provides.'

Evolution Annie

for Roy Lewis who nearly got the story right, but not quite[1]

You know all those stories of origins, those myths of our beginnings. 'A group of animals lived in the trees,' they'd start, and continue with the saga of how one day, down we came, we discovered the plains and the joys of upright posture. We stood up, looked around, and decided to stay.

I have to tell you something. That story is a myth. That wasn't how it happened, not how it happened at all.

I suppose you've read all about the importance of the dominant male in this early group, the primeval Father, and how civilisation began one day when a group of his sons got together and co-operated for the first time in rejecting their Father's authority. They killed him and ate him, or so the story goes, and that was the beginning of it all – guilt (naturally) and civilisation as the o-so-thin veneer covering the beast within, and since incest had something to do with this version of what we did to Father, this dark deed of our early days led (allegedly) to bonding outside the family group. For the greater good of the gene pool, some say, though I think that is stretching the evidence too far, imagining we knew all that back there in the Pleistocene, when of course we were just doing what came naturally. We had the trick of moving on to higher things. We had other reasons for doing the old man in.

Another story has it that we suppressed all knowledge of this dirty deed, sublimating it instead into the act of going to church on Sunday.

I ask you, does that sound a likely story? Just because it's complicated, and inherently improbable doesn't mean it has to be true. Take hold on your own common sense in these matters. It sounds improbable because it is.

Call me Annie. Evolution Annie. Come listen to my tale. Let me tell you the story of our beginnings.

We didn't decide to come down from the trees, as an act of free choice. We fell out of the trees and had to make the best of our new circumstances. It wasn't Father whom the boys killed and ate one day in the (alleged) first act of ritual communion. It was Mother who decided someone had to go, so she... but that is getting ahead of my story.

I am Annie, a diminutive prosimian, or so they will later describe me. I can tell you I am neither ape nor monkey, but something with the edge on both, as far as brains go, and their use in the skilful manipulation of what brawn I possess. Diminutive I may be, prosimian I am, but never underestimate the sheer animal cunning, the near human intellect of the humble small prosimian. Look at the merry dance our bones have led you all, look at the clever way we've let fall a hint here, a hint there, that we were far more than we seemed.

Call me names, I can take it. Come on, 'Ape-like ancestor'! Ya, heard it all before. 'Primitive' – ouch, that hurts, that really hurts. I am what I am, and proud of it. 'Primitive' is a relative not an absolute term.

We know it now, though we didn't know it then – that we didn't need to progress much further along the line we were taking when we first fell out of the trees, but nobody could predict it, back then. Least of all Mother. If only she knew she'd have made us climb back at once. Her death was to be a triumph for the simians, her rebirth a source of inspiration to us all. What we learned from Mother was that the bigger brain has not been worth the effort.

When we first fell out of the trees there was great consternation.

'This is it,' said Father, 'This is a sign from above that we must embark on a long and dangerous journey. Clearly the moment has come to get up on our two feet and take a long walk. We shall meet danger, and suffer discomfort, and we shall be sorely tried along the way, but we must go on, upwards and ever onwards.'

'That's a good idea, Edward,' Mother agreed. 'Why don't you and the boys go off and do all that, and we'll stay here in the long grass under this shady tree, and wait for you to return?' So the boys went off with Father, and some of them returned, after tests of fortitude and endurance which Mother agreed would surely have been too much for me, Annie, and my various aunts and cousins and sisters and their babies. While the boys battled raging torrents and the common cold from the icy blasts from the north, and sandy blight from the hot desert winds from the south, and lions, tigers, killer ants one way, the woolly mammoth in the opposite direction, Mother just sat underneath the tree. She taught us all she knew: sewing, rope-making, splicing, basketwork, the practical things of life, though she did not neglect our higher natures. Along the way she also devised the first alphabet, a fairly primitive affair in the light of what came later, but the little ones picked it up quickly. She baked a few clay tablets, for the cuneiform, she said vaguely, though she never did much with them, being busy at the time with plans for her funeral. Not for her the old ways, where we chewed the deceased around for a bit, and threw the bones out of the trees. She wanted something more for herself, a small burial chamber inside a largish pyramid, to keep out the hyenas, and our father, for eternity. (Though this was a passing phase. Later Mother decided the pyramid was not really her.)

Mother stayed at home and developed tools and the skills

of reason. Father and boys went out into the world and got cold and wet and suffered broken bones and falls into chasms and some of them survived frostbite, crocodiles, tigers, giant leeches that fell from the trees, snakes that rose up from the earth, poisonous berries (soon to be so labelled by my mother, the experimental botanist), killer crabs with giant pincers, elephants, and worse. So many ways for a primitive prosimian to die out there, but we were protected from it all through Mother's care and foresight. The male of the species, we knew it even back then, is more prone to accidental death. Staying home under the trees made excellent sense to us girls.

Fire, now, I'm sure you've heard their version of events. How Man the Hunter strode to the edge of the spitting volcano, bravely dodging the hissing dragons, the smoking sulphurous fumaroles, the lions, and bears that stood between him and the precious new discovery. Man the Brave strode to the edge of the bubbling lava, thrust a stick into the fire from below, and took it back, overcoming all the trials and tribulations of keeping it alight. Man harnessing an unruly Nature to his own ends. Man bringing Woman the tools of cooking. Man pointing the way to the Division of Labour, with Man the Hunter of fire, and Woman the Grateful Recipient.

No. These are stories they tell, but they are truly myths of our beginnings. They are the yarns men spin around the campfire to make them feel good about things.

Father didn't bring fire from the volcano. Fire just happened. One day there was a great storm, and a lightning strike, and fire came to the grassy plains of the veldt, and we ran before it, until it veered away from us. It left behind a few burning logs, which we kept alight out of scientific interest in manipulating and controlling our environment. Father was away doing something else at the time.

I don't want to make too much of it. Fire happened, that's all. It was an event in our lives. Fire, from which, when we lived in the trees, we frequently had to flee, but now we lived on the ground, we could discover the value of the firebreak. Properly under control, fire could become a hearth, and with the hearth came the possibilities of a true home, in the sense we now know it. We couldn't do that when we lived in the trees. The forest would burn, taking us with it.

When Father first saw the hearth on his return home from what he and the boys liked to call hunting, but I call mucking around in the bush, the first thing he said was 'Why did you have to ruin a perfectly good camp site by messing around with fire?'

Mother said, 'OK, you take it back to where it came from then. You and the boys, see that volcano over there? Kilimanjaro? Why don't you take this burning brand – mind you keep it alight all the way – and run up to the smoking crater at the top, and throw it in. Propitiate a fire god or two, and you'll feel a lot more comfortable.'

Father and the boys took some of the fire back to heaven, and they felt all the better for it, while Mother and me and the rest of us girls just got on with learning the finer techniques of cooking. Meat with the inside quite raw, and the outside thoroughly blackened, the way we liked it best.

Then Mother figured out a way to divert some water from the river down a channel and across the savannah, so that we had reticulated water and the beginning of a sewerage system.

'What are you doing, ruining a perfectly good camp site by bringing running water to it?' asked Father on his return, minus one or two of the boys. 'Dirt is perfectly natural, and we should all be rolling in more of it, such is nature's way.'

So Mother gave Father a goatskin full of water and told him to go off and find the source of the Nile, and return it to the Earth our Mother and then everything would be all right.

Before he left this time, Father called us all round him and gave us a lecture on the division of labour. 'It works like this. You women stay home, now we've got this hearth, not that I approve of fire in the home, the proper place of fire is in the volcano, but be that as it may, you girls stay here and make this place as nice as you can, in preparation for our return, and we'll go off and become the specialists in our field.' Father waved regally at us as he prepared to leave. 'You may, if you like, gather a few berries while we are gone.'

Mother saw it differently. She was developing the hearth-based multi-skilled workforce. Like Leonardo da Vinci who was to follow her so much later, Mother kept churning out the ideas, and some of them worked, and some of them were years before their time.

'Running round after wild animals will mark a dead end in evolutionary development,' said Mother, as she fed grass seed to what she called her chicks, small feathered creatures she encouraged round the campsite for their eggs. They had to be good for something, Mother reckoned. Burnt feathers tasted quite revolting.

'Without effort there can be no improvement,' said Father, kicking a chicken out of the way.

'I agree,' said Mother. 'After the Nile, you could try Mt Everest, and after you've done that once, you could try it a second time, without oxygen.' She was careful to remind him as she rescued a couple of eggs from in front of his feet, that if he was going to try Everest, he had better remember to take long strips of gazelle hide to wrap around his feet as finneskoes.

Father's trips gave Mother the peace she required to get on with the work on her gravesite. She was quietly persistent on the topic of the afterlife. 'It will be a time of peace and quiet. Calm after the storm. Rest after work.'

'What about the boys, Mother?'

'There will be boys,' said Mother, 'but they will be changed. They will be more like us.'

Naturally we scoffed.

'The savannah will bloom, and the lion will gambol with the dove...'

My sister, Sukie, fell about laughing.

'And if you don't believe me, you can go down there and help with the digging.'

We said we believed her all right.

For the afterlife, Mother knew she would need a new kind of dwelling place, but she never could work out in her own mind what it should be. She had moved on from the pyramid to the barrow, a pre-dug affair, basically a hollow chamber under a mound of dirt. 'Get cracking,' she'd say to the boys,

293

first thing in the morning on one of their increasingly shorter sojourns in the camp. 'Hollow out those shelves there for the sacred relics.'

'Sacred relics?' Father would snarl and stamp off, but we noticed he used to slink back and listen when Mother explained what she meant. 'I'll need food,' she said, 'if I'm to set out on a long voyage into the afterlife. And I'll need a few of the comforts of home, a vase or two, and a pot for the unguents.'

'Unguents are unnatural,' said Father. 'We were born to eat pulverised cockroaches, not smear them on our bodies.'

'Take no notice of your Father. You'll all miss me, when I'm gone.' The little ones burst into tears, and Father and the boys could stand it no more, and went off to explore the ancient continent of Gondwana.

The invention of alcohol took all our female skills. Who else but Mother could take the grated root of one cassava, a few juniper berries and a handful of banana skins, and make something drinkable from it? Father would have us all dead from using the wrong cassava, the poisonous variety. Mother was the one who was rock solid reliable in all botanical matters.

The problems really began when the boys came back again. They returned from the life of action and started sitting round the fire drinking gin and causing trouble.

This time they proved more than usually resistant to Mother's plans to send them to China across the overland route. 'The Himalayas and the Gobi Desert. You know, over there.' She waved her hand in a direction in which they hadn't yet gone off. 'Spices, tea, trade. That's where the future lies. The Orient and its mysteries. Why not give it a go?'

'No,' said Father firmly. 'Pour me another gin, Giselle.'

Though Giselle spiked his gin with a deadly nightshade berry or two Father survived, while crying feebly, 'Pour me another gin, Giselle. That last one packed a wallop.'

Mother called us girls together. 'Those boys will be the death of me,' she said, staring into her half completed barrow.

How could we all combine to keep Mother out of her grave

that little bit longer? Especially when some of the boys were getting rebellious. 'If she wants to go on a trip to the afterlife, why stop her?' they said. 'It's time she started going on one of those long trips she's so fond of sending us on. Let her see what it's like. And while we're about it, why not give her a shove along the way?'

Of course the girls told Mother, and she kept the boys on short rations for a week.

'I'd like a nice grave, facing the sunrise,' said Mother. 'Or perhaps the sunset. The sunset over that part of the savannah I always find particularly entrancing. Perhaps some idols in my grave, images of frog, fish and snake, to ensure regeneration after death, and propitiate the Archetypal Feminine?' She kept the girls busy inventing sculpture.

It marked the turning point in the evolution of the prosimians, the way we were tried and tested again and again, whenever the boys came home with Father. Back they'd come and settle into the joys of hearth and home, and though Mother said she was listening to the travellers' tales, she often had that faraway look in her eyes, as if she was preparing a speech to which one day they would all have to sit up and listen.

The boys came home, some of them, and rolled around the rush floor wrestling, and they took the mickey out of Mother and her funeral plans, and Father sat down in the least windy corner and expected to be waited on, and that was the first time in human civilisation that women realised how much better off they were when the men were off and away doing their own thing.

The first act of human co-operation was when we got together, Mother and the rest of the women, and worked on plans to send the men away. We held what was probably the first Council of War about it. (This was before we came to the conclusion that peace was the way to go.)

'Annie,' said Mother, 'see that tribe of *Homo habilis* over the hill?'

'What, that lot that eat giraffe?'

'They're gross,' said my sister Sukie. 'Giraffe!'

'The eating habits of *Homo habilis* may not be our own, but that is purely because they have developed the stone axe, while we are specialising in the refinements of civilisation.' Mother recognised that the stone axe gave them an edge on us with respect to carving a haunch of giraffe, but she could see further than this. She could see the potential uses to which a pre-chewed thighbone of giraffe could be put.

War, for example.

'How'd you think they'd go in a battle with Father?' Mother had to explain what she meant. 'First one of them picks up the thighbone, and hits his neighbour over the head with it. Of course, the neighbour soon gives as good as he gets, and so it goes. It's called war.'

I shall always be grateful for the things my mother taught me. Though she soon decided that war was for the future, she was the first to recognise the possibilities, and the problems. She knew that if we went down the evolutionary path to war, the boys would take to beating up the neighbours, but she could think the whole thing through. She knew that once they got the knack of it, they'd soon take to beating us.

'Murder and mayhem are thoughtless uncivilised backward looking activities, leading us one way only, back to the trees,' said Mother. She stuck to the peace, although she knew the threat of war.

Instead of warfare, Mother substituted cricket.

'See that thighbone of giraffe?' Mother asked my sister Giselle. 'I want you to go and get it for me.'

'What, go down into the valley with all those *Homo habilis* yoicks?'

'Now. This minute.'

'Why does it always have to be me? I always have to do everything.'

'Because you're so good at it,' said Mother, sending her off down the hill with a cheerful shove.

My sister Giselle was always the great whinger of the family, and the effect of whingeing on human evolution has never been studied, as far as I know. Whingeing doesn't show up in the bones, so no-one gives it any thought, but my sister Giselle was the first and the best at doing the least work round the camp and making the most fuss about it. Giselle whinged, and the more she whinged the more jobs Mother gave her to do, to take her away from the trees and out onto the savannah where the boys chased after the gazelles.

Man the Hunter, Ha! Man the accidental-tripper over the lion's left-overs, that's what those boys were. According to Mother, all this hunting business was merely a temporary abberation, useful for keeping the boys busy, but useless to anyone who wants to maintain an orderly camp routine centred round hearth and home. Someone has to mind the babies, and Mother regarded hunting as a device invented by Father to get out of his regular child-care duties.

Man the Killer Ape? I suppose when Giselle was sent off to get the thighbone of the giraffe (and Mother was right, Giselle did get it. It was thrown at her when she moaned and groaned about her wretched lot) the idea was perhaps then in Mother's mind, Man the Killer Ape. Hit Father over the head and be done with him forever. But Mother being Mother, as soon as she saw the possibilities of shaping the bone into a bat, and a lump of chewed gazelle tendon into a ball, we became instead 'Man the Cricketer.' I have to hand it to Mother. As the ball was sent flying off across the savannah and various scores called 'runs' were marked up on the wet clay tablets, the boys made use of their enormous stock of energy and their oversupply of hormones, and we found a new use for the cuneiform.

As the shadows lengthened, and the seasons changed, and the chill wind blew from the ice, Mother knew that the cricket season had come to an end. Cricket, she wanted to believe, was the game which would best inculcate the team spirit, show the boys how to be good losers, and teach them that eye-hand co-ordination so necessary for leading them gently on to the higher pursuits of reading, writing, weaving and sewing.

Alas, Mother's fond hopes for the civilising influence of cricket on the prosimian male were doomed from the start. Father and the boys soon adapted the game to their own ends, and cries of 'Up yours!' and 'Howzzat?' delivered in an aggressive and unco-operative fashion, the ball hurled down the pitch with the intention of hitting the batter square in the goolies, the ferocity of attack when the bat connected with the ball, the way it sailed high in the treetops and fell to earth on some innocent toddling prosimian, all these innovations were too much for Mother.

Worse, much worse, was to happen once winter started, and cricket gave way to football. The neighbouring hordes wanted to join in, and our pleasant campsite was invaded each Saturday by groups of loutish *Homo habilis*, who introduced the custom of spectator hooliganism and punching up the umpire.

As she began to realise the unintended consequences of her actions, Mother grew quiet and spent more of her time uncharacteristically brooding in front of the fire. It was then that it started to sink in on us that Mother was growing old. Her fur was tinged with grey, her eyesight was not as keen as once it was. Sooner or later, Mother would lie in her grave, and we knew how much we would miss her, when she was gone.

These thoughts marked the beginnings of philosophy.

The way they tell it now, back then we suddenly discovered ourselves the possessors of rather large brains, so we used the surplus grey matter for thinking.

No. That's not the whole truth. The brain was still a bit on the small side when we first fell out of the trees, but down on the ground the hands soon grew strong and skilful in their weaving and sewing. It was the skill of the hands that drove the brain on to bigger and better things.

Try telling that to Father. He simply will not listen. Father believes in brain-led innate male superiority, because he has, by sheer weight of comparative size of everything else, more brains.

'Mere quantity alone,' muttered Mother. 'Means nothing. Consider the case of the elephant. Huge brain, no sense.' She explained the steady growth of the human brain as the result of co-operative acts. It takes groups of people working happily together to erect grass humpies, to dig gardens, to create agriculture and a settled pattern of existence. The skilful use of tools in turn affects the neural connections in the brain, as new habits of life are forged, in ways not yet really understood.

Mother only knew that social change must give rise to physical change, and the prosimian brain did not lead this process. It trailed far behind.

We all knew that Father's behaviour was never any kind of argument for intelligence in diminutive prosimians, at least, in the male of the species. The females were different. There seemed some reason, in us, for the existence of sex-linked individual differences. We had the common sense. They had the wanderlust.

There were plenty of other differences.

'Is it, as Father suggests, that there is a good Father in the sky, who will guard us from harm, if we set about approaching him properly?'

'No,' said Mother. 'There is a good Mother in the earth, who asks only that the system of natural cycles of matter and energy go their own way, unhampered, through the systems of air, water, and earth. It's like this, Annie,' my mother would often say to me, for being the youngest in the family I was often about her furry knees. 'Annie, this life must be but a pale shadow of something quite other than it seems. There has to be something more to it than the endless round of gathering food, eating it, and using the sewerage system for its newly designed purpose. What are we training the little ones to collect berries for? For food, I know, but there must be another reason for our existence.'

So Mother reflected on the connections between things. She noticed the pathways in nature, how the berry changed its form and nature as it passed from the bush to become first food for the birds, then ready-mix guano fertiliser, then the new plant germinated from the seed, to berry again. Mother was the first to think this way about nature's bounty, the first to try to keep things moving round, to keep the carbon and nitrogen cycles in some kind of order. She was the first of the great recyclers.

In the rare moments when they were together, Mother and Father agreed on one thing only – the importance of stories for the moral development of the young, to encourage the

299

young into proper patterns of good behaviour. 'Heroic behaviour,' said Father. 'Warm, nurturant, co-operative, sharing behaviour,' Mother would retort sharply, wanting to instil in her brood from the beginning the virtues of co-operation over the sin of competition.

So when Father told the littlies the story of prosimian Lucy and the big bad paleoanthropologist who got the story of our beginnings quite wrong, and the bloodthirsty fate that befell poor Lucy when her bones were later dug up and displayed on TV, Mother told tales of daily life centred on the composition of the good compost heap. And if the eyes of the littlies glazed over somewhat faster with Mother's stories than with Father's tales of goodies and baddies, at least Mother's stories served the function of getting them off to sleep in a reasonably short period of time.

Mother's stories told them what Father's left out, that winning the race to be fully human was not really what it was all about. What matters is the kind of human being we develop at the end of the race, nurturing, caring, someone who will properly respect their mother's grave, when she is gone.

Sitting round the camp fire, combing each other's hair, catching the odd louse, tick, flea or other parasite, gazing into the fire, there we were, a group of happy prosimian women with but one problem in the world, what to do with the men?

'It's them!' said Auntie Elsie, as the dust on the horizon signalled a herd of stampeding gazelle, one sure sign that the men were on their way home to us, making the maximum amount of noise. Back from the away match in the camp down the road, and stoned to the gills with poisonous home brew.

'Why don't we...,' said Auntie Elsie. 'When you think of it...' She pounced on another louse at the back of Mother's furry neck, 'Why don't we just move on ourselves, leave the home fire burning, and the empty cradle rocking gently, and the shelters deserted, leave a mystery behind, and just go off and set up camp somewhere else? Leave the camp to the boys. Just walk out and leave it all, leave the stuff of mysteries behind, leave, just leave.'

'Elsie, you always were a hopeless mooning romantic,'

said Mother. 'What, leave my lovely grave?' and we knew we couldn't ask her to do that.

'The way I see it, men are some small use. In youth, when female passion outstrips common sense, reason, intellect and whatever, and our hormones send us racing in their direction for those few short heady moments of passion which lead we all know where.' To the babies playing around our feet. 'But with age comes wisdom, and the recognition it's not really been worth all that trouble. The way I see it, we still need them, for the moment, to propagate the species and replenish the stock of babies, who, you know, fall all too easily to the maurauding leopard or the rapacious fox.'

Ah, those long-lost days of the primal horde, before women invented the incest taboo. It had been all the same to us then, whether it was our brothers or our Father whom we used to create the new batch of babies. We lived, unawakened, in a state of primitive promiscuity, not realising the future harm inbreeding might cause the human species. It's not true, what they said, that it was Father who unwittingly, through the manner of his death, instituted the custom of exogamy, of marrying out of the family. No, it happened well before Father met his fate at the hands of his sons. (You remember that story, where the boys were so furious when he ordered them away from their sisters, that the boys killed him and ate him? Afterwards, it was said, they felt sorry for what they had done, and were consumed with a guilt so strong that from that day on they did what Father had ordered back when the fracas started.) Sigmund Freud invented that story, but only to conceal his own dubious motives, to hide the guilt he felt about inventing the crazy story in the first place.

No, the practice of marrying out of the horde into which one was born was the invention of Mother. When she sent Father and the boys off on their long and dangerous pilgrimages, the smartest boys soon got worn out with it all, and dropped off at neighbouring tribes along the way, where the local girls congratulated them on their cleverness, and begged them to stay. Some of the boys settled down happily, far from home, spreading their smart genes through a wider population. Genetic diversity, that's the key to evolutionary success, though we didn't think of it in quite those terms then. How could we use those words, when we barely knew the relationship between copulation and conception? Except that whenever the boys were home, conception happened all the time, and when they went away, we got a bit of a break from the child-bearing side of things.

From time to time Father came home, to replenish the supply of young males, and to take the next batch of boys on his travels. Occasionally we girls would try to get our brothers to see the light, to encourage them to think that they, too, could be weavers and potters and writers like us, but no, it was in the blood, the urge to follow a male leader, even if he led them up mountains and through bogs and into immense hardship at all times testing their endurance to the limit.

What us girls wanted to know was, why did they do it? What were they running away from? Us? What were they trying to prove? These questions remain unanswered, to this day.

According to Mother, the men could come and go, grow up and leave, after various fashions, but it was Matriarchy which provided the solid core to society, the handing of camp fire sites down through the female line to the women. It made eminent sense to her. With the care of her grave after she was gone, she knew the boys would be far too busy to weed it. Through the institution of the matrilinear descent of property, Mother knew she could achieve respect in life, and exercise some control from beyond the grave. Marrying her daughters out of the horde made sense, when she started to think about it in terms of real estate. It multiplied the number of campsites all over Africa, and round all those campsites people would sit, and remember the tales of her exploits. Big Mother, the first of her kind.

Everyone knew the campsite belonged to the women, while the men bequeathed necklaces of hyenas' teeth and similar useless objects to their sons.

With respect to the housing crisis of the Holocene, who except Mother, back in the Pleistocene, made moves to protect their descendants in this way? Big Mother, the first and best of them all.

How to explain it, the bond that developed between us sisters as we went about our daily tasks, the feelings that arose in us, for the Earth, our Mother, of which our own dear Mother represented the living embodiment of all the caring, nurturing features we held most dear, the source of warmth and nourishment, rest for the weary, unguent for the harrassed soul. We developed a feeling of unity with the bare earth under our paws. We learned to feel special, because we alone stood upright, our eyes fixed on the stars, our feet planted on solid earth.

If only we could get the boys to see things our way. Mother was starting to work on her plan, except we didn't know what was happening, until it was over.

It was too good to last. The practice of exogamy, together with the invention of team sports, combined according to some relentless inner logic that Mother could hardly have thought through, to present us with problems on a large scale. How to stem the tide of aggressive mindless violence at sporting occasions, and increasingly at weddings, that seemed to be accompanying the widespread adoption of our customs across the savannah? Alcohol contributed, too, and towards the end of her life Mother grew increasingly sad at the use to which her bright ideas were being put.

She made several attempts at civilian control. The police force was brought into being, and the institution of human slavery helped get rid of the worst offenders, but Mother could see that Paradise could never be regained, not in Africa. The years slipped by, and Mother increasingly just sat by her barrow, waiting for the moment when she would enter it for the last time.

'The boys will see it our way, when I am gone.' She believed to the end that with her passing the religion of God the Mother would begin.

When our Mother said her time was come, we knew what those words meant. We knew what we were expected to do. She had grown steadily weaker, and now she could barely move from her bed of rushes to greet the new day with her customary invocation to the sky and the sun, the bringer of warmth, and earth the bringer of nourishment.

We took her announcement to mean that she wished Father to prepare the drink from the cassava root, and ferment the juniper berries for her last meal. We knew what that entailed. Father would get it wrong, for he never properly worked out the difference between the safe and dangerous plants.

Father was pleased to be trusted with a simple action of the hearth. He didn't notice when Auntie Elsie poured the rest of the drink on the ground, once Mother had taken her cup.

Afterwards we laid Mother to rest in her barrow grave, and placed round her offerings she prized, pots of cassava flour, a jar of sloe gin, a few dull heavy stones that she predicted would be called 'gold' in the afterlife, and last of all, her precious tablets of slate and clay, with the mysterious marks of the cuneiform upon them.

According to Mother's instructions, we refused Father's offer to help in eating the remains, and we made sure we sealed up the door with heavy rocks the way she wanted it done.

That is why we are here, today, and why we worship our Mother, the earth, and why we still drink gin.

That was the end of our Mother. Our Father met with a somewhat stickier fate, but that is another story. He may now be the tallest tree in the forest, and you should pay him your respects as you pass, but don't expect an answer from him. He is too busy pursuing the thrill of the chase in that happier hunting ground.

As you pass by the smallest flower in the forest, pause and reflect that it may be our Mother. Speak kindly to her, and avoid trampling her into the dust. She has moved on to a more reflective future.

Who knows, with this simple act of your consideration, the earth may spring a little under your step, your hair may lift with a cool refreshing breeze, and your travels may be a little more joyous along the path, because of her.

---

1. The story 'Evolution Annie' was written in part as a response to the very funny but very one-sided view of human evolution portrayed by Roy Lewis in *The Evolution Man*. (This was first published in 1960 under the title *What we did to Father*.)

HELEN HODGMAN

Helen Hodgman was born in Aberdeen, Scotland, in 1945 and lived in Colchester, Essex, until 1958 when her family was shipped to Tasmania by the local Rotary Club as part of the 'Bring Out a Briton' campaign. Later she returned to England, lived in London for ten years, worked at a variety of odd jobs (including bookmaker's clerk and domestic cleaner) and spent a lot of time writing. Two successful novels were published, *Blue Skies* (1976) and *Jack and Jill* (1978) – which won the Somerset Maugham Award. 'I spent the next ten years learning to write,' she says.

In 1988, *Broken Words* was published; it won the Christina Stead prize and was renamed *Ducks* for its American publication by Harmony Books. As Helen Hodgman says, she is not an 'annual' writer; 'I long since gave up the idea, suggested to me by my first English publisher that I write a novel a year in order to gain a reputation and make a living. All that seemed all right at the time but life kept getting in the way. Art is long but life is short. I like to play. The people in my life are important. The houses I live in matter to me. There are days when I would rather work in a garden or swim in the sea than fuss with words on a page. If writing were all there was in my life I should be very unhappy indeed.'

Helen Hodgman is a drama and screen writer as well as a novelist; among her works are *The Right Hand Man* (screenplay, Australia UAA Films 1984/5) and *Giant Freesias* (television adaptation of three Elizabeth Jolley short stories, Zowie Films, 1989/90).

She currently lives in Sydney where she makes a living from writing for film and television – and works on her fiction.

'I enjoy writing scripts,' she says; 'The words will eventually fly off the page and find another form. It begins with me but doesn't end there. I am not responsible. It's disappointing when this *doesn't* happen, when the script lies about like a dead baby and in the end one has no choice but to bury it. To have even part of my unmade television script *Roundabout* published is pleasing.'

Her latest project is a novel entitled *Terrible Lizards*; 'I hope it doesn't take ten years to finish,' she says, 'but if it does, it doesn't matter. The business of writing is endless, difficult and exciting – and the process is just as important as the result.'

Helen Hodgman's novels are:

1976 *Blue Skies*. Duckworth, London.

1981, Penguin, Melbourne.

1978 *Jack and Jill*. Duckworth, London.

1981 Penguin, Melbourne.

1988 *Broken Words*. Penguin, Melbourne.

1989, Virago, London.

1989 published as *Ducks*. Harmony Books, New York.

1989 *Blue Skies* and *Jack and Jill* published in one volume. Virago, London.

Roundabout

Roundabout was a project started under the auspices of the Women's Film Fund. It was intended that it be made by an all female crew, that the key characters would be women and that the underlying philosophy would be feminist. *Roundabout* was to be screened by SBS in two ninety minute episodes. But in the end none of it happened.

The main characters:

MADELAINE: age early 40s, the power behind Eros (a luxury resort-hotel – with a difference).

LUISA: 20 years old, Italian extraction, employed as trainee house-keeper for the Eros project but wants to be a receptionist.

CHRISTINA: 19 years old, similar background to her best friend LUISA.

LIZ: late 30s, married to architect PHIL ARGENZIO and mother of three boys.

DR ALICE ROSEN: early sixties, Jewish American, famous sex therapist who is here to promote the Eros concept.

and the others:

IRINI: head of housekeeping.

PHIL ARGENZIO: 40, architect of Eros.

EARL CONNOR: 55, world famous plastic surgeon in Australia to promote Eros and to further his search for the key to eternal youth.

STEVE: 25, chef.

PARIS: 21, cab driver.

TONY: 20, gym instructor.

ROGER: MADELAINE's personal assistant.

HARVEY ROSEN: married to DR ALICE ROSEN and has come along for the ride.

the story so far...

Two days remain before the grand opening of Eros, a new luxury hotel/clinic dedicated to fitness and beauty.

Day one starts as MADELAINE *gives her new staff a pep-talk before work begins. All* MADELAINE *is concerned with is getting ready for the opening night. However, things conspire against her.*

LIZ arrives for a reunion with her estranged husband PHIL but all does not go smoothly. At the end of the day LIZ walks out on a dinner party MADELAINE is giving for DR ROSEN and EARL CONNOR and lets PARIS, the handsome Greek taxi driver, take her new dress off.

After a tiresome day spent practising vacuuming and making beds, and getting caught by LIZ and PHIL in a compromising position with

STEVE *in the state-of-the-art operating theatre (minor surgical procedures only) that lies under Eros,* LUISA *turns down* STEVE's *proposal of marriage and returns to her flat to find her best friend* CHRISTINA *in bed with a woman.*

However, the day's major drama comes when EARL CONNOR *gets carried away on the Ray Martin Show and lets slip that he is in Australia to investigate the possibilities of harvesting foetal kangaroos in order to extract their pineal glands which he believes can delay the aging process in humans.*

Can MADELAINE *control the damage?*

Will LIZ *be reconciled with* PHIL?

Will LUISA *come to terms with her best friend's sexual preference?*

Will STEVE *get over* LUISA?

Will PARIS *ever learn that no means no in any language, including Greek?*

But most of all, will Eros get off the ground?

. . . now read on.

INT.   LUISA'S FLAT   DAY

LUISA *wakes when radio alarm comes on with blast of music.*

LUISA *quickly reaches out and switches it off.*

LUISA *lies in bed, listening.*

There is a knock on the door.

LUISA *looks at door but says nothing and takes no action.*

Another knock.

INT.   FLAT   SAME

CHRIS *outside* LUISA's *door.*

LOVER *sits on couch drinking coffee, reading paper.*

CHRIS: Luisa? You there?

INT. BEDROOM SAME

LUISA *can't face* CHRIS *and her* LOVER.

She pulls the bedclothes up over her face.

INT. FLAT SAME

LOVER *looks up from a full page advertisement for* EROS.

> LOVER: Amazing! Seems some people
> think wrinkles are bigger killers than
> heart disease or cancer.

CHRIS *is distracted.*

> CHRIS: Yeah. Suppose so—
> Luisa, you there? Because we're gonna
> be late. Luisa?

> LOVER: She's already gone I bet.

> CHRIS: Luisa never gets out of bed one
> second sooner than she has to.
> And its her birthday.

> LOVER: Well in that case maybe she's
> decided she deserves to sleep in.
> If you want a ride I'll drop you – but I've
> got to go now.

> CHRIS: Wait on.

CHRIS *goes into bedroom.*

CHRIS *comes out and puts beautifully wrapped box in centre of table.*

INT. BEDROOM SAME

LUISA *lies in bed.*

The second the door slams she turns on the radio and jumps out of bed.

LUISA *rushes to her wardrobe which is a crammed up mess.*

RADIO *launches into 8 o'clock news emitting a worldwide list of disasters.*

LUISA *barely listens, daunted by her wardrobe, full of items that all look awful this morning.*

> RADIO: . . . and, moving closer to home, that colourful and controversial entrepreneur Madelaine Curtis looks as though she's in trouble this morning as the new Eros complex comes under fire from animal welfare groups across the country.

> LUISA: Shit!

In her excitement LUISA *forgets what's elapsed so far this morning.*

LUISA *jumps to the door.*

> LUISA (*cont.*) Chris!

INT.   FLAT   SAME

LUISA *opens her door.*

> LUISA: Did you hear that? Wonder what's happened. I . . .

LUISA *looks round – at* CHRIS's *open door at the unmade and rumpled bed.*

> LUISA: (*deflated*) Oh.

LUISA *spots her present.*

LUISA: (*a bit more cheerful*) Oh!

INT.   ARGENZIO SUITE   DAY

LIZ half wakes, stretches, gradually realises that PHIL *is not beside her.*

LIZ wakes up reluctantly.

Sits up.

LIZ sees her dress thrown over a chair.

LIZ lies back down, remembering the night before.

EXT.   EROS   DAY

The pristine sparkling facade of EROS *is sullied by a bloodstain which glows in the sun.*

A small car driven by a LARGE FURRY FIGURE *buzzes up to entrance of* EROS.

The LARGE FURRY FIGURE *squeezes out of the small car and proves to be a person in a kangaroo suit.*

KANGAROO *approaches* EROS...

INT.   EROS/LOBBY   DAY

KANGAROO *enters* EROS *past astonished* DOORMAN.

DOORMAN *nonetheless opens door with impeccable* EROS *style.*

DOORMAN: Good morning.

KANGAROO *crosses lobby.*

Preparations for tonight's opening bash are underway.
There's a lot of polishing/cleaning going on.
Flowers being delivered.

311

KANGAROO *keeps going, ignoring the effect it has on others.*

KANGAROO *helps itself to a flower which it tucks behind its ear.*

INT.   EROS/DINING ROOM   DAY

MADELAINE *is at a large table which, as well as serving as a place to eat, has been turned into an impromptu office.*

MADELAINE *is holding a 'council of war' with* ROGER, DR ALICE, HARVEY *and* EARL CONNOR.

Elsewhere in the room FOUR YOUNG WAITERS *are having a training session under the encouraging eye of a* JAPANESE LANGUAGE TEACHER.

Prominent on MADELAINE*'s table are the morning papers.*

The headlines sum up the situation.

The *Age:* AMERICAN DOCTOR FINDS FOUNTAIN OF YOUTH IN AUSTRALIA – AT A PRICE.
The *Australian:* ETERNAL LIFE DEMANDS WILDLIFE.
The *Sun:* PLASTIC SURGEON STICKS THE KNIFE IN.

The HEAD WAITER *stands to one side looking cynical.*

WAITERS 1 & 2 *sit at tables.*
WAITERS 3 & 4 *approach with plates of toast and put them ceremoniously down in front of* WAITERS 1 & 2.

WAITERS 1 & 2 look at their plates.

>   WAITERS 1 & 2 (*in a chorus of painful &
>   discordant slowness*): Kore wa nan desu ka?

Subtitle: *What is this?*

>   WAITERS 3 & 4 (*with equal slowness*):
>   Bejimaito tosutu desu.

Subtitle: *It is vegemite on toast.*

> HARVEY: Can I see the sports pages?

DR ALICE *hands him the papers.*

> DR ALICE: There you go, Harve.

HARVEY *proceeds to search out the sports pages and scan them. He's looking for something.*

Meanwhile ROGER *is on portable phone.*

While ROGER *is on the phone the* HEAD WAITER *brings coffee, juice and fruit to the table plus, in front of* MADELAINE, *a bowl of muesli.*

DR ALICE & HARVEY *take delivery of their breakfasts which are substantial and greeted with pleasure.*

HEAD WAITER *places an empty plate in front of* EARL CONNOR.

EARL CONNOR *opens bag and pours a rainbow stream of pills and capsules onto the plate.*

Meanwhile ROGER *carries on his phone conversation.*

> ROGER: Dr Connor isn't available for comment at this stage, no.

Pause.

> ROGER: We've made our position
> perfectly clear. Dr Connor is a
> shareholder in Eros Incorporated.
> As one of the world's leading plastic
> surgeons and experts on aging he
> also acts in an advisory capacity.
> His research work at the University of
> Human Appearance is not connected
> to Eros in any way.

313

Pause.

ROGER *grimaces, places hand over mouthpiece.*

> ROGER (*cont.*): Does Eros condone the
> mass slaughter of baby kangaroos?

> MADELAINE: Oh for God's sake!

> ROGER (*into phone*): No.

Rest of ROGER's *conversation pretty much in the background while* OTHERS *talk and eat.*

> DR ALICE: Really stuck your shoe in it this
> time didn't you Earl?

> HEAD WAITER (*adjusting a flower petal*): Will
> that be all?

> MADELAINE: It will. Thank you.

ROGER *covers mouthpiece.*

> ROGER: Hang on! I'll take a short black,
> thanks.
> (*back to phone*)
> When he's available, you'll be the first to
> know.

DR ALICE *looks anxious.*

> DR ALICE: Did you hear what he ordered?

> HARVEY: Yeah. Well, maybe slavery's still
> legal in this country and you can order
> yourself a short black any time you feel
> like it.

> ROGER (*into phone*): No worries.

Pause.

> Listen – any time, mate. You know that.

ROGER *hangs up.*

> EARL CONNOR: I feel bad about this. The
> guy asked me a question. I answered.
> I mean – he kind of caught me – and I
> made a mistake and told the truth.

HARVEY *has been getting more & more impatient with the papers.*

> HARVEY: Right. It's the American way.
> Remember that first guy who didn't
> know how to tell a lie. What had he
> done Hon? Something along the lines of
> what Earl here is planning, wasn't it?

> DR ALICE: He'd cut down a cherry tree
> Harve. And he was the first president
> of the United States. As you very well
> know.

> HARVEY: Yeah. Sure. But what I *don't*
> know is how the Seattle Seahawks got
> on against the Broncos Monday night.
> What kind of sports do you have in this
> country anyway?

> ROGER: Don't ask me.

> MADELAINE: He's not the sporting type.

> DR ALICE: Eat your eggs Harve. You'll feel
> better.

> (*to* MADELAINE)
> Okay. So what's the game plan here? I'm
> sure you've got a few ideas bubbling.

MADELAINE *nods and is about to reply when a furry paw with an envelope in it thrusts itself across her face.*

The KANGAROO *has reached its destination.*

EXT.   MELBOURNE   DAY

LUISA *walking to work.*

INT.   TAXI   DAY

PARIS *driving.*

PARIS *sees* LUISA *walking along.*

As he passes her PARIS *slows, looks back and recognises her from the pub the night before.*

EXT.   STREET   DAY

LUISA *watches taxi slow.*

As she passes taxi PARIS *winds down passenger window.*

> PARIS: Want a lift? You work at Eros, don't you? I'm going that way.

> LUISA: No thanks. I'm in a hurry.

But LUISA *stops walking, nonetheless.*
PARIS *persists.*

> PARIS: We saw each other in the pub last night, remember? Your mate whistled at me.

LUISA *allows herself to smile.*

> LUISA: Yeah. How could I forget?

INT.   EROS/DINING ROOM   DAY

The KANGAROO *is singing a song all about Earl Connor's intentions.*

MADELAINE *et al watch with degrees of amusement, annoyance, etc.*

(Music: *La Dona e mobile* – Rigoletto)

> KANGAROO:
> Poor baby kangaroo
> What is he going to do
> To get away from you
> Oh poor little kangaroo . . .

> EARL CONNOR: Is this your famous
> Henry Lawson?

> DR ALICE: No Earl. It's a kangaroo.

This KANGAROO *has a good voice.*
The KANGAROO *takes a deep breath and finishes its song with bravura.*

> KANGAROO:
> You are so cruel
> And you are a fool
> 'Cos you won't do well
> And you'll go straight to hell!

This last line is directed straight at EARL *and leaves him feeling a bit stunned.*

The KANGAROO *bows and exits.*

> EARL CONNOR: Jesus!

MADELAINE *opens envelope.*

> ROGER: Good news I hope.

MADELAINE *reads, crumples paper.*

MADELAINE: No.

Off camera a faint hissing sound carries over to...

EXT.   EROS   SAME

Close on hand holding spray can completing last stroke of a letter T.

SECURITY GUARD (O/C): Hey you! Stop that! You bastard!

Spray can drops.

EXT.   EROS   DAY

Words writ large on some prominent part of the building – BEAUTY KILLED THE BEAST.

SECURITY GUARD *has come across whoever did it just as they were finishing and is now chasing* FLEEING FIGURE *away from scene of crime.*

EXT.   EROS   DAY

SECURITY GUARD *chases* FLEEING FIGURE *into laneway where a garbage truck is picking up an over-flowing dump master.*

SECURITY GUARD *loses* FLEEING FIGURE *who flits behind the garbage truck and disappears amongst the garbage.*

STEVE, *on his way to work, turns into laneway just as the* GRAFFITI ARTIST *erupts from the pile of black plastic garbage bags he's been hiding in and makes a break for it.*

STEVE *swerves to avoid* GRAFFITI ARTIST.

The small car driven by the KANGAROO *appears at top of laneway and slows to a near stop as* GRAFFITI ARTIST *jumps into it.*

Small car zooms off.

Small car zooms past taxi where LUISA *is getting out.*

LUISA *watches it go, catching glimpse of its* KANGAROO *driver.*

> LUISA: Hey! Did you see that?

PARIS *has been too busy watching her to notice anything else.*

> PARIS: No. What was it?

> LUISA (*laughing*): A kangaroo driving a car!

> PARIS: These crazy Australians eh? (*tapping his head in gesture which indicates madness*) You never know what they'll do next!

BOTH *laugh.*

> PARIS (*cont.*): See you later then?

> LUISA: Mmmm

PARIS *grins and drives off.*

LUISA *briefly watches him go then turns down laneway.*

LUISA *sees* STEVE *and realises he's been watching her.*

> LUISA: Hey Steve! Wait!

But STEVE *turns abruptly, walks to kitchen door, enters and shuts it smartly behind him.*

> LUISA (*to herself*): Okay, if that's how you want it to be ...

LUISA *turns toward staff entrance.*

INT.   EROS/DINING ROOM   DAY

> EARL CONNOR: I'll make a statement.
> Clear this whole thing up.
>
> MADELAINE: What kind of statement?
>
> EARL CONNOR: A factual statement.
> About the role of animal experimentation
> in medical history. I'll make people think
> about the real issues. After all, where
> would human-kind be without medical
> science? Living in caves. Dying of
> disease – polio, diphtheria, tetanus,
> smallpox – I mean, come on, we have
> to face it – the animal has played a
> valuable role in helping us out. We
> love them. We have their welfare at
> heart...
>
> HARVEY: Tell that to Pavlov's dog...
>
> EARL CONNOR: But facts are facts – and
> who runs this damn planet anyway?
> (*to* MADELAINE)
> What do you think?
>
> MADELAINE: I think you'd better leave it
> to me. And Alice, if you could I'd love
> you to do something today to take some
> of the attention off of Earl.

EARL *not entirely pleased to hear this.*

> MADELAINE (*cont.*): You're on radio this
> morning, right?
>
> DR ALICE: Two shows. Usual
> format – push the book, answer a few
> questions—

(*to* ROGER): They do know I need to see
all the questions ahead of time, don't
they?

ROGER *nods.*

MADELAINE: Well Alice I'm not pushing
you for any favours – I mean, it's up to
you of course, but I'd be awfully grateful
for a bit of a plug – the positive side of
Eros – you know the sort of thing.

DR ALICE *leans over and pats* MADELAINE's *hand reassuringly.*

EARL CONNOR: Well in that case there
doesn't seem much point in me being
here at all.

DR ALICE: Oh Earl – there's nothing
personal in this you know.

HARVEY: It's business. Know what I
mean?

INT.   ARGENZIO SUITE   DAY

LIZ *on the phone to her* CHILDREN.

LIZ: Did you darling? Was it good?

A longish pause.
LIZ *only half listens, doodles on pad beside the phone, then starts slightly
as* PHIL *comes in.*
PHIL *carries the base of a draftsman's table.*
LIZ *covers mouthpiece.*

LIZ (*to* PHIL): It's the boys—
I'm getting a frame by frame description
of a video they watched last night.

PHIL *takes no notice.*
He puts the base of the table down and goes out again.

> LIZ (*into phone*): That sounds really awful
> sweetheart. I'm glad you enjoyed it. Let
> me talk to Gianni.

Pause.

> Oh, has he?

Pause.

> Yes, I forgot. He has cricket practice this
> morning.

PHIL *comes back with work top.*
PHIL *assembles this worktable during the following.*

> LIZ (*cont.*): No darling, I don't necessarily
> think cricket's only for the brain dead.
> Do you want to speak to Daddy?

Pause.

> Oh did he?

Pause.

> I see. (*frowning slightly at* PHIL)
> Well that's exciting.

Pause.

> Well... we'll see.

Pause.

> Hmmm.

Pause.

> Yes. Talk to you tomorrow. And tell
> Gianni I called, will you? And be good
> for Renata won't you?

Pause.

> (*laughing*) Okay darling. Bye.

Pause.

> Bye.

Pause.

> (*laughing*) Bye bye. Now hang up the phone.

LIZ *listens a moment before hanging up.*

> LIZ (*to* PHIL): Well, he's pleased with
> himself today. Nice to know the kids can
> survive without me. It's mean I know
> but it pleases me to think that someone
> else had to drag themselves out of bed
> to drive John to cricket practice.

PHIL *fusses with the slope of his drawing board.*

> PHIL: Gianni. His name's Gianni.

> LIZ: I know Phil. It's just that his friends
> call him John – and I forget sometimes,
> that's all.

> PHIL: You're his mother. You shouldn't
> forget.

> LIZ: Oh come on Phil! He calls himself
> John half the time. What's it matter?

323

PHIL: It matters, Liz! To *me* it matters.

LIZ: I know you've already phoned the kids this morning...

PHIL: I was worried about them.

LIZ: Gianni said you've told them about Japan. They're really excited—

PHIL: So they should be.

LIZ: I think we should have discussed it before saying anything to them. Nothing's decided yet.

Satisfied with the angle, PHIL *busily tightens a few screws.*

LIZ (*cont.*): Phil?

PHIL *deliberately finishes what he's doing.*

Then he looks at his wife.

PHIL: You made me look like an idiot last night.

LIZ: I didn't mean to. And you're changing the subject Phil.

PHIL *brushes this aside.*

PHIL: You didn't mean to? Well what did you think? Getting up and walking out like that.

LIZ: I didn't really think about it. I just wanted to get out of there.

PHIL: You didn't think. Exactly! How do you think it made me look?

LIZ: I was the one who left Phil, not you.

PHIL: You're my wife. What you do
reflects on me. And Madelaine? How do
you think Madelaine felt?

LIZ: I don't think Madelaine felt much
one way or the other. You've done a
great job for her, love. And I don't think
she'd care less if you swung from her
chandelier in your underpants. I don't
think wives rate much in Madelaine's
scheme of things. I doubt she gives what
I do or don't do a second's thought...

PHIL: People notice. People talk.

LIZ: You care more about what other
people do and say than you do about
me.

PHIL: Rubbish.

LIZ: You haven't even asked me where I
went. You never think of anyone but
yourself, do you?

PHIL: Oh for God's sake, Liz... I spend
my whole time thinking about you and
the kids. Why do you think I work so
bloody hard?

LIZ: You work hard because you love
what you do. And you've got a lot to
prove – you drag that Italian immigrant
thing round with you like a bloody
cross. And you have a lot of talent...

PHIL: Thanks very much.

> LIZ: ...so don't play the martyr and say you do it all for me and the kids. You'd do exactly the same thing whether we existed or not.

> PHIL: Is that a threat?

LIZ gets out of bed.

Wraps towelling robe round her.

Goes towards bathroom.

> LIZ: No love. It's a fact.

PHIL takes a second to digest this.
He's really disconcerted.

> PHIL: Where did you get to last night, anyway?

But the bathroom door shuts smartly on his question.

INT.   WOMEN'S LOCKER ROOM   DAY

LUISA hastily changing.

There is a poster on the wall announcing an EMPLOYEE OF THE MONTH award scheme – the ultimate prize being a trip to Hawaii awarded once a year.

There is also a new condom machine fixed to the wall.

The TELL HIM IF IT'S NOT ON IT'S NOT ON poster has been written on in various interesting ways.

The VIETNAMESE WOMAN with the locker next to LUISA's comes in.

> LUISA: Oh good. I'm not the only hopeless case.

The VIETNAMESE WOMAN *is distracted with her own thoughts and her hurry to change.*

> VIETNAMESE WOMAN: Sorry? I don't...
> (understand).

> LUISA: You're one of my mob. You're late.

VIETNAMESE WOMAN *immediately looks guilty.*

> VIETNAMESE WOMAN: Oh yes. Late. It's
> true. But it's my youngest. She has...
> dreams. Very very bad.

LUISA *is embarrassed.*

> LUISA: Hey. It's okay. I'm sorry... I didn't
> mean... you don't have to explain
> yourself to me.

> VIETNAMESE WOMAN: All night I sit. Then
> she sleeps. And I don't like... It's hard to
> wake her up to take her to day care
> when she sleeps so... so... peaceful.

VIETNAMESE WOMAN *gets locker open.*

There's a family photo taped inside the door, above the pic of Patrick Swazey.

In the photo the WOMAN *sits in a run-down suburban back yard.*
A LITTLE GIRL *plays on the dusty grass beside her.*
*TWO BIGGER BOYS & TWO BIGGER GIRLS *stand behind smiling bravely at the camera.*

LUISA *looks.*
The VIETNAMESE WOMAN *smiles.*
Touching each CHILD *in turn, the* VIETNAMESE WOMAN *names them.*

VIETNAMESE WOMAN: Kim, Lan, Giang, Hung and Ngyen.

LUISA: They're lovely.

VIETNAMESE WOMAN *smiles.*

LUISA: What's *your* name?

VIETNAMESE WOMAN: Phuong.

LUISA (*clumsy*): Phuong.

PHUONG *laughs.*
LUISA *grins and looks at her watch.*

LUISA (*cont.*): Phuong – I gotta go...

LUISA *turns in doorway.*

LUISA (*cont.*): See ya!

PHUONG: See ya!

INT.   IRINI'S OFFICE   DAY

ROOM ATTENDANTS *assembled.*

IRINI *addresses the troops.*

IRINI: Sequence of performance is important to avoid unproductive periods – waiting for a floor to dry, for example. So it's best to be systematic, working clockwise or anticlockwise round the room. Right. Now yesterday I gave you a check list of points that should be noted as you clean. Now I want you to give them back to me. Starting with you.

IRINI *looks at the* YOUNG MAN *nearest her.*

> YOUNG MAN: Check the lights – are all the
> bulbs working?

IRINI *nods and indicates next* ROOM ATTENDANT *should speak.*
With varying degrees of hesitation the following points are repeated:

> NEXT: Wardrobe ... is it clean and
> empty?

> NEXT: Dressing table ... is it polished,
> drawers empty, mirror cleaned,
> stationery in place?

> NEXT: Are the curtains easily drawn?
> TV, radio, telephone etc. all working?

LUISA *enters.*

CHRIS *turns and smiles.*

LUISA *looks away and takes a place at back of room.*

CHRIS *puzzled.*

CHRIS *turns attention from* LUISA *just in time for her turn.*

> CHRIS: The carpet ... is it vacuumed and
> does the pile run all the same way?

Silence.

It's LUISA's *turn.*

IRINI *looks at her quizzically.*

> LUISA: Uh ... bathroom. Check that the
> bath, shower, wash-basin, toilet, bidet
> and floor are all clean, that the towels

are fresh and the complimentary Eros products are all in place. And for every hair you miss when you clean the bath you lose a finger. Lose one whole hand and you're out on the street.

Some nervous laughter from STAFF.
IRINI *is amused.*

IRINI: Thank you, Luisa. I'm glad you take your work so seriously. Keep this up and you'll be on the plane to Hawaii in no time.

LUISA's *response.*

IRINI (*cont.*): Now you've all got your assigned rooms. Christina and Luisa will concentrate on the VIP suites. The rest of you will be concentrating on making sure all the rooms are ready for our first guests tomorrow ... and I do mean ready. No builder's rubbish left lying about. No dust, stray wires, flecks of paint. Double check everything to make sure it all works and do try and keep out of the way of the people getting ready for the opening. It's chaos here today.

IRINI *smiles at them encouragingly.*

IRINI (*cont.*): That's all ladies and gentlemen. You will now proceed to the housekeeping stations on each floor to pick up your equipment. But I'd just like to say that you've all done very well. And I'd also like to remind you that your in-house training will continue as and when appropriate. And one last thing – some of you may have already

> heard or noticed that we are having a bit
> of trouble over some comments made
> yesterday by one of our guests.

STAFF *response shows she is right.*

> IRINI (*cont.*): The management would
> greatly appreciate it if you say nothing
> of this if questioned by any of the media.

LUISA *looks quite excited at this possibility.*

EXT.   EROS   DAY

TWO PEOPLE *dressed in* KANGAROO SUITS *approach front of* EROS.

EACH *holds a bundle of leaflets.*

The TWO KANGAROOS *station themselves so that anyone coming in or out of* EROS *has to pass by them but not so close that the frustrated* SECURITY GUARD *seen glaring at them through the glass can make them go away.*

INT.   MADELAINE'S SUITE/OFFICE   DAY

Office buzzing.

OFFICE STAFF *flat out.*

> MADELAINE: Any important cancellations
> come in?

> ROGER: No-one who counts. A few
> people on the B list aren't coming, but
> the A list's holding steady. I imagine
> people on the A list wouldn't worry too
> much about a few dead animals. They're
> much too anxious to be seen in the right
> places. And Eros is the right place right
> now.

MADELAINE: Well let's hope they don't all suddenly develop social consciences.

ROGER *grabs a sheet of paper from the fax and gives yelp of delight.*

ROGER: That's it! They've confirmed! Nippon Australia's bought our entire Executive Stress Management Package. Plus I've had some very healthy nibbles on that 'Improve your looks improve your sales' thing. Though you might have to talk it up to some of the head honchos. Wheel them in next week, maybe? Throw in a free liposuction or something?

MADELAINE *turns with an uncharacteristically frosty look.*

MADELAINE: Days that begin with singing kangaroos don't need any more silly jokes in them. Do you know what I mean?

ROGER: I do. Sorry.

MADELAINE: Just so long as we understand each other.

ROGER *nods.*

MADELAINE (*cont.*): Good boy. And now – because I'm sure things aren't going to get any better and because I want to be around when they get worse, I'm taking my twenty minute holiday early today.

INT.   EROS/LOBBY   DAY

MADELAINE *crossing lobby.*

Sees Liz.

> MADELAINE: Liz! I've been wondering about you! What are you up to? Where's Phil?

> LIZ: Don't know. I've been looking everywhere. I seem to have lost him.

In foreground a paint-stained hand slides slowly round the thigh of one of the plastic marble statues in the lobby.

The GRAFITTI ARTIST *has made his way back in.*

The GRAFITTI ARTIST *waits until* MADELAINE *and* LIZ *have gone and when he thinks the coast is clear he heads for the lift.*

The SECURITY GUARD *spots him.*

Grabs him.

The SECURITY GUARD *slams* GRAFITTI ARTIST *against the wall and frisks him quite brutally.*

The SECURITY GUARD *finds one of the cards needed to operate the lifts.*

The SECURITY GUARD *twists one of the* GRAFITTI ARTIST'*s arms behind his back and frog-marches him smartly towards the door.*

DOOR BOY *opens door with flourish.*

SECURITY GUARD *boots* GRAFITTI ARTIST *out.*

EXT.   EROS   DAY

GRAFITTI ARTIST *lands with a thump.*

The TWO KANGAROOS *help him to his feet.*

ONE KANGAROO *shakes fist at* SECURITY GUARD *inside.*

SECURITY GUARD *gives* KANGAROO *the finger.*

INT.   EROS/POOL   DAY

A glimpse of TONY *standing naked on the pool's edge before he makes a perfect dive.*

INT.   POOL SECURITY AREA   SAME

MADELAINE *watches the above display repeated on all the monitors.*

MADELAINE *turns wistfully to* LIZ.

> MADELAINE: Gorgeous isn't he? The ultimate decorative object. I could watch him all day. But when he opens his mouth...

MADELAINE *fakes a yawn.*

> MADELAINE (*cont.*): Sometimes I wonder why the Goddess bothered to give any of them the power of speech.

LIZ *laughs.*

> LIZ: Oh come on! They're not all *that* bad.

> MADELAINE: I know, I know! Just joking!

LIZ *watches* TONY *as he climbs out of the pool – close on his muscular back and tight buttocks.*

> MADELAINE (*cont.*): Well – half joking, anyway.

INT.   EROS/KITCHEN   DAY

Busy kitchen.

Dialogue comes in immediately.

> 1st KITCHEN HAND: I don't even know
> where the G-Spot's supposed to be.
> Is it on the outside or the inside?

Food either awaiting preparation or being prepared makes this place richer and more colourful than before.

In foreground TWO KITCHEN HANDS *(one of whom has just spoken) are making stock.*

STEVE *talks to* CHINESE KITCHEN HAND *in background.*

> 2nd KITCHEN HAND: The outside.

A THIRD KITCHEN HAND *joins in.*

> 3rd KITCHEN HAND: No stupid! It's on
> the inside. And it works great. I know
> because someone showed me.

STEVE *leaves the* CHINESE KITCHEN HAND *with what looks like encouraging words and walks towards the* KITCHEN HANDS *making stock.*

Close on STEVE *tasting the stock.*

> STEVE: The G-Spot doesn't exist. I've
> tried to find it and it just doesn't exist.
> Like the flavour in this stock. That
> doesn't exist either.

> 3rd KITCHEN HAND: Oh yeah? You've
> been going with Luisa ever since it was
> discovered. Maybe hers just doesn't
> work.

> STEVE: If they existed and if they worked
> hers would work just fine.

INT.   EROS/RECEPTION AREA   DAY

The 4 RECEPTIONISTS *lined up in an apprehensive row.*

SECURITY GUARD *walks in front of them.*

SECURITY GUARD *stops at end of row and takes out the card that operates
the lift. He holds it up.*

> SECURITY GUARD: One rotten apple.

The YOUNGEST RECEPTIONIST *looks uneasy.*
The SECURITY GUARD*'s tone is conversational, casual.*

> SECURITY GUARD: That's all it takes. It's
> surprising, really. Just one. To spoil it for
> everyone else.

The YOUNGEST RECEPTIONIST *looks more uneasy.*
The SECURITY GUARD *knows this.*

> SECURITY GUARD (*cont.*): Someone who wants
> Eros to go under. Someone who wants to
> make sure everyone here loses their jobs.

YOUNGEST RECEPTIONIST *bursts into tears.*

> YOUNGEST RECEPTIONIST: That's not true!
> I didn't want any of you to lose your
> jobs! I didn't think it would cause so
> much trouble.

The OTHER RECEPTIONISTS *gather round to comfort her.*

> SECURITY GUARD: If I were you I'd tell me
> all about it, girlie. You'll feel much better
> afterwards. I can promise you that.

> A RECEPTIONIST: Oh, piss off! Don't you
> tell him anything.

The RECEPTIONISTS *surround the* YOUNGEST ONE *protectively.*

> YOUNGEST RECEPTIONIST (*to them*): My Mum
> made me do it. That man's her new
> boyfriend. She's a friend of the earth.

INT.   STAFF TOILET   DAY

LUISA *stands at row of handbasins examining her pimple.*

All the cubicle doors stand open except one.

LUISA *fishes out tube of Erase and applies it, though she's not happy
with the result.*

Sound of toilet flushing.

In the mirror LUISA *sees* CHRIS *come out of cubicle.*

LUISA *would like to run but can't.*

> CHRIS: There you are!

CHRIS *gives* LUISA *a kiss.*

> CHRIS (*cont.*): Happy birthday! Did you
> get my present?
>
> LUISA: Yeah. Thanks.
>
> CHRIS: Well? Did ya like it?
>
> LUISA: Yeah. Thanks.
>
> CHRIS: You didn't like it, did you?
>
> LUISA: I did, really.
>
> CHRIS: It's no problem. You can take it
> back and change it.

LUISA: I told you ... it's great.

CHRIS: What's wrong then?

LUISA: Jeez Chris, what do you reckon ...
that girl ... last night ...

CHRIS: Sorry Luisa. We wanted to talk to
you about it this morning, but ...

LUISA: *We* wanted to talk ...! What would
I want to talk to her for? It's *you* I'd want
to talk to. I mean I feel like a complete
idiot – you're my best friend and you
didn't even tell me.

CHRIS: I wanted to tell you but I had to
be sure about it.

LUISA: And now you are?

CHRIS: Yes.

LUISA: That was quick—
Just one night!

CHRIS: It was more than just one night
Luisa. I've ...

The YOUNGEST RECEPTIONIST *comes in.*

LUISA: Sssh. Shut up.

The YOUNGEST RECEPTIONIST *has obviously been crying.*

CHRIS *notices.*

LUISA *does not.*

CHRIS: Are you all right?

The YOUNGEST RECEPTIONIST *looks startled.*
Nods.
Goes into cubicle.
Door closes.

> LUISA: Jesus! Think she noticed
> anything?

From cubicle comes sound of paper tearing and a nose being blown loudly.

> CHRIS: God Luisa. You can be a self-
> centred pain in the bum sometimes.

> LUISA: Thanks very much.

> CHRIS: One of the reasons I didn't tell
> you is that I knew you'd feel like this.
> I'm sorry you're upset Luisa. But I'm not
> sorry about what's happened. I'm glad.

> LUISA (*whispering*): Not now.
> (*indicating closed cubicle door*)
> You think I want the whole world to
> know my best friend's a dyke?

LUISA *goes out.*
Door slams behind her.
Door opens again immediately.
LUISA *looks round door.*

> LUISA: Were you like that at school?

Toilet flushes.

> CHRIS: I think so.

> LUISA: All the time... at school... when
> we... all that stuff with boys and...
> were you?

339

CHRIS: S'pose so.

RECEPTIONIST *emerges.*

LUISA *hastily closes door on herself.*

CHRIS: Feel better?

YOUNGEST RECEPTIONIST *looks at* CHRIS.

YOUNGEST RECEPTIONIST *starts to cry again.*

CHRIS: If you cannot smile, be courteous,
be polite, be well groomed, be co-
operative, be friendly, be of service all
the time, this is not your industry—
Sounds like hell, doesn't it?

INT.   STEAM ROOM   DAY

MADELAINE *and* LIZ *lying on tiled ledges.*

They lie on their stomachs face to face, their heads close.

Their faces are hot and sweaty – a great sense of privacy and intimacy.

This is a conversation full of hesitancy and exploration of feelings.

It takes its time.

*Steam all round as they talk, obscuring body movements – bodies hidden
and fleetingly revealed – tendrils of hair, beads of sweat.*

MADELAINE: So where *did* you go last
night (*prompting*) Liz?

LIZ: I went out and got picked up.

MADELAINE (*intrigued*): Really?

LIZ: Yes.

MADELAINE: Do you do that sort of thing often?

LIZ: Never. It was the first time.

Some silence.
MADELAINE *laughs.*

MADELAINE: Was it good?

LIZ: It could have been if I hadn't been so scared by what I was doing. And I hardly know what to think about it now... in fact I've been avoiding thinking about it all day.

MADELAINE: You and Phil have been apart for weeks... why didn't you do it while he was here in Melbourne. Then he wouldn't have had to know.

LIZ: I hadn't thought of it then. I hadn't even thought about it when I walked out last night. It just happened.

MADELAINE: It wouldn't just happen for no reason.

LIZ: I know that. I just don't want to think about what the reasons are.

MADELAINE: But you do know what they are, don't you?

LIZ: Yes I do. I'm stuck at home with three kids and Phil's out in the world designing fabulous buildings for people like you who think he's wonderful...

and I know that having it off with a
Greek taxi driver wouldn't have solved
anything.

MADELAINE: I don't think Phil's
wonderful – I think he's a good
architect – but I wouldn't want to
be married to him.

Pause.

MADELAINE (*cont.*): Anyway I was married
to someone like him once...
but I outgrew him... just like you're
probably outgrowing Phil.

LIZ: You've got it all the wrong way
round. He's outgrown me, if anything.
I mean – his career's taken off – people
respect him – and I feel like I've done
nothing with my life.

MADELAINE: You're not giving yourself
enough credit. You're much more real
than he is. Okay – he's an architect – but
who is he?

LIZ: I don't know. Whenever I try to talk
to him about anything that matters to
me he has no idea what I'm talking
about – it always ends up being about
him. He thinks it's enough to tell me
how much he loves me and the kids but
I don't think he has any real understanding
of any of us, including himself. I did
know Phil once... when we were young
it was terrific... but somewhere along
the way he changed... or we both
changed... but I've lost track of him...
and worse still... I've lost interest.

MADELAINE: Will you leave him? I think he's very frightened of that happening. He's hated being here without you.

LIZ: I know he has. And I do know he's frightened. But it's been really good for me with him away. When he was around there were some mornings I'd wake up and feel like I was dying. And I don't want to feel like that any more. He's not a child and I can't go on holding his hand forever.

LIZ *almost in tears.*

MADELAINE *comforts her.*

EXT.   CORRIDOR OUTSIDE VIP SUITES   DAY

LUISA *up ahead.*

CHRIS *hurries after.*

CHRIS: Wait, Luisa.

LUISA *waits.*

CHRIS (*cont.*): This is dumb. We've got to work together, at least. Let's just get through the day huh?

LUISA: I just think it'd be better if we worked separately today, that's all.

CHRIS (*getting fed up*): Okay. Whatever. We'll divide up the rooms.

INT.   SAME CORRIDOR   DAY

Two cleaning trolleys emerge side by side from housekeeping room one pushed by LUISA *and the other pushed by* CHRIS.

343

Without looking at each other LUISA *and* CHRIS *stalk off in opposite directions.*

It looks funny but it is sad at the same time.

INT.   EROS/KITCHEN   DAY

STEVE *is looking at the engagement ring he tried to give* LUISA *the night before.*

TONY's *voice breaks in on his reverie.*

> TONY (*high pitched voice*): Oh Stevie!
> I thought you'd never ask!

STEVE *looks shattered.*

TONY *adopts a softer tone.*

> TONY (*cont.*): Sorry mate. Tell you what.
> Take a break. Let's sit down. Tell me all
> about it.

> STEVE: Nothing to talk about.

> TONY: Well in that case you can just
> make me a cup of coffee.

TONY *sits down.*

Clearly he will not be moved.

STEVE *smiles.*

INT.   ARGENZIO'S SUITE   DAY

LUISA *letting herself in.*

Once in, LUISA *has a bit of a sticky-beak around the place.*

LUISA *looks briefly at a family photograph.*

LUISA *checks temperature and her blood pressure on the Timex portable healthcheck unit which is standard equipment in* EROS *suites.*

Then LUISA *sees the dress* LIZ *wore the night before.*

LUISA *takes this dress, feels its fabric, holds it against herself, closes her eyes and—*

LIZ *comes in.*

LUISA *sees her in the mirror.*

> LIZ: Lovely isn't it – that dress.

LUISA *quickly puts it back where it came from.*

> LIZ (*cont.*): Look I'm sorry about yesterday. It was embarrassing for both of us.

> LUISA: Well we didn't expect anyone to come in.

> LIZ (*laughing*): No. well I think I knew that!

LUISA *relaxes a bit.*

Almost smiles.

LUISA*'s starting to revise her opinion of* LIZ.

> LIZ: I felt quite jealous.

> LUISA: Really!?

> LIZ: It looked so romantic.

LUISA *at a loss as to what to think of this.*

> LUISA: Aah... well I'll just... I think...
> I think I'll just go and do the bathroom.

INT.　　　　　EROS/KITCHEN　　　　　　　　DAY

STEVE *and* TONY *drinking coffee and eating croissants while the kitchen toils around them.*

TONY *eats enthusiastically.*

> TONY: Luisa didn't know when she was
> well off. They're all the same. Don't let
> it get to you mate. There's plenty more
> where that came from – plenty more
> fish in the sea like they say. Make these
> croissants, did you?

STEVE *nods.*

> TONY (*cont.*): Tell you what mate – if I
> didn't know better... well what I mean
> to say is if I'd known at school you were
> going to turn out to be a cook I'd've had
> you picked for a pooftah, that's for sure.
> And that bloody Ron! Bloody great chain
> of hairdressing salons and I'll tell you
> what, there's nothing wrong with him.
> All ready for the big night?

> STEVE: Still got my centrepiece to do. No
> good doing it too early. The timing's got
> to be just right with those things.

> TONY: Not to worry. You'll be right.
> Gotta go. Meeting my mate Paris for
> a workout. You know Paris?

> STEVE: No.

TONY: Drives a cab – and I'll tell you
what – the stories that bloke can tell
about what he gets offered instead of
Cabcharge – reckon you're lucky to be
shot of Luisa when you think how much
of it there is walking round out there.

STEVE: You might be right.

INT.   ARGENZIO SUITE   DAY

LIZ *pouring orange juice over ice.*

LIZ: Sure you won't?

LUISA: Well I...

LIZ *hands it to her.*

LUISA (*cont.*): Steve's all right. But he's
not romantic, like you think... except
about food maybe. But otherwise he just
wants to get married, buy a house, have
kids...

LUISA *remembers the family photo.*

LUISA (*cont.*): ... not that there's anything
wrong with that.

LIZ: Except that there must be more.

LUISA *bit surprised to hear that.*

LUISA: I think so... but *you've* got more.
Well – he's got more. He has. Your old
man. He's got all this. And a lot of other
buildings round the place. And heaps of
people telling him he's great all the time.
Hasn't he?

LIZ: Oh yes. He's got more. But I
haven't.

LUISA: Yeah. But still... it must be...
I bet you get to travel a lot. At least
it's not boring. You must meet a lot
of famous people. Like Dr Alice.

LIZ: I think I'm invisible to most people.
Wives mostly are.

LUISA: Why d'you do it then?

LIZ: Because Phil wants me to. He needs
me with him. And because, whenever
I think about it, I can't decide exactly
what I do want to do. And whatever it
was, Phil wouldn't think it important
anyway.

LUISA: My dad was like that... he didn't
design buildings or anything but
everything he did do he expected my
mum to back him up and tell him he
was wonderful all the time and nothing
she did was as important as anything he
did. Or if things stuffed up at work or
something he'd come home and take it
out on her. I mean I know it's not the
same because your husband's famous
and you've got money and a nice house
and everything but the *idea's* the same,
isn't it?

LIZ: I suppose it is, yes.

LUISA: I get really scared sometimes I'll
end up like my mum – that if I don't get
a proper sort of job soon – like a career or
something to get some decent money so

> I can do what I like instead of what some
> guy wants.

INT.   EROS/KITCHEN   DAY

STEVE *stands contemplating a good-sized block of ice.*

HE *looks at it from all angles.*

DR ALICE's *voice is issuing from the radio throughout the above and
through to end of scene.*

The RADIO INTERVIEWER *is a woman.*

> DR ALICE: I like to start out this way – I
> like to say something like: 'I'm sure that
> the walls of this radio station, TV studio
> – whatever it is – have never heard words
> like ejaculation, lubrication, penis, vagina,
> orgasm, masturbation.' That way, if the
> audience is on edge waiting for some
> explicit language, they can relax.

> RADIO INTERVIEWER: Okay everyone –
> relax. Dr Alice – do you ever get bored
> with sex?

> DR ALICE: Yes and no. If the questions
> were all about sex, then I'd be bored. But
> the questions are really about
> relationships.

STEVE *opens drawer and chooses one of a number of ice-chisels.*

STEVE *approaches his ice block.*

It is a crucial moment – STEVE *lines up his chisel and makes the first
tentative chip.*

HE's *pleased with it.*

INT. IRINI'S OFFICE DAY

DR ALICE*'s radio show continues over and carries on throughout.*

> INTERVIEWER: That goes against the image
> most people have of you.

> DR ALICE: Images! The whole sad world's
> so hung up on images.

MADELAINE *is in Irini's office.*

IRINI *isn't.*

MADELAINE *is looking at the* ROOM ATTENDANT *pictures pinned to the wall.*

> INTERVIEWER: That's interesting. I'm sure
> you're aware that a place like the Eros
> Complex exploits our insecurity, our
> need to present a desirable image to the
> world, our desperate fear of aging.

MADELAINE *unpins* LUISA*'s picture, puts it on the desk.*

MADELAINE*'s getting more and more nervous at what she's hearing.*

MADELAINE *sees pack of cigarettes and matches on* IRINI*'s desk.*

MADELAINE*'s hand sneaks towards them.*

MADELAINE *brings it under control with difficulty.*

> DR ALICE: I'll give you my personal
> answer to that. People don't like the
> way I look – too bad. And as for all these
> wrinkles . . . I earned each and every one
> of them. I wear my wrinkles with pride.
> But maybe someone else doesn't feel
> the same about their wrinkles – then let
> them get rid of them – it's a free country,

thank God. Where's the exploitation?
The Eros Complex serves a need. It
didn't create that need.

INTERVIEWER: So despite some bad press
you stand behind the Eros project, do you?

DR ALICE: Stand behind it? I'm staying
there. And I've stayed a lot of places
round the world and I know when a
place has class and when it hasn't – and
Eros is as good as anywhere in the world
and better than most.

MADELAINE (*relieved and subdued*): Thank
you.

IRINI *sweeps in.*

Spots photograph.

IRINI: I knew it!

MADELAINE *is instantly restored to normal.*

MADELAINE: Can't be helped. I'm short
a receptionist.

INT.   ROSEN SUITE   DAY

CHRIS *is listening to the interview while she cleans the Rosen's bathroom.*

Things are revealed in bathrooms and this one is no exception.

CHRIS *has never seen so many indigestion remedies in her life.*

INTERVIEWER: And now we'll take our
first question. We have our first caller
and it's Margaret from Kew. Go ahead
please Margaret.

MARGARET: Yes. I'm here. Good morning Dr Alice.

DR ALICE: Good morning Margaret. What's your question?

MARGARET: It's difficult.

DR ALICE: I know it can be, Margaret. But you just go ahead anyhow. Just talk to me.

MARGARET: It's my husband. Last night I saw him masturbating in front of the television.

DR ALICE: Margaret – let me ask you this – what programme was he watching while he was doing this?

MARGARET: One of those nature programmes on the ABC.

DR ALICE: About what?

MARGARET: It was about rhinos.

DR ALICE: Did he know you saw him?

MARGARET: No.

DR ALICE: Don't tell him. For all you know he was thinking of you.

CHRIS *finds this amusing.*

A knock on the door of the suite.

CHRIS *turns radio off.*

LUISA (V/O): Chris? It's me. You there?

CHRIS *opens door.*

LUISA: Guess what? She wants to see me.
Madelaine. Upstairs. What've I done?
D'you reckon it's because I was late
again? But why should she notice me
being late? You'd think she'd have
better things to worry about. I don't get it.

CHRIS: Well perhaps if you just go and
find out ... and get hysterical afterwards.

LUISA *laughs.*

Starts to go.

Stops.

LUISA: Do I look all right?

CHRIS: You look fine. Go on, get out of
here – go!

LUISA *starts to go.*

LUISA *stops.*

LUISA: Catch you later? When I've got
the sack.

CHRIS: Well if that's the case we'll have
time for a drink. It'd be good if Steve
could come.

LUISA: I'm not seeing him anymore.

CHRIS: How come? What's up? Why
didn't you tell me?

353

> LUISA: Because I wasn't bloody talking to you, that's why.

And LUISA*'s gone.*

INT.   MADELAINE'S OFFICE/SUITE   DAY

MADELAINE*'s on the phone.*

ROGER *and* OFFICE STAFF *are working – phones ringing etc.*

> MADELAINE: Okay. That's on green.

Pause.

LUISA *enters frame.*

MADELAINE *sees* LUISA *and watches her as she continues to talk on the phone.*

LUISA *goes first to an* OFFICE GIRL *who points in* ROGER*'s direction.*

ROGER *has* LUISA *sit down and wait.*

> MADELAINE: Day-glo orange would certainly stand out better, but what we're aiming for here is a soothing effect – not to mention a degree of environmental awareness.

Pause.

MADELAINE*'s low chuckle.*

> MADELAINE (*cont.*): It's never too late, darling. And the copy reads – 'free of animal products, tested only on humans.' And put lots of glue on the back. I want this message to stick.

INT.   OFFICE   DAY

A full page glossy advertisement for EROS *flicks into view as* LUISA *turns the page.*

LUISA *looks up from the magazine she's flipping through.*

Beyond the page MADELAINE *is bearing down on* LUISA.

LUISA *tries to get up but the chair seems to hold her.*

> MADELAINE: Luisa! I've had my eye on you! Come with me. I'm going to throw you in at the deep end...

INT.   EROS   DAY

ROGER *takes* LUISA *into a room where the staff uniforms are stored.*

Life-like models wearing all the different EROS *uniforms stand around the room.*

LUISA *looks at the skinny dummies and* ROGER *looks at* LUISA.

> ROGER: ... not quite the perfect size ten I think... try this.

ROGER *plucks a receptionist's uniform from rack and hands it to* LUISA.

LUISA *takes it.*

> LUISA: Now?

> ROGER: When would you prefer?

LUISA*'s getting scared she'll blow this opportunity.*

> LUISA: Oh, *now.* Now's fine. Only...

> ROGER: Go ahead. I won't look.

While LUISA *changes* ROGER *looks through artists' impressions of uniforms, all for* EROS, *all different.*

> ROGER: We went through hell over these uniforms. Took ages to find a designer who could come up with the image Madelaine wanted. I hope I've finally got it right. What do you think?

LUISA *has changed and stands in front of mirror.*

> LUISA: It's great.

> ROGER: Over there.

LUISA *goes to chair* ROGER's *pointing at.*

ROGER *takes out a beauty case full of* EROS *products.*

> ROGER (*cont.*): Hair. Then make-up. But first something you want. Tell me what you most dislike about your face.

> LUISA: I...

LUISA *looks at* ROGER *and decides she can trust him.*

> LUISA: This hair. Here on my top lip.

> ROGER: Right.

> LUISA: It won't hurt, will it?

> ROGER: Sweetheart you won't feel anything but better!

INT.   EROS/KITCHEN   DAY

STEVE *working on his ice sculpture.*

A shape is slowly emerging.

STEVE *is very delicate in his movements as he chips off each gleaming piece.*

INT. EROS/LOBBY DAY

LIZ *approaches reception desk.*

> LIZ: Do you know where Phil Argenzio is?

> RECEPTIONIST: Yes Mrs Argenzio. He's on the roof.

EXT. EROS/ROOF SAME

PHIL *is giving an interview.*

He talks into tape recorder.

The INTERVIEWER *is a young woman.*

There's a PHOTOGRAPHER *too, taking pictures.*

> PHIL: I'm not interested in recycling the past.

LIZ *has entered frame.*

She stops and watches.

Only PHIL *is aware of her presence.*

He looks at her and doesn't take his eyes away.

PHIL*'s words may well be aimed at her.*

> PHIL (*cont.*): Which is not to say I see no logic in preserving old buildings of historical significance – but I see no logic

in repairing or reconstructing the facades
of things when they no longer have any
context.
(*to* INTERVIEWER/RECORDIST):   Excuse me.

PHIL *walks over to* LIZ.

PHIL: I won't be long. Will you wait?

LIZ *nods.*

PHIL (*cont.*):   Good.

LIZ *watches him return to the interview.*

There are tears in her eyes.

INT.   MADELAINE'S OFFICE/SUITE   DAY

Office activity in background.

LUISA *wears receptionist's uniform.*
Her hair, her make-up all perfect.
LUISA *has the* EROS *gloss.*

MADELAINE: You've missed the training
sessions but I'm sure you can cope.

LUISA *can't stop looking around.*

LUISA *sees intriguing glimpses of Madelaine's private living area.*

MADELAINE *slightly amused.*

MADELAINE: Some people think it odd
I live up here in the best part of Eros.

LUISA: I'd live up here. I mean – if I built
something I'd think I might as well
enjoy it.

MADELAINE: Exactly! Luisa – how good
are you at solving problems?

LUISA: Well I . . . I'm all right, I suppose.
I haven't had to do anything like that
since I left school. Do I have to pass a
test?

MADELAINE: Not really. But I'd like your
advice.

LUISA *can't imagine what advice* MADELAINE *could possibly need from
her.*

INT./EXT.   WINDOW   DAY

MADELAINE *and* LUISA *stand looking down at the increasing activity
in front of* EROS.

A van covered with Animal Liberation slogans has set up outside.

EVERYONE *coming into or passing by* EROS *now has to run a minor
picket line of* TWO PEOPLE *plus the* TWO *in* KANGAROO SUITS.

*As well as handing out leaflets they are now asking for signatures on
what looks like a lengthy petition.*

MADELAINE *and* LUISA *watch as some large and possibly decadent but
definitely frivolous items being delivered for the party tries to negotiate
its way past them.*

MADELAINE: They're not going to let me
off easily, are they? What can I do?

LUISA *looks at her.*

MADELAINE: What would you do?

LUISA *tests a few ideas in her mind.
Finally, tentatively . . .*

LUISA: Feed them?

MADELAINE: Feed them?

MADELAINE *and* LUISA *look at each other.*

MADELAINE *smiles slightly as the idea grows on her.*

MADELAINE (*cont.*): Feed them. Yes.
I'll bear it in mind.

LUISA: Did I pass the test?

MADELAINE *smiles.*

EXT.   EROS/ROOF   DAY

INTERVIEWER *and* PHOTOGRAPHER *packing up equipment.*

PHIL *shakes hands with* INTERVIEWER, *nods his thanks to* PHOTO-
GRAPHER *and strides over to* LIZ.

PHIL (*referring to* INTERVIEWER *and*
PHOTOGRAPHER): *Architectural Digest.* Went
well I think.

LIZ: I'm glad. I've been looking for you
all day.

PHIL (*playing a game*): But I've been
around! You couldn't have looked very
hard. Or did you just lose me? Like your
purse?

LIZ: Stop it Phil. It doesn't help.

PHIL: What would help? Ask me.

LIZ: A walk would help. I'd like to get
away from Eros for a while.

INT./EXT.   EROS   DAY

LIZ and PHIL cross the lobby.

PHIL catches what is apparently his first sight of what's going on outside today.

> PHIL: What's going on?

> LIZ: Doctor Connor stirred a lot of people up yesterday. Remember?

> PHIL: God yes. Of course I do. It won't affect anything d'you think? I don't want tonight messed up.

DOOR BOY opens door for them.

> DOOR BOY: Good afternoon Mr and Mrs Argenzio.

LIZ smiles at him.

PHIL hurries through door.

EXT.   EROS   DAY

PHIL brushes aside a leaflet offered by KANGAROO SUIT.

LIZ takes one.
Reads it.

> **ANIMAL BILL OF RIGHTS:**
> All animals should have:
> Freedom to move and exercise.
> Freedom from mutilation.
> Freedom from stress and pain.
> Access to habitat suited to their needs...

PHIL's voice breaks in

PHIL: Liz. Please. Come on.

LIZ *puts leaflet in her pocket and follows* PHIL *toward the street.*

LIZ *stops on the way to sign the petition.*

PHIL *waits impatiently.*

As PHIL *and* LIZ *walk away—*

> PHIL: I don't see why you're on their side. They could really mess things up for me tonight.

> LIZ: I don't think you should worry about that. Your building will still be here tomorrow.

PHIL *smiles at her and relaxes.*

> PHIL: You're right. Liz love... I have to say you usually are. Now – where would you like to walk? We could take a cab anywhere you like.

> LIZ: Let's just walk.

INT.   EROS/LOBBY   DAY

LUISA *approaches the Reception desk.*

There's some flash looking luggage on a porter's trolley near the desk.

The RECEPTIONIST *who came to the defence of the* YOUNGEST RECEPTIONIST *is busy behind the counter.*

> LUISA: Excuse me. I'm the new...

> RECEPTIONIST (*sharp*): You're the new receptionist, I know.

LUISA: Madelaine said ...

RECEPTIONIST: I know what Madelaine said. Madelaine said I'd show you the ropes. Didn't she?

LUISA *nods.*

Maybe being a receptionist is not so great after all.

RECEPTIONIST (*cont.*): Well you'd better come round this side then hadn't you? I can't show you the ropes with you standing over there, can I?

LUISA *tries a smile.*

RECEPTIONIST (*cont.*): That's a lot better. 'There are no difficult customers – only demanding ones.' That's your first rope. Hang on to it.

LUISA *takes this in.*

RECEPTIONIST (*cont.*): And a soft answer turneth away wrath. That's my own bit of wisdom. You can take that one or leave it.

LUISA*'s beginning to like this* WOMAN.

EARL CONNOR *comes up.*

EARL CONNOR: Call me a cab, would you?

RECEPTIONIST: Straight away, sir.

EARL CONNOR *goes and stands by his luggage.*

> EARL CONNOR: Tell them it's to the
> airport and tell them I'm in a hurry!

EXT.   EROS/STREET   DAY

*PARIS pulls cab into kerb, grabs sports bag from seat beside him, jumps
out and runs towards EROS.*

INT.   TAXI   DAY

> TWO WAY RADIO: Come in 459?

Pause.

> 459?

Pause.

> Where are you, you lazy Greek?!

INT.   EROS/LOBBY   DAY

PARIS enters.

> EARL CONNOR: Taxi for Connor?

PARIS shakes his head.

> PARIS: Sorry mate.

> EARL CONNOR: Things sure are slow
> round here.

> PARIS (*sympathetic*): I know. It can be
> murder sometimes, getting a cab in this
> town. Nobody does an honest days
> work anymore...

PARIS stops.

PARIS *has seen the new-look* LUISA *in her receptionist's uniform.*

LUISA *turns to see* PARIS *who suddenly looks much more like the average Greek hero than a mere man who drives a cab for a living.*

THEY *stand gazing at each other for a few moments, taking in these facts.* PARIS *and* LUISA *are falling in love.*

A COURIER *arrives to break the spell.*

COURIER *puts box containing the stickers* MADELAINE *ordered on the counter between them.*

EXT.   YARRA   DAY

    LIZ: I'm leaving you Phil.

    PHIL: Just like that? Twenty years and
    just like that? Snap! Boom! Over!

LIZ *very quiet and distressed.*

    LIZ: Not like that.

LIZ *looks at* PHIL *who stands miserably staring out over water, his shoulders hunched, his pose defensive.*

LIZ *can't bear it.*

SHE *goes toward him to touch him.*

PHIL *shies away, turns his back.*

    PHIL: God Liz! How could you?

    LIZ: Listen Phil – I want you to know
    this – what I'm doing – it's not a vote
    against you – it's a vote for me.

PHIL *explodes with anger.*

> PHIL: 'It's not a vote against you it's just
> a vote for me.' Where'd you get that one
> Liz? Off a bumper sticker?

INT.   EROS/LOBBY   DAY

LUISA *sticking Free of Animal Products sticker on rows of* EROS *products.*

She doesn't find it very stimulating.

She picks a sticker up on the end of her finger and looks at it.

> LUISA: You'd think the whole bloody
> world would have the message by now
> wouldn't you?

> PARIS: Can I help you?

> LUISA: Haven't you got anything better
> to do?

> PARIS: Not 'better', no. I'm here for a
> workout with Tony. You know Tony?

LUISA *pulls face that indicates that she does.*

PARIS *laughs.*

> PARIS (*cont.*): He's not so bad ... when
> you get to know him. And your friend,
> the girl who whistled at me in the pub
> last night, she works here too doesn't
> she?

> LUISA: Yes. You remember Chris do you?

> PARIS: How could I forget? I never got
> a wolf-whistle from a girl before. She's
> really something!

LUISA *looks at* PARIS.

LUISA *blurts it out.*

> LUISA: Last night I came home and found
> Chris in bed with a woman.

Pause.

> LUISA (*cont.*): I mean this has been – like
> I was really upset at first. But now...
> well, I guess I'm getting used to the idea.

> PARIS: Well yeah... she's still your
> friend – the same person I mean only...

> LUISA: Only what?

> PARIS: Only she doesn't look like a
> man-hater.

> LUISA: What does a man-hater look like?

PARIS *shrugs.*

> PARIS: Well you know... not like Chris
> does anyway.

> LUISA: Why do you think Chris hates
> men?

> PARIS: She goes to bed with women. She
> must hate men.

> LUISA: Well you go to bed with women.
> But that doesn't mean you hate men,
> does it?

PARIS *laughs.*

LUISA: You know what really worries me about Chris?

PARIS: No.

LUISA: I'm scared people might think I'm like that too. Because we share a flat and because she's my best friend.

PARIS: Impossible. They'd see you with me and they'd know. I'd keep you so satisfied you couldn't want anything else.

LUISA *laughs.*

LUISA *looks at him speculatively.*

LUISA: That good?

PARIS: Find out.

PARIS *and* LUISA *exchange a lustful look across the ranks of* EROS *products.*

LUISA *looks at the shining ranks of room keys.*

LUISA: So many empty beds...

TONY *lopes up.*

TONY: Been looking all over for you, mate. Thought you were coming to the gym.

PARIS *finds it hard to take his attention from* LUISA.

PARIS: I was ... am.

TONY (*to* LUISA): Heard about you and Steve. Too bad eh? Want to talk about it

> do you? Need a nice broad shoulder to
> cry on? Tell you what. Meet me after
> you knock off. We'll go to my place.
> Talk about it over a cup of coffee.
> (*to* PARIS): Coming?

PARIS *and* LUISA *burst into laughter.*

> TONY (*cont.*): What's funny? Did I say
> something funny?
> (*to* LUISA): D'you think I'm funny?

> LUISA (*to* PARIS): D'you think he's
> funny?

PARIS *looks at* TONY *and, still laughing, shakes his head.*

TONY *looks from one to the other in bewilderment.*

PARIS *puts his arm round* TONY'*s shoulders and hugs him.*

PARIS *is taller and chunkier than* TONY.

TONY *shakes himself free.*

> TONY: Hey!

TONY *smiles.*

TONY *laughs and shakes his head.*

> TONY (*cont.*): Jeez you're a bloody
> madman!

EXT.   YARRA   DAY

LIZ *and* PHIL *walk slowly back in the direction of* EROS.
There is a physical distance between them and they do not speak.

INT.   EROS   DAY

PARIS *and* TONY *walking away along a glass walkway – a new sign
reading* GYMNASIUM *and* POOL *points the way they're going.
They walk close together, talking.
They break apart, laughing.*

>   TONY: Listen to you – It must be love!

PARIS *leaps in the air, one arm raised in a victory salute.*

INT.   ARGENZIO SUITE   LATE DAY

PHIL *sits at drawing board.*

PHIL *picks up pen and makes a couple of aimless marks.
Tears diagram off board.*

Turns to see LIZ *who's wearing swim suit.*

>   PHIL: Swimming!? At a time like this.

>   LIZ: It helps me Phil. Swimming lengths.
>   It straightens out my thoughts.

>   PHIL (*sarcastic*): Oh well – in *that* case.

>   LIZ: Stop it Phil. Please. I try to talk and
>   you don't like the words I use. I don't
>   know what to do.

>   PHIL: Yes you do. You're leaving.

>   LIZ: I was hoping...

>   PHIL: Hoping what? We could still be
>   friends? Share the kids? Get together
>   once in a while? Be civilised?

370

Close on LIZ'*s face. She was hoping for all of the above.*

INT. EROS/GYMNASIUM LATE DAY

PARIS *and* TONY *working with weights.*

DR ALICE *is doing her aerobic routine in front of large video screen (new addition) to music.*

HARVEY ROSEN *is on the computerised rowing machine.*

LIZ *walks across on her way to pool.*

PARIS *looks up and sees* LIZ.
It's as if the intensity of his gaze interrupts her own thoughts.

LIZ *looks across the gym and all its glittering hi-tech equipment at* PARIS.

TONY *notices and crudely nudges* PARIS.
TONY*'s voice breaks in on* PARIS*'s thoughts.*

> TONY: Hey look. It's her – the one I was telling you about. Jeez she's got a great body.

Without thinking PARIS *turns on* TONY *and shoves him away to stop him talking.*

TONY *lashes out.*

PARIS *and* TONY *wrestle and struggle amongst the gym equipment.*

DR ALICE *and* HARVEY *stop what they're doing and watch, half amused.*

PARIS *gets the better of* TONY.

> TONY: All right. All right. Get off me!

PARIS *lets him up.*

TONY *gets to his feet, resentful.*

> TONY (*cont.*): What's your bloody
> problem anyway?

PARIS *walks away without answering.*

He looks over to where LIZ *was, but she has gone.*

PARIS's *face reflects his feelings.*

> TONY (*cont.*): What about Luisa?

> PARIS: This has nothing to do with Luisa.

TONY *and* PARIS *stand glaring at each other.*

Then the ridiculousness of the whole thing strikes them.

TONY *and* PARIS *lighten up.*

> TONY: You're a crazy sort of bastard, you
> know that don't you?

PARIS *grins.*

> PARIS: You want to finish this workout
> then or what?

TONY *and* PARIS *go back to the weights.*

> DR ALICE: What do you think all that was about?

> HARVEY: Oh you know, honey – boys will
> be boys.

> DR ALICE: Yeah Harve ... and girls will be
> women.

EXT.   MELBOURNE   EARLY EVENING

A sunset shot ...

EXT.   EROS/LANEWAY   EVENING

TWO IMPECCABLY DRESSED WAITERS *wheeling food trolleys out of back door and round to the front of* EROS.

They negotiate the hazardous laneway with great aplomb, startling a DERELICT *asleep in a cardboard box who wakes to think he must still be dreaming.*

EXT.   EROS   EVENING

The TWO WAITERS *stand at front of* EROS *with their trolleys.*

The TWO WAITERS *raise silver covers to reveal a splendid array of vegetarian food – fruit, salads, vegetables, an impressive variety of breads and cheeses.*

The TWO WAITERS *approach the* KANGAROO SUITS *first.*

At first there is some resistance—

> KANGAROO SUIT: Is this an organic tomato?

> WAITER: It's biodynamic sir. It bounces.

KANGAROO SUIT *helps himself.*

> OTHER KANGAROO SUIT (*to other waiter*): You wouldn't have such a thing as a ham sandwich would you mate?

The TWO OTHER ANIMAL LIBERATIONISTS *help themselves.*

This is starting to attract the attention of a few PASSERS BY.

TWO WAITERS *emerge from front doors bearing trays of champagne and juices.*

This is a popular move.

LUISA *and* RECEPTIONIST *come outside.*

> LUISA: This was my idea.

> RECEPTIONIST: Go on.

> LUISA: No, really. Madelaine asked me what I'd do with these people hanging round outside.

A few more PASSERS BY *are stopping.*

ONE *or* TWO *help themselves to a drink.*

> LUISA (*cont.*): I couldn't think at first. Then I asked myself what my Mum would do. And that's when I got the answer.

DR ALICE *comes out.*

DR ALICE *approached by autograph hunters.*

HARVEY *comes out with an armful of* DR ALICE's *books.*

HARVEY *sells.*

ALICE *signs.*

INT.   MADELAINE'S SUITE/OFFICE   SAME

MADELAINE *turns laughing from the window.*

> MADELAINE (*to* ROGER): God she's wonderful. She doesn't miss a trick. I love her!

> ROGER: You're pretty good yourself. This feeding the savage beast idea of yours was a shrewd move.

MADELAINE *tries to resist temptation but can't.*

> MADELAINE: Yes, wasn't it?

EXT.   EROS/STREET   SAME

PASSING MOTORISTS *slow down to see what's going on.*

A MINOR TRAFFIC JAM *is developing.*

A television news van comes into view.

Pulls up outside.

EXT.   EROS   SAME

CAMERA CREW *setting up.*

LUISA's *talking to a* MIDDLE AGED MAN *who's stopped to watch.*

> LUISA: You should come in when we're
> open.

> MAN: No. All that's for the ladies. What
> could you lot do for an oldie like me?

> LUISA: You'd be surprised!

INT.   EROS/KITCHEN   SAME

STEVE *is working on his ice sculpture.*

The winged figure of EROS *is nearing completion.*

KITCHEN HANDS *gather round* STEVE.

> KITCHEN HAND: Well, I vote we all go
> outside. It's all happening out there –
> and here *we* all are – stuck in the kitchen
> as usual.

375

STEVE: What is this? A mutiny? How's it going?

STEVE *looks up.*

The party preparations are nearly finished.

Gorgeous food.

STEVE: You're all terrific. You know that, don't you?

The proud smiles of the KITCHEN HANDS.

INT.   ARGENZIO SUITE   SAME

LIZ *packs.*

PHIL *watches.*

PHIL *goes to* LIZ, *gently shuts the open lid of her suitcase.*

PHIL: Liz. Listen. You've come so far with me ... We've come so far together. I wouldn't be here tonight if it hadn't been for you. I know you're leaving. I accept that. But Liz – please – don't go tonight. Stay and share this with me.

LIZ *will stay.*

PHIL *puts his arms round her.*

THEIR *faces reflect the regret and tenderness they feel.*

EXT.   EROS   SAME

MADELAINE *comes out of* EROS.

ROGER's *behind her, but it's* MADELAINE's *moment.*

MADELAINE *stands poised for the* CAMERA CREW.

OUT OF THE CROWD *comes a tall* OLD WOMAN, *dressed in long black dress, black hat, black veil.*
She bears a wreath.

The CAMERA CREW *whirls to film her.*

MADELAINE *shoots a questioning look toward* ROGER.

ROGER *shrugs.*

The OLD WOMAN *is a compelling presence as she makes her way slowly toward the front door of* EROS.

ALL *watch.*

PARIS *comes up to* LUISA *who doesn't notice him until he takes her hand.*

The OLD WOMAN *reaches the door.*

The CAMERA CREW *follows her all the way.*

The OLD WOMAN *kneels before the doors of* EROS *and places her wreath on the ground.*
It is a dignified and moving act.

The OLD WOMAN *props an 'in memorium' card next to the wreath.*

On the card are a list of names.

> *The Tasmanian Tiger*
> *The Hairy-Nosed Wombat*
> *The Boobook Owl*
> *The Pig-Footed Bandicoot*
> *The Paradise Parrot*
> *The Western Swamp Turtle*

The OLD WOMAN *bows her head briefly, then rises and makes her way
back through the silent* PEOPLE.
And goes.

PEOPLE *move.*

PEOPLE *start to talk.*

The spell is broken

LUISA *looks across to where* MADELAINE *talks to* TV REPORTER.

> MADELAINE: And I promise you – you
> have my personal commitment that Eros
> will never ever use or cause harm to any
> living creature.

REPORTER *nods.*

Filming stops.

> REPORTER: Could you just step over here?

The TWO KANGAROO SUITS *step forward.*

> REPORTER (*cont.*): One on each side?

The TWO KANGAROO SUITS *move to stand one on each side of* MADELAINE.

ROGER *comes over with* BABY KANGAROO *in his arms.*

ROGER *hands* JOEY *to* MADELAINE *who flinches a bit but does her best
with it.*

MADELAINE *stands holding the baby.*

The TWO ROO SUITS *stand on either side.*

MADELAINE *smiles as the cameras roll ...*

EXT.   EROS   SAME

Close on LUISA *and* PARIS *as they stand before the doors of* EROS *watching the scene...*

And then LUISA *and* PARIS *turn to each other and kiss.*

A long kiss broken by LUISA.

> LUISA: You don't want to get married do you?

> PARIS: Never!

LUISA *smiles and resumes the kiss.*

EXT.   EROS   SAME

MADELAINE *turns.*

MADELAINE *looks toward* EROS.

The lights are coming on inside.

The first PARTY GUESTS *start to arrive.*

Their laughter heard as they hurry toward EROS.

MADELAINE *smiles the smile of one who is about to realise her dream...*

INT.   EROS/KITCHEN   SAME

All is ready.

The ice-statue stands splendid and gleaming – the centrepiece of the circle after circle of exotic finger foods that radiate out from its base.

Slowly EROS *begins to turn.*
As it turns it catches the light.

The gleaming STATUE *turns and turns.*

ELIZABETH JOLLEY

Elizabeth Jolley was born in 1923, in the industrial
Midlands in England. She is half English, half
Viennese; (her father met her mother when he went
to Austria with the Quaker Famine Relief after the
Great War). She was educated at home, with French
and Austrian governesses, until the age of eleven,
when she was sent to a Quaker boarding school.
She worked as a nurse during World War II. In 1959
she moved to Western Australia, with her husband
and three children.

Elizabeth Jolley has taught creative writing, and
literature, at a variety of institutions (and is currently
at Curtin University). And when not reading, writing
or teaching, she continues to cultivate an orchard
and to rear geese. Landscape, she says, is important
to her; she makes use of the regional features of both
Australia and Europe to provide setting, and to
parallel certain aspects of her characters.

Her Quaker upbringing is still influential: 'I was
brought up to believe all war is wrong. I still believe
this, and feel helpless in the face of the terrible
suffering caused by the many wars around the
world.' And she is disillusioned about politics: 'How
can anyone have faith in "politics" when so much
dishonesty and corruption is uncovered, only to be
covered up again? Having four grandchildren makes
me even more concerned about war, and about the
environment.'

'In my writing I try to explore and celebrate
the small things in human life,' Elizabeth Jolley
comments: 'I am interested in people and their needs

and feelings. I work with imagination from moments of truth and awareness. Characters stay with me for years.'

Since leaving school in 1940, and except when the children were very young, Elizabeth Jolley has worked, every year, but only recently has she earned her living from writing. 'It is not possible for me to explain anything about writing as a way of life or as a means of existence,' she says. 'I think that if I could understand and explain something about the mysteriousness of being a writer, I probably would not write. And I hope that I do not, in the future, make the mistake of trying to go on writing when I really have nothing more to say.'

Elizabeth Jolley has won many literary prizes: The *Age* Book of the Year Award, and the *Age* Award for Fiction. The Premier's Prize for Fiction (NSW), The Miles Franklin Award and the Canada/Australia Literary Prize. She has written numerous radio plays, as well as her novels and short stories, and much of her work has been translated into other languages.

Among her publications are:

1976 *Five Acre Virgin and Other Stories*. Fremantle Arts Centre Press, Fremantle.

1979 *The Travelling Entertainer*. Fremantle Arts Centre Press, Fremantle.

1980 *Palomino*. Melbourne House, London; Outback Press, Victoria. 1989, University of Queensland Press, St Lucia.

1981 *The Newspaper of Claremont Street*. Fremantle Arts Centre Press, Fremantle.

1983 *Mr Scobie's Riddle*. Penguin, Melbourne.

1983 *Woman in a Lampshade*. Penguin, Melbourne.

1983 *Miss Peabody's Inheritance*. University of Queensland Press, St Lucia.

1984 *Milk and Honey*. Fremantle Arts Centre Press, Fremantle.

1985 *Foxybaby*. University of Queensland Press, St Lucia.

1986 *The Well*. Viking Penguin, Melbourne.

1988 *The Sugar Mother*. Fremantle Arts Centre Press,
   Fremantle. 1989, Penguin, Melbourne.
1989 *My Father's Moon*. Penguin, Melbourne.
1990 *Cabin Fever*. Penguin, Melbourne.
Her books are available in the United Kingdom
from Viking Penguin and in the United States and
Canada from Harper & Row, Persea and Viking
Penguin.

Supermarket Pavane

It's the small things I take, only the small things.
Small things which will slide from my pocket into the lining
of my coat, a bread roll, a tea-bag in its envelope, a tiny three-
cornered cheese wrapped in foil, an egg lifted carefully from
a carton of eggs, a small chocolate bar, a tomato and perhaps
an onion. Not all at once, Mr Afton, you understand because
there are special people who watch for thieves.

Thieves. I never thought I would be a thief. I never thought
that I would ever spend time sitting on these benches in the
arcade where the supermarket is. In winter it is bright and
warm here and in summer – well, it is cool. All the time, at all
times of the day there are people passing. And children. I like
to see the children very much. You remember, I know, how
fond I have always been of children.

Some days I do not take anything because I feel watched.
There are people who watch, Mr Afton. The assistant in the en-
graver's kiosk and the cobbler, I think they are watchers. Uniformed women police walk round, in pairs, sometimes. Their
black polished shoes are the epitome of efficiency and authority. Some days I do feel watched. I have always been inclined to imagine, haven't I Mr Afton, that people are watching
me or talking about me. Or both. Sometimes I even have suspicions about the breakfast-sausage woman. I expect I have
told you about her, Mr Afton, but in case you have forgotten
I'll tell you again. Often, you see Mr Afton, there is a woman,
dressed in a white overall, cooking something. She has a fry-
pan on a little table and she offers small pieces of what she

is cooking to the people who are shopping. The smell is very appetising and I dare say the people, who can afford to, buy the particular product. Most days in the supermarket you will see a woman cooking something and offering tastes to people. It is stupid of me, isn't it, to feel the breakfast-sausage woman is watching me...

Sometimes when I am sitting on one of the benches in the arcade alongside the supermarket I think about the concerts in the town hall years ago. I remember every concert. Perhaps it is the wooden benches and the plants in tubs which remind me. Do you remember the potted palms in the town hall, Mr Afton? Clementi, you said Mr Afton, was the Father of the pianoforte as we know it today. We took the senior girls and the music students to the concerts. You always said it was of benefit to us all to hear the sonatas of Clementi played as they should be played. I remember too what you said when I wept during Ravel's *Pavane pour une Infante défunte*...

It is when I am in my room at Mrs Porter's that I miss the music most. I know I have the piano there. I am afraid to play the piano.

I'm not giving any music lessons today. I suppose that's a part of it all; I'm not giving music lessons at present. I'll be perfectly truthful, Mr Afton, I haven't had any pupils either for the piano or for dancing for some months now. To be quite honest, and I have always been honest with you, Mr Afton, the dancing class has not been on all year. Mrs Porter, that's my landlady, I always mean to tell you about her, she says it's all for the best really because even though I have the downstairs front room, practically on the street, the noise, the thumping of the children dancing was a bit much (her words) for the other boarders even though Miss Vales said she 'never ever heard a thing' and Mr Treadaway didn't know what I was talking about when I said to him one day:

'Oh Mr Treadaway I do hope my callisthenics and the *pas de deux* do not disturb you.'

The music lessons Mrs Porter said, right from the start, were all right if the piano was on the outside wall and in the mornings. Mornings, she said, for the music and the dancing because at that time I was the only boarder not out to work. Miss Vales is on a pension now (an invalid pension though I have no idea what can be wrong with her). It was Mrs Porter's idea that she apply for the pension. And Mr Treadaway, he is the one the young men in the upstairs front room have nicknamed the Cupboard Queen, I always envy people who have nicknames because it implies affection, that people are fond of you; well, Mr Treadaway is now more fully retired and *he* has a pension cheque too. The other young men upstairs at the back I know nothing about. I don't even see them at the breakfast table which is a part of the arrangement with Mrs Porter. I expect I have told you some of these things before, Mr Afton, but as I can only talk to you in my head, it doesn't really matter, does it.

Anyway today is the day Mrs Porter plays cards. She is out all day when she goes out for cards. They usually play at a Mrs Gordon's house. She is confined to a wheel chair and all the ladies go to her. This morning, before she went out, Mrs Porter said again she couldn't imagine what had happened to those two nice little girls who came for their piano lessons twice a week and what would I be doing for expenses? She hoped, she said, that I was bearing in mind that she, with all *her* expenses would soon be obliged to take bigger cuts from the pension cheques to cover the rents and water rates and everything. She had no need, Mr Afton, to ask me about the Willmot twins as she was here the day their mother called to explain about them going away to school. I think I am upset today, Mr Afton because, before she went out, Mrs Porter asked me (and she has asked me before) if I couldn't bring myself to do some babysitting. She has this agency, d'you see, and Miss Vales and the young men, upstairs-front, do babysitting regularly. The upstairs-back young men go out at night too.

'Oh, Mrs Porter,' I said to her then, 'I'm far too nervous to go out at night. I'm sorry.'

'It's on your own head then, my dear,' Mrs Porter said. 'People these days can't be too highly strung to earn their living.'

The upstairs-back young men are always very nicely dressed when they go out. Once or twice I have seen them on the stairs (the bathroom is upstairs). Once I asked Mrs Porter about their work. It was because of their bright hair in curls and their ear rings and really, Mr Afton, they have rouge on their cheeks and lips. Mrs Porter said yes they were pretty boys. I was not to worry about them. They were in theatricals, she said, and if they were not in till the small hours that was their funeral. But I do know, Mr Afton, that they sleep in every day and have cooked breakfasts taken up by Mrs Spence (Mrs Porter's maid) on big trays. Mrs Spence does not live here but comes in every day for an hour or two.

Mrs Porter does not allow dressing gowns and slippers in the front hall or on the stairs so I have to dress to go up to the bathroom.

Miss Vales is in great demand, days and evenings. She has several 'regulars'. She says she's sure I would like that kind of work and why don't I have a go. But I'm too nervous, Mr Afton, about being in charge of other people's children alone in their houses. I do love little children so very much, but it was different being at school with them.

'Mrs Porter,' I said my first evening here, 'I think my room is damp, it will be harmful to my piano if the room is damp.'

'Miss Mallow,' Mrs Porter said, 'you have the best room in the house. If there is an error in the building of the house, since I did not build it, I can hardly be responsible.'

I showed her the damp patches on the wall paper, Mr Afton, and she told me that was the pattern. She said mine was the room she showed people. 'It's my showpiece,' she said. It is true, mine is the room where anyone from the Town Council, or a prospective lodger, is taken.

Though they say it's no longer possible for you to know me when I visit you, Mr Afton, I tell you things because I have always told you everything. Because of the damp the piano is out of tune. When I talk to you about the piano I forget that your poor pale hands lie in the same position all day on the turned down sheet. I like to think of your fingers, nimble and firm, racing across the keys. I can't help wishing, Mr Afton, that everything could be as it used to be. I wonder if, in your silent world, you remember the children singing in the school hall. I see you *clearly* turning your head to smile as your hands, leaping, came down to a wonderful harmony of chords. Do you still see in your mind, Mr Afton, the dancing we always had on the Headmaster's lawn, your lawn Mr Afton? *Allemande – Courante – Sarabande* and *Gigue*. Long afternoons of spotted muslin, home made scones and tea. And then there was that last day when we packed up the books and the teaching materials to be stored because the school was being closed. You told me that day that I should not indulge too much in recollection of past pain. I often think of that last day, Mr Afton, and what you said to me then . . .

He's such a dear little boy. I know I won't be able to have him for long. He has stopped crying at last and is standing by the gas stove. He seems to want to be in the kitchen near the stove. Perhaps it is because of his mother. She is sure to have a stove and she probably stands by the stove a great deal, in that place where he is standing now. Perhaps he thinks if he stands there she will come and fetch him. I'll stand by the stove. There. I'll smile at him. There. Close to him and close to the stove. Now that he has stopped crying perhaps he will eat something. I'll cook something. I'll make bacon. Children always like bacon. Mrs Porter's sure to have a bit of bacon left over.

He did not want to come with me at first but I held his little arm and I pushed and pulled him. I held his fat little hand tight and dragged him to the main road. A few people passing glanced at us. It is not uncommon to see an elderly person trying to manage a small wayward child. Children do not always behave as they are expected to. It would not be unusual for someone to hold a child tight by the hand at the edge of the busy street.

The little boy, though he seems very young, is not all that small. I have no idea how old he is. He is a big little boy. He might be three years old or just four. While he was crying he seemed very young. He cried like a baby cries, a baby with an adult knowledge of all the cares and troubles of this world. He cried without words except for something I couldn't understand, it might have been his own baby name for his mother.

'What's your name?' I have asked him the question several times. 'What does your mummy call you? Does she call you Jack?' Wasn't I stupid, Mr Afton, it occurred to me straight away that no children are called Jack these days. Not even dogs are called Jack as they used to be. Oh Mr Afton, remember all the Jacks we had at school?

When I first saw the little boy he was at the entrance to our shopping arcade. The new place where the big supermarket and the variety stores are. There is a sandwich bar there and shoe repairs, an engraving kiosk and a hairdresser, the chemist is on the corner opposite the bank. At the engraving kiosk they will cut keys while you wait. As I said, I saw the little boy on the pavement, his fat little face crumpling up with oncoming tears. Twice he called something which sounded like a baby name for mother. His voice, timid with fear, did not carry at all. I was the only one among all those hurrying people who could see that he was lost. I could see him looking first up the street and then down as if in a bad dream – the place strange and not one familiar person in sight.

He's lost I said to myself at once. 'Where's Mummy?' I asked him. 'Is she over there in the bank? Do you think she's in there?' Bending down to him I indicated with my arm the big glass doors of the bank across the street. There was a queue of people inside; not one of the people was looking anxiously through the plate glass to see if their little boy was out alone in the street.

He's frightened I said to myself. Without meaning to I frightened him more by bending down to him and telling him: 'Let's go over and look for her in the bank and if she's not in there we'll find her in one of the shops.'

Suddenly, Mr Afton, this wish to feel the child in my arms is so strong that there is only one thing I can think of and that is to take him home and look after him. I want to feel the roundness of his forehead and cheeks close to my face and I want to take his little hand and hold it in mine. So, that's when I start to pull him along the footpath. And that's when he starts to really cry. He cries in a heartbroken way as if he, being lost, has lost everything he ever had. The more he sobs the more I want to hold him close to comfort him. At the corner of the main street we have to wait for the green light.

'See the red lights?' I know children like things like traffic lights. I hold his arm tight. 'See the red light,' I say. Children start to learn their colours this way. 'There's a sheep carrier,' I point it out to him as the huge trailer crosses the intersection in front of us. 'All those sheep,' I say, 'are going across the sea to the Arabs. They will go in a big ship,' I tell him. 'They'll go alive.' He is not able to look at anything. I try to wipe away his tears with a tissue. He does not try to stop me wiping his face and he does not seem to notice a concrete mixer as it roars by.

It is then that I notice his clothes. He has neat little clothes and his sandals are of good quality leather, not plastic. There are no marks or bruises on his knees, nothing on his knees except left over dimples. Usually little boys have scraped knees and toes. As I said, his knees are unmarked. He must be well looked after I think to myself. I keep hoping he will stop crying.

The park is deserted. I notice as I hurry him along the path that his little knees knock slightly against each other.

'Look at the birds,' I tell him. I quicken my step and hurry him more.

At home I try everything. He seems unable to stop crying. I am worried that he might need the toilet. He is crying too much to concentrate and he slips away, sideways, from me while I try to pull at his little pants. I can't help wondering, Mr Afton, if, in my intention, I have done him a lasting harm. A stranger pulling down his clothes, undressing him, violating his small privacy like that! This worries me dreadfully, Mr Afton, and I think I should write a note and pin it in his pocket so that the incident can be explained to someone – should an explanation ever be required. I am wishing now that I had never tried to take him to the bathroom at all.

Kneeling beside him on the kitchen tiles I ask him if he would like to see the chickens. I lead him through the veranda and down the garden to the pen where the four brown hens are. Mrs Porter's hens.

'Cock-a-doodle-do!' I try to make him smile. I explain that the old rooster is dead now. We can't hear him crow, 'Cock-a-doodle-do' any more. The little boy stumbles on the path and I hold his hand. I love his little hand. I think of the soft little bed I will make for him. While he is asleep I shall sit by him and breathe in his baby fragrance. I wish that I had a little folding bed, the kind of bed people have for visiting children. I wish too that I had some toys put away, a teddy bear and some bricks and farm animals, things like that. A little toy horse would be nice to have even if it wouldn't stand up because of a damaged leg. The little horse could be leaned up against something, like the one we had at school, do you remember, Mr Afton? How the children loved the horse?

The neighbours in this street might have things put away in their houses. Stored up in their rooms there are things which, kept and then looked at, show how lives come to a halt at certain times. They will have kept things which were thought to be important and useful and which might be needed at some time. A collection of calendars has nothing more than the years all piled up, yellow at the edges and covered in dust.

Neighbours label children, the religious one, the pretty one, the clever one and so on. This little boy? How would they, the neighbours if they knew him, label him? How would other people speak of him? The fat one, the sturdy one, the sweet one, the lost one. Mrs Porter? What would she say if she came home unexpectedly; the stolen one?

Every morning there is a stillness in my ugly room and the light is sombre. I like to think of it, Mr Afton, as being like the light in the Garden of Gethsemane. Two flickering eyes of light appear far apart and high up on the wall facing the window. Gradually a pattern of light and tremulous shadow moves down the wall until the whole wall is illuminated with the light from the rising sun as it comes through the thin swaying leaves and branches of the street tree outside my window. Every morning I watch this illumination. For a short time, as the light increases, my room seems serene, free from trouble, and the shabbiness of the carpet is of no importance. The smooth surface of the piano and the polished corner of the mantelpiece gleam. Something made of brass shines in the empty fireplace and the chair looks as if made of cherry wood. Even my clothes, over the back of the sofa, seem enriched as if they are of a better cloth. This transformation of my room takes about half an hour. It is then, Mr Afton, that this room is like the room you used to have. The little boy's bed, the bed I make for him, ought to be made in the place where the first light of the morning will bless him.

'My sweet little boy. Don't you cry any more. See, here. See here are the brown hens. Aren't they lovely?'

Though he is still drawing breath and sobbing, Mr Afton, he does seem quieter. The fowls turn their heads and regard us with experienced eyes.

The eldest son next door, when I was a child, was the musical one. He went away to sing. All the sons went away to be what their labels told them to be. The good one, the funny one, the quiet one, the bad one. And one, I remember, went to be a soldier.

'I'll tell you about the rooster,' I tell the little boy. 'You know, the rooster must have been a saint! When the rooster died, he was very old...' I'm making a little story about the rooster. 'When the rooster died Mrs Porter left him there in the pen. Perhaps she thought he would be too heavy to move and that he might have...' I think it is better not to tell my little boy about the smell of death. 'Perhaps,' I say, 'Mrs Porter couldn't remember where the garden spade was. Well, one day I find the spade. One day when I am alone here, like today. There it is over by the fence. See the spade? So, I go in the fowl pen and I scoop up the old rooster WHAM on to the spade and I bring him out through that little gate there. 'Because,' I say, 'I must bury him. All things that die must be buried. So I bring him out through here.' I show my little boy where I carried the rooster. The tears are still filling his eyes and running over his cheeks. His face is puffed up with his grief. I have never seen a child so drenched in grief as this one is. Little children do not usually cry without noise.

His mother's face. Her face will be all puffed up with grief and tears. She'll be blindly going first one way and then the other, never looking long enough in one direction. Too frightened to tell anyone she's been fool enough to lose her baby. Young women these days do not take enough care, Mr Afton, remember some of the mothers at school? This little boy, abandoned on the footpath, walked straight into my arms. Perhaps his mother is, at this moment, touching his pillow, his little pyjamas and his folded down little sheet, knowing in her heart she will never see him again. She will go to the kitchen because she must get up some idea of cooking. She'll try and, after pulling out the saucepans, she'll cry some more. Hopeless crying and she'll go off out once more to search again. She'll see him lost and frightened, drowned, burned and run over. She'll imagine him suffocating. And she'll see him again and again in her memories as he was, warm and sleepy, smiling and rosy faced when she picked him up out of his little bed on the last morning they were together. She'll come home, Mr Afton, and stand by the stove as she always does and as if he could be playing by himself, talking softly in his own language to himself, in the next room. She must know, Mr Afton, the mother must know, surely, that only death can keep him with her forever.

I try and take your advice, Mr Afton, you know – about not dwelling too much on painful memories. I recall too your explanation about the *Pavane*. You remember don't you the Ravel, *Pavane pour une Infante défunte*. The tenderness in this elegy, you said, is not intended as a consolation on the death of a child but is a haunting and majestic dance to honour a royal princess after death. I have always regarded little children as being little princes and princesses. That is, after all, how their mothers will think of them. My little boy is someone's prince. Surely to hold the memory in a fragment of music after death is the greatest of blessings.

What happened to the middle son next door, the one they called the religious one? It's no use asking questions which have no answers is it, Mr Afton. Sometimes it seems as if I can hear the boys next door, as if I am back in my mother's house and the boys next door have all come home once more. I seem to hear their voices talking to and fro on the other side of the fence. Not what they are saying, only the sounds of their voices, back and forth, loud and soft, all night sometimes they are talking and talking.

'The funny old rooster,' I say to the little boy, hoping that he will smile, 'the rooster was a saint. Not every person can be a saint.' I'm talking in my Grade one dinosaur-story voice, Mr Afton. 'Not every person can be a saint and roosters aren't ever saints. But *he* must have been one.'

I don't know why I tell him about the rooster, Mr Afton, it's just a story. Children like stories. I'm not sure if he understands it is a story for him.

'The rooster is a saint,' I tell him, 'because when he died he had no smell. His feathers, his magnificent black and green tail feathers, brushed against the rosemary at the side of the gate. See the rosemary there? And he was fragrant with the spicy sharp scent.' I pull a bit of the rosemary and hold it out to him. 'See here,' I say. 'See how nice the rooster smelled.'

The little boy is not able to smile at the lofty happiness of the canonised bird. I never spoke of it to Mrs Porter either. You see, Mr Afton, she would never have understood the ultimate. And it was the ultimate. Mr Afton, in my head I seem to hear your voice singing, your silvery tenor voice which deepened with the tenderness and the grief in the *Kindertotenlieder*. Even when you sang without the words the meaning was there and it was there too even in a few bars on the piano. Sometimes I long for music, for Mahler, and for your voice. In Mrs Porter's house we are all discarded people, in a kind of wilderness, and there is no music.

The little boy turns his face away from the bacon. He turns away from the bread and butter and the glass of milk. I stand in the kitchen, quite still, not knowing what to do next. He slides off his chair and stands beside it. Though I know Mrs Porter will not be back for hours I begin to feel uneasy about her return. There is not much time left for the little boy. Miss Vales and Mr Treadaway and the young men are out most of the time but there is always the possibility that one or all of them will come home. Mrs Porter plays cards all day, Mr Afton, can you imagine anyone playing cards all day?

The breath of sleeping children is pure and sweet and their flesh is cool and soft to touch. I think Medea says this when she holds her sons for the last time before she has to follow her destiny. She has to kill her children, Mr Afton.

A peacefulness is in the room, in the whole house, when a child sleeps. Everything in the house is restored through the sleeping child. This is true about death too. I think of the rooster and the peaceful fragrance of the rosemary.

I am trying to remember where, in my room, those things are. The things I will need for the little boy's bed. A pillow and a little blanket.

I will play the piano and sing for my little boy and he will sleep. I will play the melody from the *Pavane*...

'Keep the piano,' you said to me that last afternoon, Mr Afton. 'I'd like you to have the piano,' you said.

'Oh I couldn't possibly, Mr Afton,' I said. 'Really I couldn't.'

I found a flat and at first I thought it was nice. A comfortable place suitable for a retired lady. Quite soon, though, it seemed sinister, yes sinister, Mr Afton, and ugly and cold. Having the gas heater full on would cost an awful lot, I thought, so I was cold, cold all the time. And sad. And the piano, it was out of place there. Quite quickly too my little store of savings was being eaten up by the rent. Whenever I went out and came back to the place the walls seemed to come up close, to shut me in, in sadness.

The piano was never closed in your room, Mr Afton, except on that last afternoon. Do you remember that day? It was autumn. The pupils had gone home and the school was finally and officially closed. And you said to me to come to your room. The piano in the special light of your room, Mr Afton, was noble and the ornamental candle holders were shining and grace-ful. You seemed to have a kind of halo. The sun was shining through the amber panes of your window. It rested on your white head and on the piano.

'Walnut,' you said. And you stroked the veneer.

'It's shabby now,' you said, and then you closed the lid very gently. You smiled and told me that the piano needed a room in which shabbiness did not matter. You said I should find a room, similar to the one you were leaving, for the piano.

The rent for the flat was too high. I found this room in Mrs Porter's house and had the piano brought here. I meant to go on visiting you, Mr Afton, in your nursing home, promising myself your affection and advice. They tell me that since your illness you do not recognise and know anyone. I don't believe them. If I don't visit you it is because I am talking to you all the time in my head, and not because of what they say.

Without your wall of books, Mr Afton, the piano has always seemed bereaved.

I am playing the piano very softly for my little boy. I made his bed on the sofa. I want him to sleep the deep sweet sleep of childhood. The deepest sweetest sleep of all.

I think this is the kind of room, Mr Afton, you hoped I would find for the piano. The carpet is suitably threadbare. Perhaps this room is like the one Beethoven had where he spoiled the carpet pouring jugs of cold water over his head trying to cure his deafness. Do you remember when we read about Beethoven? Mr Afton? His landlady, like Mrs Porter, treasured a thin worn-out old carpet.

I have been trying to sing for my little boy. He is restless and gets up from his pillow and stands by the door. When I open it he goes back along the passage to the kitchen and stands by the stove, as if prepared to stand there forever waiting for his mother.

The afternoon is nearly over. Mrs Porter will be back directly. Miss Vales and Mr Treadaway will be returning each with their small packages of shopping. The same sort of small shopping we all bring in. Small money saving shopping. Little suppers to last until the breakfast we have by agreement with Mrs Porter. When I was living at the school, during all those years, Mr Afton, I never considered once how I would be living later on.

Mrs Porter often says it is a misfortune for her too that savings aren't what they promised to be. Others, she says, are in the same boat (her words) and doesn't she know it! (still her words). Boarders, she says, all have the same excuses when it comes to rent. She has been obliged to drop the breakfast egg and is having second thoughts about cereals. I know I ought to take on some work through her agency but after Miss Vales' *terrible experience* I am even more nervous. I realise that Miss Vales may by her own behaviour, she is rather excitable, vulgar perhaps, she might by her own way of behaving invite certain undesirable circumstances...

My little boy looks very pale. He must be tired and hungry. It is getting late and any minute now Mrs Porter will be coming home. Where can I hide my little boy? Mrs Porter always goes straight to the kitchen. She puts the kettle on as soon as she comes in. She does not come to my room as a rule but she might today because I have not tidied the kitchen. Boarders are not allowed to use Mrs Porter's kitchen. I will have to hide my little boy. We can make a little game of hiding. I have put his pillow and the little blanket in the wardrobe...

Every mother is a Goddess, you said, Mr Afton, you said this more than once. Every child you said belongs to his or her own Goddess that means, you said, that everyone is loved and cherished even if only for a short time.

It is starting to get dark. The park will be almost deserted. My little boy's mother, unable to eat or to rest, will wander once more, mourning, through the places where she has been before. She will not give up her search. This is the way of all mothers. She will return and return, always searching and asking and hoping.

It is because of Mrs Porter, Mr Afton, that I am not able to tell anyone except you about my little boy. No one at all knows where he is. If I did tell someone, what would I do if they came to Mrs Porter? Because of Mrs Porter there is only one thing I can do now.

The check-out girls at the supermarket will be working as fast as they can. It must be almost closing time. This always seems a sad time to me, Mr Afton, because it is a time when people put off going home to their dark houses. The trolleys will be being brought up in long lines from the car parks and the aisles will be swept even while people are still crowding in to the bright lights and the wonderful sense of plenty.

Perhaps as she makes her way through the dusk, the little boy's mother is praying that he will come safely back to her. If I could pray, Mr Afton, it would be to ask you to intercede for me, to tell them that I need the little boy and that I would look after him well. Mr Afton, I would say, answer my prayer please because you know how it was always said at school that I was good with children, especially the little ones. If I pray, Mr Afton, it is always to you. Your face is the face I see as God's face. I can't pray, can I, against the mother's prayer?

My little boy is restless. I can hear his little hands pitter patter on the inside of the wardrobe. 'Time for sleep,' I tell him and I hold the door.

I dislike the little boy's mother. She is probably out shopping still. She will have been to the hairdresser and her hair, cut fiercely square, swings gleaming to her shoulders. She has her own way always. Her hair swings steel blond and selfish from her cold heart across her handsome dark glasses as she turns and tosses her head. Her hair cuts the dusk.

My little boy's mother is in the fitting room of an expensive shop smoothing, with snake-like movements, the scales of her new dress – down over her breasts, her waist and her hips and thighs. With cool elegance she surveys herself in long mirrors. She lights a cigarette while her parcels are wrapped.

The loudspeaker girl will be calling customers to the part of the supermarket where, for five minutes only, whole roast chickens are being sold off at a ridiculously low price.

My little boy's mother might be flustered in the dress department of the variety chain store. Not knowing what to buy she tries to buy something quickly because she knows she must hurry to find her little boy. Her fat childish body is hot and trembling as she tries to squeeze into a cheap narrow frock.

Perhaps I should go to the place where the hot roast chickens are. The offer will be repeated until they are all sold. Perhaps I should go there with my little boy. Because we are hungry we could take the chicken and eat it together in the dark park.

I have been standing here in the arcade for quite a long time. My little boy, with an uncanny fortitude and patience, is standing beside me. His little legs are planted with his feet far apart and his knees pressed back. He lets me hold his hand. He hasn't tried to run away in the crowds of people as they come and go. I have promised him his mother will come soon. She is sure to come by directly, I tell him, keeping my voice low so that the passers by do not hear what I am saying.

My little boy stands quite still and I, without moving my lips – so that people going by will not think I am talking to myself – am asking you, Mr Afton, to get some sort of heavenly permission for me to keep this sweet child. Perhaps some kind of accident could cause the little boy to have no one to care for him?

The little boy's mother is perfectly still under a white sheet being carried slowly on a stretcher.

'Will you take him?' they ask me. 'Will you take this little boy?' They plead. 'Please take him,' they beg. 'He has no one at all in the world.'

Close to where we are standing there is a woman in a white uniform. She is cutting up and frying some slices of breakfast sausage. She puts little plastic sticks in each piece and holds them out on a plate to people as they pass. She is familiar. She is often here with samples of quickly cooked food. She smiles and holds a piece of the sausage out to my little boy who does not look up and take it. I shrug and shake my head with a smile which is half grimace as much as to say: 'Silly little boy. My little boy is very shy.' I wish so much that he would turn to me for one precious moment. Mr Afton, I do wish this.

Because I am standing here with the little boy for such a long time I imagine that the breakfast-sausage woman is looking at me with curiosity. Perhaps this is not the case. I have always been too imaginative about people either looking at me or talking about me. Suddenly it seems to me that she is hostile. Perhaps she knows something. She is condemning me in an unspoken opinion. I tell myself not to be stupid. I know really that she is concerned with something else. There is a shabbily dressed man who has cleared her plate of cooked samples twice already. The plate of samples is meant to attract several people. This man also seems familiar. Perhaps it is his respectable shabbiness which is something I have often seen. It is something else about him which makes me feel I have seen him before. Perhaps it is his shoes, not in keeping with the rest of his clothes, perhaps they remind me of some kind of uniform. He is returning once more. He seems eager. Chatting to her again in a good-natured way, he seems to divert her attention and once again eats all the fresh pieces she has just finished frying. The smell of the breakfast sausage is certainly appetising. I try to catch her eye with a knowing and sympathetic glance but she, listening with half an ear to his boring talk while he eats, seems only to be concerned over the disappearance of her samples. During the whole time that we, my little boy and I, have been here she has not sold one packet of sausages. I can't help wondering, Mr Afton, if and where I have seen her, this new breakfast-sausage woman, before. I do have this very strange feeling, Mr Afton, that for some reason she has turned against me. Once or twice she has looked intently first at my little boy and then at me. Her greedy customer disappears for a short time and then comes back. She has not fried any more for the time being. The customer stays as if waiting for her next frying. It is as if they are in a conspiracy, as if it does not matter that he has eaten her samples and that she has not made a single sale. Because I feel conspicuous I take my little boy more firmly by the hand and walk slowly away. Not too far away and certainly not too fast either because, Mr Afton, you see, I know they will come for him, for my little boy. This is the place where they come. This is the place where we have everything, the supermarket, the sandwich bar, the hairdresser, the engraving kiosk, the shoe repairs and the chemist. The chemist is on the corner if you remember.

When they come, Mr Afton, I would like to tell them that the little boy's mother is not the only mother to lose her child. Years ago our neighbours lost all their children, one by one, the musical one, the religious one, the clever one, the pretty one, the good one, the funny one and the bad one and one went to be a soldier. But that is everyone's love story isn't it, Mr Afton. Women of a certain age have the soldier lover, who never came back, at their faithful fingertips to explain their unmarried, their unchosen state. One, more than one, went to be a soldier...

The little boy is not lost. He is with me. Even so I know they will come for him. They will come and take him from me. It is only a matter of time, quite a short time.

The breakfast-sausage woman, followed closely by her devoted client is moving unobtrusively in my direction. Her little table, like a small counter, is self-contained on small wheels. They steer it together, lovingly, skilfully between the people – a kind of dance, slow and precise and full of grace. Perhaps they hope for more customers at this other end of the arcade. The people, interested, begin to move towards the little counter and away again. A *Pavane* for the supermarket, and all the time they are coming nearer and nearer.

They will come for the little boy, Mr Afton, and his mother will come with them. They will come very carefully. Gradually they will close in on all sides. She, the mother, is sure to be young. The little boy may well be her first born. She is sure to be plump. The little boy is soft and chubby, Mr Afton, and probably takes after her. When he sees her he will rush and hide his face, as if ashamed, in her skirt, close in by her knees. And she will laugh and cry at the same time and sink down on her knees and enfold him in her arms. Her lips will caress his soft hair and the smooth skin of his forehead and cheeks.

The breakfast-sausage woman and her accomplice are coming closer. I remember now, Mr Afton, as I see their well polished black shoes coming steadily towards me, where I have seen them before.

'You should get out more Mr Treadaway.' Mrs Porter says this to him most mornings. I don't know really why I should think of this now but this morning I passed Mrs Porter and Mr Treadaway in the front hall.

'Mr Treadaway,' Mrs Porter said, 'I'm telling you straight for your own good, for your health, you should go out more of an evening. What about Bingo Mr Treadaway? How about you come out once in a while to Bingo?'

'Mrs Porter,' Mr Treadaway said in his soft voice, 'Mrs Porter, I was not expensively educated in order to spend the last years of my life playing Bingo.'

'Suit yourself then Mr Treadaway,' Mrs Porter said. It was then, Mr Afton, as I passed to go upstairs that I saw Mr Treadaway was crying.

The breakfast-sausage woman is standing very near to where I am standing with my little boy. I remember her. I remember too, Mr Afton, that I have told you all this on a previous occasion. But since, they say, you can never *know* it does not matter.

When my little boy's mother is here with her arms round her little boy neither of them will glance once in my direction, Mr Afton, why should they?

❧ JOANNE BURNS

Joanne Burns was born in Sydney in 1945; she grew
up in the eastern suburbs. Her response to her
Catholic education was to deliberately fail 'religion'
in her final school year. She went on to become a
teacher (after graduating from Sydney University in
1966); she has taught in Australia and England and
since 1975 she has worked part time in order to have
the opportunity to write.

'So far the money I have earned from publication,
broadcasts, and public readings of my writing, has
been only a tiny fraction of my annual income,' she
says. 'But I am loathe to commit myself to a full time
teaching position with no time to write outside of
school holidays. If I taught full time I fear that I
would never write more than an intermittent dribble,
and that would be like a slow death. My life would
feel empty.'

Even though she is a well published writer, Joanne
Burns does not see herself earning a living from writing.

'Because my writing does not fit conventionally
or conveniently in either of the genres of poetry
or fiction, and is basically a blend of poetry, prose
poem, and short fiction, I don't see my work as being
much of a commercial success, or having solid
acknowledgement in mainstream literary culture.
I know the lack of capitals in my writing irritates
some people who regard such rawness as either
gimmickry or inferior – a form of cultural primitivism.
However, to me, unless the capitalisation is
significant to the specific meaning I see capitals
really just as elements of stylistic fashion which

ascribes artificial importance to certain words owing
to their syntax or their "properness" as nouns. They
are part of a consciousness that opens car doors for
ladies, and extends courtesies to the queen.'

As a result of an Australia Council Writer's
Fellowship for 1991, Joanne Burns has the luxury
of being able to write full time. She is concentrating
on longer works, a collection of futurist fictions –
'a stab in the dark', which includes a novella,
'australia who'; and a collection of monologues (of
obsession, of disturbance), 'epistemology and the
sticky beak'.

Her publications include:

1972 *Snatch* (poetry). Strange Faeces, London.
1973 *Ratz* (poetry). Saturday Centre, Sydney.
1975 *Alphabatics* (children's stories). Saturday Centre,
Sydney.
1976 *Adrenalin Flicknife* (poetry). Saturday Centre,
Sydney.
1977 *Radio City 2am* (poetry, with Stefanie Bennett,
Ruth K. Fordham). Cochon, Townsville.
1979 *Correspondences* (prose poems, with Pamela
Brown). Red Press, Sydney.
1981 *ventriloquy* (prose monologues). Sea Cruise,
Sydney.
1988 *blowing bubbles in the 7th lane* (poetry, prose
poems, short fiction). FAB Press, Sydney.

A collection of poetry/prose poems will be published
in 1992 by the University of Queensland Press.

found parable

i.

there once lived a girl who suddenly when she
was nearly thirty realised what being a girl meant. before that
she'd been happy to be just margaret or maureen or elizabeth
or whatever name it happened to be and she'd been happy

to help others (i.e. mostly boys) to live their lives. she just took it for granted because trust was something you were supposed to have. she was always busy helping, both at work and in her spare time, of which you can imagine there wasn't much. but one day when she was nearly thirty she woke up and for the first time she remembered a dream she'd had. i dreamt she said to everyone who was around (mostly boys), i dreamt i was flying a plane of people across high mountains away from danger. and they replied that's make believe, you're only a girl. get going and cook us some breakfast and iron our pants and clean our toilets. but she kept on waking up. she wanted to make her dream come true.

ii.

one of the first things she did was to discover the muscles in her back, arms, legs. all over in fact. and most importantly the appearance of what went on between her legs. she examined all these parts of herself carefully, with the aid of mirrors and other girls she began to meet. they all discovered the power of the girls. which because it was new and more interesting than she'd thought for so many years, took all twenty-four hours of the day to discuss. and so she grew very poor because there was no time to go to work in the world (some called it the patriarchy) that was all around the moment she stepped out the front door. she talked lots about her lack of money in connection with her being a girl. one would have thought she'd say woman like the others did, but she wanted to start her life all over again so why not make girl a good word. lots of her friends said we are women not girls. but i feel so young and fresh and new and strong she replied. in time (and it didn't take long) the majority won out. she needed to talk to others. women, that is.

(once she'd forgot and she said 'you guys'. the women in the room had nearly died.)

iii.

now that she was a woman she began to listen
to her own words more carefully, when she was not listening
to all the other women (her father had said she was such a
good listener). she discovered she spoke of her self more than
she had realised – 'for me it's', 'what i really feel'. but who was
her true self. she had a hunch she was another person deep
inside, not the person she appeared to others. maybe her real
self was trapped somewhere deep inside her body. maybe if
she improved the condition of her body, loosened it, cleaned
it up, her self would find it easier to come out into the 'light'
(she'd just learned how to use this word. old words were
beginning to have new meanings).

she tried massage. she rubbed and they rubbed. backs,
muscles, bones. she felt warmer, more relaxed. but it wasn't so
easy to reach the self inside. and the oil was so slippery. she tried
all sorts of different diets and half starved trying to remove all
the impurities from her body quickly (she was in a bit of a hurry)
but nothing really big really happened. her self still seemed to
be stuck inside. maybe she'd made a mistake she thought. one
night in the middle of her sleep she sat bolt upright and declared
'i am not my body'.

iv.

so she visited some friends (i.e. women) who
talked of how they had begun to feel they weren't getting far
enough with their lives although they had felt they were getting somewhere. it's a long long journey they sang around the
fire with some hope of reaching the destination flickering
across their faces. one of them anxious to speed up the process,
found a place for them to go from a friendly advertisement on
a noticeboard. this would be a place where they could let go
of the feelings inside their bodies which were holding them
back from working through to their selves (true), or souls as
a few of them preferred to say. a poet among them called it
spiritual mining. she knew things.

and so every week some of them started to go along to this

place (it was called a course) where they began to start to let go of many things that were in the way of where they wanted to go in themselves. they used words and tears and laughing and dancing, and lots of acting out of their childhood experiences. it was all very human. amazingly real the poet said. our girl (i.e. woman) mimed being a baby in her mother's womb and she got born all over again. for this activity she was in a small group. everyone was very supportive. she found it hard at her age to roll herself up womblike. she had such long legs and neck trouble which had not been fixed through all the massage. but the rebirthing did get rid of a lot of pain from the past. it was well worth it she said during the evaluation session.

word got round that this was a good place in which to grow. to find yourself in. have your feelings. because the course was growing (more and more people wanted to come. men too. nice ones) bigger premises were found. everyone began to grow so friendly, so loving. everyone hugging each other. i'm learning new things about men she thought, and women too. we are all human beings. by hugging people's outsides she had begun to feel their insides. we are all the same really. so warm.

after the hugging part of the session they would go with a partner and communicate for some time. she felt at last she was finding herself when she did this. she didn't just speak. she talked. i am learning so much, she wrote in her diary.

v.

after she had spent quite a lot of time growing she began to feel tired nearly all of the time. it wasn't just from the job she'd taken to pay for all the courses she had completed. it was a tiredness from somewhere deep inside her self. all she wanted to do was sleep. she decided to cancel the next weekend course she had booked her self into even though it meant losing the $100 deposit. it's well worth it to sleep she told herself. and so she slept a deep deep sleep and in her dreams a rather large cloud opened and said to her

> self is an illusion
> nothing is everything
> everything is nothing

it was as if she had almost touched these words with her whole being, she wrote down later. and she felt new again. her developing intuition told her this message had something to do with 'transcending the world'. she'd done a bit of it here and there along the way but she had a strong feeling it was now time to get into it totally. a new path was opening before her. she'd learnt by now to trust her feelings (although soon she would be taught to forget them) and she rushed off to the nearest neighbourhood noticeboard to check up on the current meditation centres and their various courses. she felt so terrific. everyone was very polite and helpful on the phone or in person. everyone seemed very calm. when she inquired as to the cost of a course (some called it contribution) they all replied

you'll get out of it
what you put into it

vi.

there once lived someone who got up in the morning and went about the business of the day year after year until her number was up and she lived as long as anyone else had been able to. sometimes (in her spare time) she collected postage stamps.

❧ELIZABETH RIDDELL

Elizabeth Riddell was born in New Zealand in 1910. In her final year of boarding school, with a reputation as a poet, she was invited to Australia by Ezra Norton to work on his newspapers. She went on to make a distinguished name for herself as a journalist and critic as well. In 1986 she was awarded Critic of the Year by the *Australian Book Review* and in 1989, her most recent book of poetry, *From the Midnight Courtyard* was shortlisted for a Banjo Award.

Throughout her career she has changed papers and employers many times. In 1942 she was sent by Ezra Norton to open a US Bureau and in 1944 she moved on to Britain; she worked in Fleet Street, gained accreditation with the British War Office, and saw out the war in Europe.

Back in Sydney, she worked for the *Australian* and has for some years now concentrated on book reviewing, and arts feature writing; her heart, however, is in poetry.

She has written two songs (with music by G.S. English) – 'Songs for a Crowning' and 'Country Tune'.

Among her other publications are:
1940 *The Untramelled*. Viking Press, Sydney.
1948 *Poems*. Ure Smith, Sydney.
1961 *Forebears*. Angus & Robertson, Sydney.

Reviewing

Let me start with an outrageous quote from Evelyn Waugh:

'The chief function of the reviewer is to rebuke the impudence of publishers in laying so much trash before a weary public.'

One is encouraged to draw a line between 'reviewing' and 'criticism'. The latter may commonly be found in literary journals, those which are usually attached to the English Departments of universities, have deplorably small circulations – not stimulated by newsagents who hide them behind more popular magazines about football, cars or fashion – publish from four to six times a year and are funded by their parent institutions and the Literature Board of the Australia Council. This benevolence on the part of the Council is because the literary journals publish a small component of fiction and poetry and pay contributors. This kind of journal also exists in the US where it is naturally able to call on a much larger audience than that available in Australia.

The tendency of these Australian journals is to be bland, but then blandness is endemic to all Australian reviewing. Reviewers as well as 'critics' pull their punches in case they should be seen to inhibit the very recent growth in the publication of anything Australian. After all, we and they (in whatever category) had to wait a long time to have anything to criticise or review.

I think it would be more honest of me to confine my comments to the business of reviewing rather than to the business of criticism. Those little postscripts which many editors of Literary Pages (which should correctly be called Book Pages) append to a review often conceal an implication that if the reviewer is a teacher at any kind of tertiary institution (and here is instant trouble if they are described as a teacher rather than a member of the English Department of Whatever-it-is College) their remarks will be more acute, informed and worth listening to than the remarks of anyone else on the same page. In fact a reviewer needs to be identified by profession or status only if their interests relate to the book he or she is discussing.

What every book editor longs for is a star, one who will be read even if they are reviewing a book devoted to the statistics of beetle infestation in mealie crops in Zaire. But stars are hard to come by. The most intelligent and stylish reviewing comes, and has a history of coming, from 'outsiders', not from the groves of academe.

There is a good deal of competition in the groves. I remember that when I attended the inaugural Wordfest in Canberra – now grown out of all expectations to the point when it could more accurately be called a Talkfest – a Tasmanian book editor revealed that he paid only occasionally for book reviews. Instead, he handed the incoming books over to a friendly chap on the university staff (I am sure long retired) who distributed them among colleagues always wanting another work on their special subject. At that Wordfest a publisher said that reviewers were an arm of the publishing trade and should regard it as their duty to write 'selling reviews'. This is, of course, no part of the reviewer's duty. Reviewers have to tell the public what the book is about, whether it fulfils its aim, what claim it has to interest people and if it is well or ill written; and, if it is not fiction, whether it is telling the facts or making out a good case for its opinion, or both. Some reviewers, like me, will applaud style, good English, and will complain of poor editing, ham-handed production and printers' errors which occur with ever more frequency. Some of us will also complain about 'alright' instead of 'all right' and 'onto' instead of 'on to'. A lot of good it will do us.

Where do book reviewers come from? Who knows? But we know why they come. They come because of a firmly held belief of publishers/editors that their newspapers and magazines will not be taken seriously unless these include book pages. These pages are relatively cheap to produce, can be put together well ahead of the rest of the paper, do not often attract libel suits, can be contained neatly within columns of advertising and dropped altogether in case of emergency. Books are received free from the publishers, the reviewer is paid an inconsiderable fee. In most cases reviewers are allowed to keep the book which is considered to compensate for the smallness of the fee. Indeed, it does. Editors, or managers, are sometimes irked by the reluctance of book publishers to advertise on the

Book Pages, pointing out that real estate agents and money lenders support pages dealing with their industries.

Over the years I have been reviewing books for a variety of publications I have identified certain pressures in the market. Editors tend to want reviewed books that they consider are 'news' or which are about newsworthy subjects, but which are often part of a promotion and have nothing to say, and in any case say it ineptly. There is also, because of the size of what can be called the bookworld, the use of terror tactics by authors and their relatives. I'm joking, of course. But twice, when I have hinted in print that a novel was not a latterday *War and Peace*, infuriated spouses have urged the editor to remove me from the reviewing panel. Readers do not seem to get into such emotional states. An editor is astonished if he gets more than a handful of letters a year related to the reviews he has published.

The anonymous book reviewer is now a rare bird. Probably the last English-language journal to publish unattributed reviews was the *Times Literary Supplement* which abandoned the practice some time ago. My feeling is that the *TLS* has lost some bite since then. But reviewers have to stick by the rules or take the consequences. It is the book that must be reviewed, not the writer. Reviewers may criticise the author's plot, punctuation and style but not his or her personality, or you will be in court in no time.

A few years ago I won an award from the *Australian Book Review*, a journal published monthly as a show window for Australian books only, as 'best reviewer'. The first of these awards – there were only two – had been offered to Humphrey McQueen but he had refused it, doubtless on moral grounds. The award, which was funded by publishing and bookselling bodies, has now lapsed. It was at least an acknowledgement that reviewing is an important component in the book industry, a link in the chain of information, inspiration and entertainment that has no discernible end.

I mention this because at the time the *National Times*, now defunct, asked me to comment on the job. I wrote:

Book reviewing is a privileged trade. Do not pay any attention to those who complain that they cannot get into their houses because of the number of books pressed on them by literary editors. The most hypocritical comments come from academics as the richly-scented, gloriously-upholstered volumes shower upon their desks, brought by couriers through rain, hail, heatwave, etc.

There are some hazards to reviewing. One of them is the neighbour's dog. A week or so ago a courier expertly landed a jiffy bag containing two novels at my front door. He had another package but missed with his second throw so that *The Collected Letters of Dylan Thomas* flew into the next garden and the jaws of a German Shepherd. Luckily the householder heard the thump and retrieved the book just as Micky was about to chew one of Dylan's many letters to his wife beginning 'Darling Caitlin' and ending with a request for money.

Another difficulty occurs when you are asked to review an author you may have happened to meet or one that you see regularly. There is no percentage in this. It is better to leave their books alone, especially if your reviewing over the years has been mostly of British or American authors, which suggests you have no context of Australian writing to draw on, apart from a few heroes such as Henry Handel Richardson, Patrick White, Christina Stead, Martin Boyd, Barbara Baynton, David Malouf. This has been my experience and has led some people to believe that I do not care for Australian books. Perhaps I should have a photograph of my bookshelves to hand out, showing titles of Australian books past and current.

One of the pleasures of reviewing is the chance it gives to boost a book when you think you are really on to something good. To stick your neck out now and again is a positive thrill. The next book written by your genius may be a dud. So what? There is no law against being the author of only one good book.

In fact too much is expected of authors. Like film directors, they should be permitted a few failures and not expected to come up with an annual masterpiece...

Which is about what I have been saying so far in this article. In other words – and this has been said about other forms of journalism, such as art and performance reviewing – a book review should be an intelligent, well-thought-out coherent set of prejudices.

Books are reviewed on radio and there have been moves to give them some space on television. But the review in print is more significant than either of these because the print review lives. It can be referred to in a file or on microfilm; it can be clipped, photocopied, passed on to agents and publishers, pasted in a scrapbook. A printed review has substance, whether favourable or not. It is as much the space allotted the review as the opinions expressed in it that counts. For the casual reader of literary pages, half a column on a book guarantees its importance even if the reviewer fails the author on plot, construction, grammar and relevance.

If Australian reviewing is fraught with problems, so apparently is that of Britain. D. J. Taylor, who reviews for serious British newspapers, recently published *A Vain Conceit* (Bloomsbury paperback) in which he castigates British novelists for sticking to the old safe forms and reviewers for putting up with it, or welcoming it because it makes life easier. Enlarging to an interviewer on his ideas, he says:

Book reviewing is a racket, a pleasant and sweetly conducted racket but a racket all the same in which everybody more or less knows everybody else and gamely conspires in mutual backslapping.

This certainly does not apply to Australia.

Taylor offers some good quotes from other people. George Orwell said: 'Until one has some kind of professional relationship with books one does not discover how bad the majority of them are.' And Julian Barnes, novelist and television critic:

Some Italian critic once wrote that the critic secretly wants to kill the writer. Is that true? Up to a point. We all hate golden eggs. Bloody golden eggs again, you can hear the critics mutter as a good novelist produces yet another good novel; haven't we had enough omelettes this year?

I don't know about other reviewers, but I have a lot of the missionary, or hot gospeller, in me. Sifting through three years' reviews, trying to define my attitude towards the job, I noted how often I pressed the claims of writers (fiction and non-fiction) little known in Australia, some of them Australians. The list is a long one – Michael Ondatjee, Timothy Findlay, Alice Munro, Anne Tyler, Ann Beattie, Margaret Atwood, William Gaddis, George V. Higgins, J.F. Powers, Brian Moore,

Jonathan Raban, Bruce Chatwin and Paul Theroux (before they became famous), Murray Bail, Helen Hodgman, William Boyd, Joan Didion. I was confirmed in my belief in the enduring talents of William Trevor, Saul Bellow, John Updike, Ruth Prawer Jhabvala, Nadine Gordimer, Janet Frame, Paul Fussell, E.L. Doctorow.

I also found in this file reviews of several books that I wanted/ want everyone to read. But of course everyone doesn't. Or hasn't. Among them is *The Wars* by Timothy Findlay, which slipped into Australia only in a Penguin paperback. Another is *In Fifteen Minutes You Can Say a Lot* by Greville Texidor. It contains short stories and sketches, her only published work. She lived in Britain, Spain, NZ and Australia and deliberately ended her life in a cottage in Hazelbrook in the Blue Mountains of NSW.

Another is *Darlinghissima: Letters to a Friend* by Janet Flanner. Flanner, an American, was for forty years the Paris correspondent for *The New Yorker* magazine which has published some of the most accomplished and thoughtful writing on politics, the arts, and the changing social scene in the English language. Flanner's beat was Europe. The letters are to her lesbian lover, Natalia Danesi Murray, an Italian married to an American. These are marvellous letters, on an extraordinary variety of people and events. I hope they have penetrated into the darkest corners of male and female prejudice.

After a Funeral by Diana Athill is another one-off, the very moving and candid story of a 'relationship' (much abused word) between Athill, a partner in the publishing firm of Andre Deutsch, and Didi, a young Egyptian temporarily in Britain from guest-working in Germany. No good was ever going to come of this affair but, I wrote: 'the book adds a new dimension to the literature of suicide as well as to the literature of friendship.'

Two more remarkable books that I hoped would acquire readers were *Contact* by A.F.N. Clarke and *A Life in Egypt* by Bimbashi (Joseph) McPherson, edited by Barry Carman. Clarke first: he was a captain in the Parachute Regiment, on duty in Ulster. He says in a foreword: 'The book is written in anger, anger at previous attempts to portray the British soldier and anger at the violence and hatred that became part of a way of life.'

It is clear from Clarke's narrative that the serving soldiers hate the Catholics and Protestants equally. I wrote:

I expect the commanding officer of the regiment has already denied that Clarke's story is true (he resigned from the regiment when his contract was up) but I fail to see why he would want to write it unless it were the truth. His publishers have taken a chance but neither they nor he will make money from it. A film is out of the question. No romance, see?

Now for Bimbashi McPherson, whose name was Joseph but who was known as Bimbashi, roughly the equivalent of major in Arabic, by everyone in Cairo when, after World War I, during which he served on a hospital ship at Gallipoli and before joining the Camel Corps he was appointed as a kind of high sheriff to clean up the city. This meant getting rid of revolutionaries, drugs and brothels. The book would not have existed except for the persistence of the late Barry Carman, an Australian journalist, broadcaster, geographer and traveller who made a radio series for the BBC from the twenty-six bound volumes of letters written to his family by Bimbashi and treasured by his great-nephew. The series became a book, then a paperback, published under another title.

Reviewing as an art, or trade, or craft, or occupation began in Britain in the early part of the nineteenth century and many established writers, such as Thomas Carlyle, looked on it with horror. Doctor Johnson is said not to have been perturbed by this intrusion. Several journals with the word 'review' in their titles, appeared and disappeared. At one stage two of these had a combined circulation of 100 000.

John Gross, himself a notable man of letters, writes in *The Rise and Fall of the Man of Letters* (Weidenfeld & Nicolson, 1969) that critics must be prepared to be challenged on their own ground by a whole battery of specialists.

Encircled by this expertise, the critics may well protest that their main business is still simply to give a reasoned (or unreasoned) account of their feelings about a book in the language of everyday life. They may take a certain pride in being the last amateur in a world of professionals... But all the same, he knows that there are people who know more than he does about things he is supposed to know about and, if he has any professional pretensions at all, it is hardly a thought calculated to raise his self-esteem.

Gross says:

Whatever the future holds, the first qualification for being a good critic will always be an interest in literature for what it is rather than for the ends which it can be made to serve. But the second qualification, no less essential, will be a commitment to the life that lies beyond literature, by which it must finally be judged.

Criticism remains the most miscellaneous, the most ill-defined of occupations. At any given moment it is liable to turn into something else: history or politics, psychology or ethics, autobiography or gossip. In a world which favours experts and specialists, this means that the critic is increasingly liable to be dismissed as a dilettante or resented as a trespasser. But if his uncertain status puts him at a disadvantage it also makes possible, ideally, the breadth and independence which are his ultimate justification.

ELIZABETH RIDDELL
on Canada's chilling expert

Atwood's survival kit

Cat's Eye, by Margaret Atwood. Bloomsbury. $29.95

Margaret Atwood is a star turn on Canada's literary scene, possibly on the world scene, since she almost won the Booker Prize in 1986 with *The Handmaid's Tale*. (Perhaps we should stop acceding to the Booker's view of itself as the most important award, rather than the best-promoted.) Atwood's new, quite long novel – 421 pages, handsomely put together – is nearest in tone to her dark, sardonic, sometimes chilling (Atwood is good at chill) *Life Before Man*.

The reader may at first fear that she has joined the 'childhood in all its detail' school (dangerously secluded gullies near school, rude boys, dog-poo on the shoe, mummy and daddy in bed), but her preoccupation with Elaine's chancy childhood has a reason other than the usual drippy nostalgia. In fact, there is not an aunt in sight: deranged, alcoholic, pentecostal, frigid or otherwise.

Elaine is first seen at eight, and last at 40. She is examined on two levels. On one, she is in Toronto, pleased but apprehensive, and certainly sceptical, for a retrospective in a private gallery of her paintings.

She has left Ben, her comfortable second husband, behind in Vancouver and is staying in the studio of her first husband, raffish Jon who does 'installations', while he is in Mexico. But he is about to return. There are no flies on Elaine; she knows what will happen and is prepared to enjoy it, no offence meant, none taken, she hopes.

Atwood is a witty writer and the novel is rich with big and little funny scenes. Among them is an interview with Andrea, a palpably hostile reporter from the lifestyle section (formerly women's pages) of the local newspaper. Andrea is out to get Elaine, and does.

Elaine's family consists of a father, a mother and a brother. The father and brother are 'brains', the mother a greenie before there were Greenies. Father's specialty, which eventually gives him a chair at what I presume to be York University, is an insect pest called the spruce budworm. I am sure we have an equivalent in Australia. His hobby is to follow chains of thought through to their logical conclusions, which makes for some interesting dinner conversations.

Father says that, were he a betting man, he would put his money on the insects, which are older than people and have more experience at surviving.

Much of the novel relates how, between the ages of nine and 12, Elaine is the slave of three friends of the same age. 'Slave' is not too strong a word for the way they go to work on her. The experience is probably not rare.

What is fascinating is to have Atwood explain how Elaine survives. There are some good tips for little slaves. For one thing, learn to faint in order to get out of awkward situations. Elaine becomes known as the girl who faints. And learn to forget. Elaine says, 'I've forgotten things. I've forgotten that I've forgotten them.' When her mother refers to 'your bad time' (when she was persecuted almost into suicide by the little fiends/friends, the most hauntingly awful of whom is Cordelia), she thinks of it only as 'the missing time'.

The male characters in *Cat's Eye* (the title relates to a marble Elaine keeps, without conscious decision, in a desk drawer) are not as visible as the female, but as important. On radio recently Atwood said, 'It's a lot easier to write a male character from your own culture... because you have the language and the detail, you have the reactions. Women spend a lot more time listening to men than men do listening to women, so we have a lot of material at our disposal. Men do not usually sit and have a two-hour conversation about the intricacies of the psyches of their wives and girlfriends, whereas women do this routinely.'

Among other things, Atwood is a marvellously acute observer, an honest reporter of events and careful of the language. When you add imagination and a rigorous appraisal of the way people live (Canada, Australia, New Zealand, any old reconstructed colony) the result is a deeply satisfying novel.

A fairy story from NZ

The Carpathians, by Janet Frame. Bloomsbury. $32.95

Janet Frame's latest novel is a complicated, ironic fairy story or fable. It is not about those Carpathians in which Dracula was supposed to hang out; it is just that Frame sees the brooding mountain range – in whose benign shadow an extended family of mixed-blood New Zealanders takes up a way of life different from the one they had anticipated – as being as far, or as near, as the Carpathians. The puzzling nearness or farness of things is an important part of her story.

Frame calls this her second novel, after *Owls Do Cry*, which seems to imply that it has been tucked away until now while 10 other novels and a three-volume autobiography were written and published. Yet it has a truly contemporary feeling. It emphasises the way New Zealand, like Australia, enthusi-astically promotes tourism (for the inward flow of cash) by seizing on myth and legend to make itself interesting, whereas a few years ago such things would have been dismissed as old-hat, boring and a real liability to progress.

The particular myth under discussion is that of the Memory Flower commemorated by a plaster sculpture on the outskirts of a town named after it. Puamahara in the west of the North Island. It has 13 000 people and all-the-usual facilities – retire-ment homes, a hospital, pubs, policemen and institutions to take care of wayward children as well as the Memory Flower. Attracted by an article in the *New York Times* (no doubt filed by a stringer in a dull week) the unostentatiously rich Mattina Brecon – who works as an editor in a publishing house – decides to investigate the Memory Flower and its environs.

She takes a house in Kowhai Street, named after the national flower, pronounced cow-eye by some and an approximation of Ko-fie by others which blooms in golden wreaths on trees that line the pavement. And she investigates the residents: Hercus the old soldier, Joe the piano tuner, Ed the computer salesman, eccentric Dinny Wheatstone (who has Mattina's measure, but is looking for a publisher) and the part-Maori Hanneres.

Mattina, while disclosing nothing of her past to the locals, lets the reader into a bit of history. She is married to Jake, who has spent 30 years trying to write his second novel. He con-tracted writer's block immediately the first was published, to acclaim. A son, John Henry, does better than dad by getting his first into print before Jake's second.

One night in Puamahara a deadly rain falls on Kowhai Street, activated, one assumes, by the Gravity Star. This is a star at once close and distant, near and far, here and there. People dis-appear from Kowhai Street and the real estate agents find it a real problem. The chamber of commerce doesn't like people to talk about the night of the rain. Like chambers of commerce everywhere (and tourist bureaus) the notion of mysteries, puzzles, ambiguities, the unexplained, the unresolved, sends them into nervous fits.

Jake finds them nervous when, after Mattina dies of cancer (caused by the midnight rain?) he visits Puamahara out of curiosity and to look over the real estate.

New Zealand is noted for its turbulent seas and exploding earth. 'Jake had the image of a cliff, the size of populated Kowhai Street, falling into the sea or over the edge of the world into nowhere, and the wound in the earth healing overnight; and no one remembering; but the Kowhai trees remained in the street!'

Janet Frame is an amazing storyteller with a marvellously fresh, lucid style. Among novelists, nobody even thinks the way she does. Her novels have received critical acclaim and some prizes. It would be nice if the reading public appreciated her, too.

❧ SARA HARDY

Sara Hardy was born in Torquay, Devon, in the
summer of 1952. Her mother, Pat, was politically
active, with the result that the very young Sara
attended Ban the Bomb marches (and other
protests), in her pram. She grew up believing that
singing and performing and politics was a natural
part of living.

Schooling was not satisfying, or satisfactory. Sara
Hardy wanted to act; at fifteen she left school to
attend a secretarial course, becoming a stupendously
bad shorthand typist. But determination led to acting
training at Dartington College of Arts, where she was
stretched in mind and body. At the same time she
was also writing poetry, and very long letters. 'It was
the crafting of these letters, the desire to make them
entertaining, good to read, which was the beginning
of my learning to write,' she says.

A potentially successful straight acting
career – beginning with *Toad of Toad Hall* and thirteen
and-a-half different animal parts (including the *front*
of the horse) – was curtailed by feminism and an
introduction to sexual politics.

'I saw a play – *Any Woman Can* by Jill Posener – at
the Institute of Contemporary Arts in London. It
was about a woman who was having a lot of trouble
because she kept falling in love with other women,
and then she finally discovered she was a lesbian,
and that was more trouble, coming out and
everything. And then she discovered feminism...

'I left the theatre in shock. Half the play was about
me. The other half I just had not lived yet.'

421

❧

A year later Sara Hardy was touring England and Europe with Gay Sweatshop Theatre Company and was devising, (and typing) and writing plays. From tutoring at drama school in 1979, and working with the Half Moon Young People's Theatre, she moved to Australia. She arrived in January 1981 and didn't ever use her return ticket; in 1984 she became an Australian citizen.

After acting in Sydney and Adelaide (and living in Melbourne) she adapted a playscript about the relationship between Radclyffe Hall and Una Troubridge (entitled *Radclyffe* it was chosen to be one of the three main plays in the Celebration '90 Festival in Vancouver). She then wrote a companion piece, *Vita! a fantasy*, about the relationship between Vita Sackville-West and Virginia Woolf. 'Writing it was a kind of lovely agony,' she says; it took over a year to complete.

Sara Hardy acknowledges that it is very strange performing one's own work. 'In rehearsal I have to pretend someone else has written it. This works until I see my name appearing in public places as the author!'

Having received a research and development grant from the Victorian Ministry for the Arts and a 1991 Writers' Fellowship from the Australia Council, Sara Hardy is still concerned about the economic future; her own and that of the arts in general.

'With the economic climate as it is, theatre will suffer very badly. My sort of theatre may find it almost impossible to survive. And my own problem of earning enough to live on from writing (and acting) is not improving with age. Now I am in my late thirties I am entering that fallowest of periods when there are even fewer parts for women. (Maybe this is why I am inclined to write parts for women over thirty-five.) I do not want to write just for me, however. I have so much work to do to discover/ explore what my writing *is*. I have left it so late to seriously begin. I cannot afford restrictions that bind me to writing myself into my next play. At the same time I do hope that I *do*, because that is how I have been earning my living lately.

'Since I have become a *writer*/performer, certain strategies for survival have emerged. I work almost as hard at selling my writing as creating it. I write a lot of letters, grant applications, and I send off a lot of scripts and publicity packages. I sell my product. It is like pushing a lot of little boats out into the sea. Most are never seen or heard of again. One, maybe, will find a harbour.

Vita! – a fantasy

For Lois, without whom...

CHARACTERS

VITA SACKVILLE-WEST, who is also ORLANDO.
VIRGINIA WOOLF, who creates Orlando and acts out all the characters who play opposite Orlando, i.e. HARRIET, MRS GRIMSDITCH and SHELMERDINE.

The play travels through the 1920s and 1930s; history and fantasy.

It is important to note that the character Virginia is set in 1941, the year of her death (she was 59). The play is revealed through Virginia's eyes, so the character Vita is conjured up as Virginia remembers certain encounters during their twenty year relationship. Vita is remembered young and vital, at the height of her powers. The *writer* Virginia supplies the other voices for the Orlando passages, but Vita becomes Orlando.

Vita! – *a fantasy* was first presented by Radclyffe Theatre Productions at the Universal Theatre, Melbourne, on 15th August, 1989, with the following:

VIRGINIA WOOLF	– Marion Heathfield
VITA SACKVILLE-WEST	– Sara Hardy
DIRECTOR	– Lois Ellis
DESIGNER	– Diana Stewart
LIGHTING DESIGNER	– David Cohen
DRAMATURG	– Lois Ellis
MUSICAL ADVISOR	– Lorraine Milne

The development and production of this play was assisted by funding from the Victorian Ministry for the Arts and the Australia Council, the Federal Government's arts funding and advisory body.
Copyright enquiries to: Sara Hardy
                           c/o Radclyffe Theatre Productions
                           16 Barnett Street, Kensington,
                           Victoria, 3031, Australia.

ACT ONE

VIRGINIA *Enters. She wears clothes of the late 1930s. She reflects, and to the audience says:*

VIRGINIA: For the most part, I have been very, very, happy.
              [VITA *enters, as if conjured up by* VIRGINIA. *She wears a 1920s dress, and to the audience says:*]

VITA: They say she's quite mad!

VIRGINIA: They say she's a Sapphist, with a bugger for a husband!
              [*They greet each other.*]

VIRGINIA: I'm so very pleased to meet you Mrs Nicolson.

VITA: Mrs Woolf, the honour is all mine. I've been so dazzled by the glamour of your writing that I feel I should bow before you! It is an honour to meet you.

VIRGINIA: Mrs Nicolson! I've yet to get used to the idea that you've even heard of me, let alone read me.

VITA: I'd be a very slovenly scribe if I hadn't read *you* Mrs Woolf.

VIRGINIA: Then it is I who must curtsy before you, for I confess, I haven't read any of your books.

VITA: And please don't, they're dreadful!

VIRGINIA: Surely half the population cannot be wrong.

VITA: Steady on, I'm not that well read. Honestly I
           loathe my early novels, I'd be ashamed if you
           read any of them; some of my poetry is all right.

VIRGINIA: You tend toward the traditional form I believe.

VITA: I've always been rather more 1560s than 1920s.
           My strongest desire is to be a poet – a good poet,
           but it seems the hardest of battles.

VIRGINIA: Ah but those battles are the most exciting.

VITA: Absolutely.

VIRGINIA: I shall make a mental note – buy the poems of Mrs
           Nicolson.

VITA: Oh don't do that – there aren't any! I publish
           under my *own* name: Sackville-West. I would
           consider it an honour if you would allow me to
           send you a copy as a gift.

VIRGINIA: Mrs Nicolson! I shall have to curtsy all over again!

VITA: Oh it's purely a selfish gesture, that way I'll en-
           sure you read the better ones, rather than the
           worse.

VIRGINIA: I suspect you are far too modest. Now if you're
           a Sackville perhaps you know something of the
           Palace of Knole in Kent. I was reading that Queen
           Elizabeth gave it to Thomas Sackville the poet.

VITA: But Mrs Woolf I was born there! Knole is my
           ancestral home. Queen Elizabeth gave Knole to
           Thomas Sackville because she'd made him High
           Treasurer and wanted him to live closer to her.

VIRGINIA: How extraordinary to have such a precise knowl-
           edge of your heritage – how far can you go back?

VITA: William the Conqueror on my father's side,
           Spanish gypsies on my mother's.

VIRGINIA: Do you think that you could be persuaded to call
           me Virginia?

VITA: Only if you will call me Vita.

VIRGINIA: Vita – 'life'.

VITA: Life.

VIRGINIA: You publish with Heinemann I believe.

VITA: They've published my last four books yes, Virginia.

VIRGINIA: I wonder, Vita, are you honour bound, or could I seduce you into writing a little something for our publishing venture – the Hogarth Press?

VITA: I'd be delighted. But what do you want?

VIRGINIA: (What I want is illusion, to make the world dance) – anything you fancy for our *Spring Catalogue*.

VITA: Spring? Gosh!

VIRGINIA: Yes, I told Leonard it was too short a notice – *I* couldn't possibly do it, perhaps later on in the year… Autumn?

VITA: I can never resist a challenge – you'll have a manuscript by the beginning of Spring, you may not wish to publish it, but you'll have it.

VIRGINIA: Spring – what a delightful expectation.
[VITA *exits.*]

VIRGINIA: Let us go, then, exploring, this summer morning, when all are adoring the plum blossom and the bee… Should she say, if I rang her up to ask, that she were fond of me? If I saw her would she kiss me? If I were in bed would she.. ! I'm excited by an idea: Vita as 'Orlando'. I've been making up the first chapter.

'Vain trifles as they seem, clothes have, they say, more important offices than merely to keep us warm. In every human being a vacillation from one sex to the other takes place, and often it is only the clothes that keep the male or female likeness, while underneath the sex is the very opposite of what it is above. Of the complications and confusions which thus result everyone has had experience.'

From the earth green waters seem to rise over me, and I let myself down, like a diver, into the last sentence I wrote yesterday, and I take my voyage away from the shore.
[VIRGINIA *gestures to indicate the arrival of* ORLANDO: VITA *dressed as a male youth in Elizabethan costume.*]

[VITA/ORLANDO *enters.*]

ORLANDO: I shall be valiant, I shall be victorious. No challenge shall go unanswered. No adventure denied!

[ORLANDO *suddenly spies* VIRGINIA *who 'plays out' her part as* HARRIET. VIRGINIA *is in the act of creating* ORLANDO.]

ORLANDO: I fear thou hast strayed unwittingly onto private parts.

HARRIET: Do not fear kind sir, your privates are safe and my wits are much about me.

ORLANDO: May I have the honour—

HARRIET: Unhand my honour sir! Though thy legs be fulsome and thy reputation long I will no wise fall between 'em!

ORLANDO: [*aside*] (Methinks the lady is quite mad, and thus I tread with caution.) Permit me mad madam—

HARRIET: Do not finger the oyster at me sir!

ORLANDO: I am the Lord Orlando, and you trespass upon Knole, my ancestral home and garden.

HARRIET: Lord Orlando I knew thee, and if virginity permit I would pursue thee for a bosom friend hereafter. I am the Archduchess Harriet Griselda of Finsterd-Aahorn and Scarr-op-Boom in the Romanian territory.

ORLANDO: Archduchess! [*bows low*] I hope I did not offend thee.

HARRIET: Be calmed Lord Orlando, though 'tis true, my nature is like to the virginal – highly strung and close fretted.

ORLANDO: A beautiful instrument, though difficult to pluck!

HARRIET: Aye, there's the rub. Dost thou finger a musical instrument?

ORLANDO: When a boy I mastered the flageolet, but now I have another calling.

HARRIET: And would thy lips let fall the call?

ORLANDO: Archduchess—

HARRIET: Fie upon Archduchess – call me Harriet, even though I am the Queen's cousin.

ORLANDO: [*rushes to her*] You do me a great honour Harri—

HARRIET: Careful – we are highly strung and apt to break.

ORLANDO:	Forgive me Harriet I was too bold, I will study to play thee with the utmost care.
HARRIET:	Practice may prove tedious for the instrument is warped with the worm and past croning.
ORLANDO:	Past croning?
HARRIET:	[*aside*] (His leg is faultless but his wits are dull.) 'Tis but my way of saying that a crone who gathers sticks in the snow is past midling.
ORLANDO:	Past midling?
HARRIET:	She who carries faggots to market is full blown.
ORLANDO:	Ah, I fathom thy meaning.
HARRIET:	[*aside*] ('Twas but a pebble in a puddle but we will swim on.)
ORLANDO:	But my dear Harriet—
HARRIET:	Oh the vibrations!
ORLANDO:	Dear, dear Harriet—
HARRIET:	La Sir!
ORLANDO:	Is not the oak tree a thing of great glory in its full majesty?
	Is not the red wine matured from an old vine a taste more divine?
	Is not—
HARRIET:	Lord Sir thou art a poet! [*aside*] (Would that he were a gardener!)
ORLANDO:	Since ever I could hold a quill betwixt thumb and finger I have tried to write, and due to a certain childish melancholia, where solitude was my best play fellow, I have writ such a mountain of belaboured works that it does make me blush to speak of it.
HARRIET:	Prithee speak some more for thy blush becomes thee.
ORLANDO:	I have read, I have studied the great masters, the Greeks, the classics, I have tried to emulate them but 'tis all for nought for my ink runs to water.
HARRIET:	Hast thou tried to *not* emulate the masters?
ORLANDO:	Surely one must write to the fashion?
HARRIET:	Then 'tis fame and not quality thou seeks.
ORLANDO:	Surely one is married to the other.

HARRIET: Ah Orlando, let me touch the down on thy cheek for an honest simple creature. Gadzooks sir! 'tis fire between us. Phew!

ORLANDO: How did a *woman* come by such wisdom?

HARRIET: 'Tis a form of madness though some call it genius – 'tis all one tee hee.

ORLANDO: Art thou married Harriet?

HARRIET: I am betrothed these past twenty years to one Leonardo.

ORLANDO: Leonardo – would I know him?

HARRIET: He is a lowly Jew but I love him well enough.

ORLANDO: You love him yet you do not wed him.

HARRIET: Though he be fond of the music Leonardo has not the way with the virginal, more's the pity.

ORLANDO: If *I* were to rehearse a delicate touch and a careful fingering wouldst thou be drawn to the music?

[ORLANDO *takes her hand and kisses it.*]

HARRIET: Phew! Lorks a-lassy what a fiery melody!

ORLANDO: 'Tis a beautiful instrument.

HARRIET: Oh I am all a-flutter and must run home.

ORLANDO: Dost thou live close by?

HARRIET: I have a Room of My Own 'pon the river and five hundred pounds a year to live by.

ORLANDO: Then may I visit thee before my departure?

HARRIET: Departure?

ORLANDO: I am to be Ambassador to Teheran.

HARRIET: Teheran?!

ORLANDO: Persia.

[ORLANDO/VITA *exits.*]

VIRGINIA: She is so much in full sail on the high seas, while I am coasting down the backwaters. Of course her brain and insight is not as highly organised as mine; but then there is her capacity to take the floor in any company, to toss off ten pages a day, to control silver, servants, dogs; her motherhood, her voluptuousness – her being in short (what I have never been) a real woman. I must ask her if she minds my dressing so badly.

[VITA's *voice is heard, as if a memory for* VIRGINIA.]

VITA: I was summoned to see the crown jewels at the Palace. Darling I am blinded by diamonds. I have seen Aladdin's cave. Sacks of emeralds were emptied out before my eyes, sacks of pearls. *Literally*. I came away shaking the pearls out of my shoes! All this in a squalid room, with grubby Persians drinking little cups of tea. Oh *why* weren't you there! P.S. Call me 'Honey' when you write.

VIRGINIA: Oh yes I liked her, the loveliness of her and, if life allowed I would attach myself to her for all time; like an oyster to a ship. But she was doomed to Persia. To attend her husband in Persia.

[VITA's *voice as before.*]

VITA: Persia has turned magenta and purple: avenues of judas-trees, groves of lilacs, torrents of wisteria, acres of peach blossom. We are going to Isfahan tomorrow, but heaven knows if we shall get there. By 'we' I mean Harold, Harold's lover Raymond, and I. For Raymond arrived, safe and sound.

Soon I shall wave goodbye to Harold and to Persia, and will be on your doorstep on the first day of Spring waiting to carry you off in my little blue motor!

VIRGINIA: I liked her, I liked being with her – she shone in the grocer's shop with a candle lit radiance, pink glowing, grape clustered, pearl hung; legs like beech trees. Of course I looked like a damp duster, incredibly dowdy. She said she couldn't care less for personal appearance, she said no one put on things in the way I did – and yet, so beautiful... she said.

She was off to Persia. I'd been sick and I was desperate to see her because I knew that if I didn't – if I didn't – then – I never would. It was Leonard who persuaded me to write.

[VITA *enters in 1920s dress.*]

VIRGINIA: Vita!

VITA: Yes!

VIRGINIA: Vita...

VITA: Yes?

VIRGINIA: Vita, I ...

VITA: Yes?

VIRGINIA: Why do I feel like a virgin, a shy schoolgirl.

VITA: I don't know, because you are neither.

VIRGINIA: Vita ...

VITA: Yes.

VIRGINIA: Oh this is awful.

VITA: Try.

VIRGINIA: Do you remember – at Knole, in Charles II's bed-room, where he went with Nell Gwynne ...

VITA: Nell Gwynne, yes.

VIRGINIA: Well, do you remember, you probably don't, do you remember, you ... caressed me?

VITA: Oh dear, I knew I shouldn't have done that, it's just that you looked so lovely, I really am a silly oaf, do please forgive me.

VIRGINIA: No, well, I didn't you see—

VITA: Yes?

VIRGINIA: I wanted you to know—

VITA: Yes?

VIRGINIA: I liked it.

[*Pause.* VITA *goes to embrace* VIRGINIA *but* VIRGINIA *backs off.* VITA *understands and withdraws.*]

[VITA *is up stage in silhouette.* VIRGINIA *to audience:*]

VIRGINIA: 'Orlando beheld a skating figure, which, whether boy's or woman's for the loose tunic of the Russian fashion served to disguise the sex, filled him with the highest curiosity. When the boy, for alas, a boy it must be – no woman could skate with such speed or vigour – swept past him, Orlando was ready to tear his hair with vexation that the person was of his own sex, and thus all embraces were put out of the question.'

[VIRGINIA *addresses* VITA *who rejoins her.*]

VIRGINIA: Tell me about your love life.

VITA: My passions might scare you off!

VIRGINIA: Who was that geranium woman you ran away with – your cousin.

VITA:	Violet wasn't my cousin.[1]
VIRGINIA:	Wasn't she?
VITA:	No, she was a childhood friend.
VIRGINIA:	Oh, I must have misunderstood.
VITA:	I did run away with Violet.
VIRGINIA:	When you were children.
VITA:	Violet would have loved that! But I wasn't under her spell enough then.
VIRGINIA:	What was she like?
VITA:	She was the only child who could match me – ancestor for ancestor, palace for palace, jewel for jewel – we both boasted a romantic heritage, her mother was the King's mistress.
VIRGINIA:	Could you match that?
VITA:	My grandmother was a famous Spanish dancer – Pepita, and my mother was illegitimate – yes, I could match that.
VIRGINIA:	And you played together.
VITA:	Yes, she'd come to Knole or I'd go to her castle in Scotland, or her palace in France.
VIRGINIA:	Gracious.
VITA:	It seemed quite ordinary to us, I told you, I'm very 1560s.
VIRGINIA:	So it was amongst palaces and kings that you fell in love with Violet.
VITA:	Not in love with her, no, not that I was aware of. I secretly admired her, she was a brilliant, extraordinary, almost unearthly creature. She was two years younger but in every instinct she was by far my senior, yet I treated her with unvarying scorn – out of arrogance to begin with – I was a terrible snob – and then I discovered that the more I spurned her the more she adored me.
VIRGINIA:	She loved you?
VITA:	Passionately. But it took me years to notice!
VIRGINIA:	But you finally did.
VITA:	On rare occasions she would kiss me, on the mouth, that was very disturbing! But I didn't understand my feelings. I just knew that there

was an extraordinary bond between us, she *be-longed to me.*

VIRGINIA: Belonged?

VITA: Yes, I can't rationalise it, but she was *mine*, and in some way always will be.

VIRGINIA: And so you finally noticed her affections and you ran away together.

VITA: Oh no, I finally married Harold. I became a diplomat's wife in Constantinople.

VIRGINIA: Yes.

VITA: When I became pregnant, we came home, I found Long Barn to live in, 'time flew' and before I knew it I had two boys, and a garden.

VIRGINIA: Yes.

VITA: I was thoroughly domesticated. Violet would bombard me with letters saying 'cast aside the drab garments of respectability and convention, lead the life Nature intended you to lead.' Otherwise I'd be a failure she said, instead of being one of the most scintillating and romantic figures of all time I'd be Mrs Nicolson, who had written some charming verse! I couldn't have cared less.

VIRGINIA: So you never ran away together.

VITA: Oh yes, we were gone for nearly a year.

VIRGINIA: How did it happen?

VITA: It was 1918, the last year of the War, Harold had been recalled to the London Foreign Office so he usually came home at weekends. Violet had just been dismissed from her latest war effort work in a soldiers' canteen – she'd made a cup of cocoa for a visiting General out of knife cleaning powder. She invited herself down to Long Barn, I could hardly say no, but the thought of trying to entertain her was frankly very boring, and I wanted to write. Anyway she came. We spent a ghastly few days when we both got on each others nerves and then it happened.

VIRGINIA: It?

VITA: I'd seen a photograph of the uniform that the new Women's Land Army was wearing – there

was a scandal because they'd demanded to wear
breeches because of the sort of work they were
doing, and I thought well I'm doing all this gardening and farming why don't I get some, so I
had some breeches made up and when they
arrived Violet demanded that I put them on.
Well, I went into wild spirits. I ran, I shouted, I
charged, I vaulted over gates – and all the while
Violet followed me, through fields and bogs and
woods, hardly saying anything, but never taking her eyes off me. And in the midst of all my
exuberance I knew that the old under-current
was back. After dinner we went to my sitting
room, and, after some limp attempts at conversation, we finally talked. She was so skillful! She
struck deep into the secret of my duality, challenging me to reveal myself. I spoke with sincer-
ity and pain long into the night, revealing my
innermost self not only to her, but to me. How
my femininity and gentleness was brought out
by Harold, but how there was another half, a sort
of masculine half, that I kept concealed. She was
so much more experienced – I felt like a boy of
eighteen with a woman of thirty-five! That same
year Harold had to tell me he'd caught a venereal
infection – from another man. Honestly I didn't
know what he meant! He had to explain it, I was
so innocent. It was only *then*, when I had to
grapple with Harold's duality that I began to
analyse my own. Violet was infinitely clever – she
didn't scare me, she didn't rush me. She retraced
incidents in our friendship which I couldn't
pretend to have forgotten. By this time I was
drunk with the liberation of half my being.
During the hours of talking, she had moved
closer and closer to me. She took my hand, and
for each finger she told me a reason why she
loved me. She wore a dress of red velvet that was
exactly the colour of a red rose – and with her
white skin, and tawny hair and lovely voice, she

was seduction itself. She pulled me down, very
gently, until I kissed her. I kissed her. And that
was the beginning.

VIRGINIA: And then you ran away with her.

VITA: Yes. Then I ran away with her.

VIRGINIA: What brought you back?

VITA: The first time? We ran out of money I think.

VIRGINIA: It happened more than once?

VITA: We were possessed. We could not keep apart
even if we wanted to.

VIRGINIA: And Harold?

VITA: Harold suffered, he complained, he stressed his
fears for the children, for our reputation, but he
didn't ultimately try to stop me. Violet and I were
under enormous pressure, our families became
tyrannical, they feared a terrible scandal; that's
why Violet was forced into marriage.

VIRGINIA: Lord!

VITA: In name only – she married on her terms, that
was strictly understood; we'd sworn fidelity, she
and I.

VIRGINIA: Who was he?

VITA: Denys Trefusis.

[VITA *starts to leave.*]

VIRGINIA: And?

VITA: Oh… We… finally came back.

VIRGINIA: You're not going to tell me!

VITA: No, I'm not going to tell you. I've written it down,
so, one day, perhaps.[2]

[VITA *exits.*]

VIRGINIA: To write *Orlando* I needed to know all the in-
timacies of Vita's nooks and crannies. It took
exquisite degrees of coaxing, but she finally told
me the ending to the Violet story:

They had fled once again to Europe, but this
time they were pursued by a brace of husbands
in an aeroplane! They were run to ground in a
Paris hotel where the four of them argued hys-
terically about the virginity or otherwise of the

435

blushing Violet (though, technically speaking, the deflowering of Violet had long been in Vita's hands). There was no clear answer to the question.

Denys Trefusis, with the honour of a gentleman, said different things to different people; Violet protested, a little too much; and Harold, well Harold turns out to have been a better diplomat than I had thought, for it was Harold who had raised the question of consummation in the first place.

Vita, proud, confused, and deeply wounded, went home and wrote a book about it.[3]

I pressed Violet between the covers of *Orlando* – she became Sasha, a Russian Princess, a creature soft as snow and with teeth of steel.

[VIRGINIA *indicates the approach of* VITA *as* ORLANDO – *now a man, he is dressed in restoration costume (1670s).* VIRGINIA *speaks on behalf of Mrs Grimsditch.*]

[ORLANDO *enters creating poetry.*]

ORLANDO: 'There is a garden in her face
Where roses and white lilies blow'

Face, face, umm place, base? Oh no, no, um—

'Her lovely laughter there does show
Of orient pearl a double row
Pearls like rosebuds filled with . . . snow'

Oh agony, agony! This affliction of the Muse shall kill me, yet am I not half dead with melancholy? Am I not poisoned with cupid's arrow dipped in gall? Did she not deceive me, she who had given herself to me alone? I am done with women! My only pleasure now is the solitude in which I read the great literature of the past – for there is no greatness in the literature of the present, only precious conceits and wild experiments. If I could but emulate those great masters. If I could but

squeeze from my pen just one little book that was
famous. Fame!

GRIMSDITCH: The strumpet.

ORLANDO: Poetry!

GRIMSDITCH: The harridan.

ORLANDO: Greatness!

GRIMSDITCH: The sop. Hm hm hm. My Lord.

ORLANDO: What is it Mrs Grimsditch?

GRIMSDITCH: If I may be so bold your Lordship this room needs
cleaning.

ORLANDO: Can't you do it some other time?

GRIMSDITCH: I've been waiting a hundred years already.

ORLANDO: Oh very well – though how a man is to capture
the Muse with all this going on I see not.

GRIMSDITCH: 'Tis true, there's a lot of the palsy going about,
and the dropsy and them's as died of the quinsy.

ORLANDO: 'Twas not an ailment I referred to Mrs Grimsditch, but the Muse, though perhaps ailment is
right, for to be without the Muse is to suffer such
an affliction as to drive one mad.

[*He goes into a daze.*]

GRIMSDITCH: [*to audience*] This wanton Muse is as changeable
as a midsummer morning that shines one minute
and throws down her waters the next; for do I
not observe him write, and it seems good, read
over, and it seems vile, cross out, write again, tear
up, cut out, put in; be in ecstasy, then in despair;
then in a fixed nothing with the gaze of a dead
fish from cock crow to candle light all for the lack
of a line that scans and a word to rhyme with
wasp!

ORLANDO: Wasp, wasp, wasp . . .

GRIMSDITCH: 'Tis most strange to serve him his supper for he
does mumble and mouth all his characters' parts.
I do serve him his victuals as if it were to many
people! The mutton might be fallen upon as
'twere by a roguish knave, the wild fowl sucked
upon as by a buxom blackamoor and the mince
pie hacked upon as by a victorious knight in full
armour. And as for his ale, 'tis brought to his

	mouth betimes as if by one who knew naught but the whore house or as by one so simple and so delicate one would swear he be a flower.
ORLANDO:	Genius.
GRIMSDITCH:	Madness.
ORLANDO:	Life! Adventure! What man can be a great poet if he has not had a great adventure?
GRIMSDITCH:	I know not, I lack the privilege of learning. But I say this: What woman can make a mince pie if she has not the wherewithal?
ORLANDO:	I shall to Mistress Gwynne. Sweet Nell has a fondness for me and might vouch me an audience with King Charles. I shall beg His Majesty to send me as Ambassador to Constantinople!
GRIMSDITCH:	Would my Lordship wish me to humbly attend thee on thy travels?
ORLANDO:	No good Mrs Grimsditch, you stay here and clean the house.
GRIMSDITCH:	Then all the while I shall imagine thy adventures and wish thee safe returning.
ORLANDO:	Thank you. Oh, and do thou also some restoration, after Cromwell's rabble I must refurbish the whole house.
GRIMSDITCH:	What all 690 rooms Sire?
ORLANDO:	Yes, and dig up the garden. I shall bring back exotic plants from the East!

[ORLANDO *exits.*]

VIRGINIA:	'The sound of the trumpets died away and Orlando stood stark naked. No human being since the world began ever looked more ravishing. Chastity, Purity, and Modesty, inspired, no doubt, by Curiosity, peeped in at the door and threw a garment at the naked form which, unfortunately, fell short by several inches – for we have no choice but to confess – he was a woman. The change of sex, though it altered their future, did nothing whatever to alter their identity. His memory – but in future we must, for con-

vention's sake, say 'her' for 'his' and 'she' for 'he' – her memory then, went back through all the events of her past life without encountering any obstacle.' Ha Ha!

[VITA *enters in 1920s dress.*]

VIRGINIA: Hallo Mrs Nicolson.

VITA: Hallo Mrs Woolf.

VIRGINIA: How very nice to see you.

VITA: Likewise I'm sure.

VIRGINIA: And how was the Persian Gulf?

VITA: Very wide.

VIRGINIA: And the Bakhtiari Mountains?

VITA: Very steep.

VIRGINIA: I hear you ran into a Polish revolution.

VITA: I went round it.

VIRGINIA: And Teheran?

VITA: Full of Europeans.

VIRGINIA: And Harold?

VITA: Full of Diplomacy.

VIRGINIA: And Vita?

VITA: Full of you.

[*Pause.*]

VIRGINIA: Leonard has resigned from the *Nation*.

VITA: I wish Harold would resign from the Empire.

[*Pause.*]

I missed you terribly.

VIRGINIA: Did you finish your poem?

VITA: Yes; and you your book?

VIRGINIA: Oh I'm still wading to the lighthouse – but surprisingly quickly for me.

VITA: Good.

[*Pause.*]

VIRGINIA: Would you like to come with me on the 18th to—

VITA: Yes!

VIRGINIA: Oh good, well that's settled then – and have you heard about Rose Macaulay's party – no of course you haven't, well there was Clive and I being silly and brilliant in a whirl of meaningless words surrounded by second rate writers in second rate dress clothes (Leonard and I had rushed straight from the press, covered in ink) and I was just about to let myself float above the clamouring of those baldnecked chickens when I thought I heard Mr O'Donavan say, 'Holy Ghost' when in fact he said, 'The whole coast' and I asked, 'Where is the Holy Ghost?' and he said, 'Wherever the sea is' and I thought – 'am I mad or is this wit?' – 'The Holy Ghost?' I repeated, 'The Whole Coast' he shouted, and so we went on, in an atmosphere so repellent that it became, like the smell of bad cheese, repulsively fascinating.

VITA: Virginia—

VIRGINIA: And then poor Leonard got very nervous with his shaking arm, and rattled his way all through dinner getting more onto the table cloth than into his mouth; he suddenly dives under the table to pick up what he took to be Mrs Gould's serviette, only to discover that he was lifting her petticoat, right up to the thigh, and the foundations of that tenth rate literary respectability collapsed before us – and I kept saying to myself Vita would love this.

VITA: Virginia—

VIRGINIA: I had a million things to tell you and now I can't think of one – oh yes I can – we now have *two* water closets at Rodmell, one paid for by *Mrs Dalloway*, and the other by *The Common Reader*, both dedicated to you, seeing as it was your idea.

VITA: I'm honoured.

VIRGINIA: Don't be, they don't altogether work yet.

VITA: What was it I let myself in for on the 18th?

VIRGINIA: Cambridge. I've been harassed by the women of Girton.

VITA: Why?

VIRGINIA: They want a lecture on 'Women and Fiction' so I'm going to tell them to be androgynous in a room of their own!

VITA: Lord!

VIRGINIA: Will you come?

VITA: Oh yes I'll come.

VIRGINIA: That's my Vita. I've been plagued with a vision
            of you for four months.

VITA: Good. What is it?

VIRGINIA: You're stark naked, very beautiful, brown as a
            satyr and treading grapes. Now have you been
            treading grapes?

VITA: I've been stuck in a river, I've crawled through
            snow, been attacked by bandits, been in a burn-
            ing train; I've worn silks one day, sheepskin the
            next, I've seen Kurds and Medes and caravans,
            I've received the most wonderful letters imagin-
            able – but I haven't been treading grapes.

VIRGINIA: Pity. And are you still my Vita?

VITA: I used to call your name to the moon and the stars
            and the sun – didn't you hear me?

VIRGINIA: Every day and every night. I've missed you
            in a way I never thought possible – you terrible
            terrible creature.

            [*They embrace*]

            And you're all right?

VITA: I am now!

VIRGINIA: Despite a Polish revolution?

VITA: Despite all sorts of things! I was so relieved to
            step on to the platform at Victoria Station I swear
            I almost kissed the porter!

VIRGINIA: So instead you went sporting with lewd lasciv-
            ious oysters till four o'clock in the morning.

VITA: Who told you?

VIRGINIA: Ah Ha!

VITA: How you Gloomsburies stick together.

VIRGINIA: Lethargic loose lipped oysters.

VITA: There was nothing in it, as you well know,
            though I'm heartily pleased to see you jealous.

VIRGINIA: Wicked creature. If you've given yourself to that
            Mary woman I'll have no more to do with you –
            you'll find Virginia's soft crevices lined with
            hooks – and what's more, the world shall read
            about it in *Orlando*.

VITA: Orlando?

VIRGINIA: It's a revolutionary form of your biography, about the lusts of your flesh and the lure of your mind – heart you have none, who go gallivanting down the lanes with Mary. You're an excellent subject – five hundred years of nobility, which gives me licence for florid descriptive passages and so on, and, dare I admit it, the opportunity to untwine and retwist some very odd, incongruous strands in you.

VITA: Lord!

VIRGINIA: Now use your Donkey-West brain on this: suppose there's the kind of shimmer of reality which sometimes attaches to my characters, you know, like the lustre on an oyster shell? – well suppose I write it and people we know read it and say, 'There's Virginia gone and written a book about Vita' – shall you mind? Of course I may not write another line, but what do you think?

VITA: Basically you're saying, will I give you permission to publicly unwind and retwist me, and thus provide you with the perfect tool to wreak vengeance should you ever feel the misguided desire to seek it.

VIRGINIA: Something like that.

VITA: I'm thrilled and terrified! How wonderful. Yes, absolutely yes!

VIRGINIA: Give yourself time to think—

VITA: No, do it, I want you to do it, only, if I'm going to be drawn and quartered I think you might dedicate it to your victim.

VIRGINIA: Done! Oh and I was wondering if you'd pose for the illustrations.

VITA: What? Illustrations?

VIRGINIA: Of Orlando – it's a biography after all so I thought it should show Orlando in his – er *her* – various guises throughout.

VITA: Hmmm?

VIRGINIA: Of course you don't have to, I could perhaps find someone else, though I was rather hoping to

	include a portrait of Thomas Sackville and you do of course look so much like him.
VITA:	Clever Virginia.
VIRGINIA:	And now we shall never speak of it – except I have a thousand questions to ask and I'll need to visit Knole – which will be the model for Orlando's ancestral home, and of course I'll have to spend a great deal of time with the subject.
VITA:	Clever, clever Virginia.
VIRGINIA:	That's just what your husband says.
VITA:	You've heard from Harold?
VIRGINIA:	A very loving letter which is more than I can say for *you*.
VITA:	Rot, I wrote you excessively loving letters, what did he say?
VIRGINIA:	He says that I'm not to worry about his having any 'feelings', that he wants your life to be as rich and as sincere as possible and that he knows I have an excellent, repeat excellent, influence over you and that he isn't jealous.
VITA:	Dear Harold.
VIRGINIA:	That is as long as you don't go running off with any Mary, Kitty or Flo.
VITA:	He did not say that.
VIRGINIA:	Does he *know* all about us?
VITA:	Pretty well, yes. And Leonard?
VIRGINIA:	Leonard is a very intelligent man.
VITA:	I like Leonard.
VIRGINIA:	He likes you, which is remarkable because he hardly likes anyone.
VITA:	Gosh, does he really like me?
VIRGINIA:	Oh yes, in fact he's so keen on you he's asked if you wouldn't mind keeping me company at Rodmell, when he has to stay overnight in London, nursing the Hogarth Press.
VITA:	Oh I say! Tell him I'll have to think about it.
VIRGINIA:	Beastly creature! Don't think you are the only one with admirers. I am loved, by a man.
VITA:	A what?

443

VIRGINIA: A man with an aquiline nose, a nice property, a wife of title, and furniture to suit.

VITA: Who is it?

VIRGINIA: He made a proposal.

VITA: I'll kill him, who is it?

VIRGINIA: I so want to tell you but I'm sworn to secrecy.

VITA: I'll have him, I swear.

VIRGINIA: That's rather what he proposed to do with me.

VITA: Damn him!

VIRGINIA: You're very beautiful when you're angry.

VITA: Look here I really mind.

[VIRGINIA *stays silent,* VITA *begins to storm out, just in time* VIRGINIA *stops her with:*]

VIRGINIA: Philip Morrell.

VITA: Him? But he's nothing but a— did I just find a hook in a soft crevice?

VIRGINIA: It was a very small one – I know you like just a little pain with your pleasure.

VITA: You know too much.

VIRGINIA: Never enough, never enough.

[VITA *exits.*]

VIRGINIA: 'But to give an exact and particular account of Orlando's life at this time becomes more and more out of the question. As we peer and grope in the ill-lit, ill-paved, courtyards, we seem now to catch sight of her and then again to lose it. The task is made more difficult by the fact that she found it convenient to change frequently from one set of clothes to another. For the probity of breeches she exchanged the seductiveness of petticoats.'

[VITA *enters, in 1920s dress. Both address the audience, each from within a tight spot of light.*]

VITA: I behaved honourably, it was she who seduced me!

VIRGINIA: What I want is illusion, to make the world dance.

VITA: At first it was a mental thing, a spiritual thing.

She inspired a feeling of tenderness – I suppose because of her strange mixture of hardness and softness – the hardness of her mind, and her terror of going mad again. At first I treated her as someone very frail, as if the slightest jolt might push her back into madness. But, apart from a very few occasions, she's positively robust! She will always tell me the state of her mind – if she needs to rest. In some strange way I think that the precarious balance of her mind feeds her creativity.

VIRGINIA: I take my writing board on my knee and I let myself down like a diver, very cautiously, into the last sentence I wrote yesterday. Then perhaps after twenty minutes or more I see a light in the depths of the sea, and I stealthily approach with a net which I fling over some sea pearl which may vanish. And if I net the sea pearl, if I bring it to the shore, it isn't anything like what it was when I saw it, under the sea; but sometimes it is, and that is the great excitement of life.

VITA: Making love with Virginia is like making love with a rainbow. It's like swimming naked by moonlight in a phosphorescent sea, wildly sensual, exhilarating, a touch dangerous, but not exactly sexual.

[VITA *exits*.]

VIRGINIA: It was fun, spontaneous, fast flowing. Diving in was a rapture; my cheeks would flush with the surge of it. I became like a transparent globe flung high by a powerful fountain, exhilarated, suspended, drenched with sensation. Vita – caught between my covers for all time!

Leonard says that *Orlando* will buy us a car.

The idea has come to me that what I want now to do is to saturate every atom. I mean to eliminate all waste, deadness, superfluity: to give the moment whole; whatever it includes. Say that the moment is a combination of thought; sensation; the voice of the sea. Waste, deadness, come from the inclusion of things that don't belong to the moment; this appalling narrative business of the realist – getting on from lunch to dinner – it is false, unreal, merely conventional. To saturate, that is what I want to do in *The Waves*. It must include nonsense, fact, sordidity: but made transparent.

[VITA *enters, in 1920s dress.*]

VITA: I don't know what to say; I'm hopelessly dazzled, enchanted, bewitched.

VIRGINIA: I'd made myself quite ill, it suddenly struck me – what if she's angry, or hurt?

VITA: But Virginia it's wonderful. It's the loveliest, wisest, richest book that I have ever read. It's like a vision that you've miraculously caught solid and brilliant in words. How did you – I just can't express – it touches me too deeply – so many passages – and Knole! My wonderful Knole!

VIRGINIA: I tried to make it *your* Knole. Did I catch it?

VITA: It made me weep it was so beautiful... Queen Elizabeth's visit by torchlight, and the skaters on the Thames, and Oh so much – wonderful phrases, and the birds singing 'Life!'

VIRGINIA: 'Let us go then exploring'? Yes I thought you'd like that.

VITA: But Orlando! How could you dress me in so glorious costume?

VIRGINIA: And I was hoping for cold and considered criticism.

VITA: Well I don't think I'll ever be able to give you that, I'm suffering from a strange form of Narcissism as it is – I'm in love with Orlando!

[*Pause.*]
Darling did you say you were ill?

VIRGINIA: Just a headache.

VITA: Why didn't you tell me you were ill?

VIRGINIA: Because I'm not ill. I had an attack of pre-publication horrors that's all. I don't sleep for fear I'll wake to find myself exposed as a fraud!

VITA:	Oh it's agony that feeling, doubting every sentence.
VIRGINIA:	Every word.
VITA:	Knowing it's all too late because Virginia's already posted off the review copies!
VIRGINIA:	And vile voices scrape through the brain – 'it's a failure, it's no good, you're no good.' Obscene, derisive, vicious; I fear those voices, they herald my madness. They always threaten when I'm about to have a book published. Don't look so worried, I've learnt to control it.
VITA:	I know, but you have to be careful, and rest.
VIRGINIA:	No! I go for long walks and mow the lawn.
VITA:	I thought it looked a bit odd.
VIRGINIA:	Thank you.
VITA:	Were you worrying about *Orlando* when we went to France?
VIRGINIA:	No, not at all.
VITA:	Good, I'd hate you to think me an insensitive clod.
VIRGINIA:	Insensitive – never.
VITA:	Anyway, you've been rightfully exposed as a genius, they say *Orlando* is a poetic masterpiece!
VIRGINIA:	They also hint at Knole and V. Sackville-West.
VITA:	I know, isn't it exciting! People keep giving me odd looks!
VIRGINIA:	They've been giving me those for years.
VITA:	And someone called me Orlando!
VIRGINIA:	Who?
VITA:	Hilda Matheson, that lovely woman at the BBC, she's asked me to do a series of talks on modern poets.
VIRGINIA:	Ah, Miss Matheson.
VITA:	She's going to ask you to do something on writing and women.
VIRGINIA:	Oh yes.
VITA:	And she wants to order more copies of *Orlando*, and so do I, and Oh, Virginia you've poured such riches on me I feel like a cup held under Niagara! If only I could say what I feel.
VIRGINIA:	I'll have to ask your biographer – who by the

	way is selling almost as well as the popular V. Sackville-West.
VITA:	Bravo!
VIRGINIA:	They say that old Mrs Woolf has finally written a book that everyone can read!
VITA:	Must be the illustrations.
VIRGINIA:	Must be.
VITA:	You see you really must stop trying to revolutionise the form of the novel.
VIRGINIA:	I know, it's so unlucrative.
VITA:	What are you going to do with the proceeds?
VIRGINIA:	Leonard will buy a car, and I have bought a rubber dinghy.
VITA:	Crikey!
VIRGINIA:	I shall row up and down the river whipping up ideas.
VITA:	And a heavy swell. I say, I can't swim!
VIRGINIA:	Death. Against you I will fling myself, unvanquished and unyielding... How does a woman buy face powder?
VITA:	I'll show you.
VIRGINIA:	Will you give me a driving lesson?
VITA:	What, now?
VIRGINIA:	Why not, and when I'm changing gear you can tell me all about Hilda Matheson.
VITA:	Ah.

[VIRGINIA *goes up stage into silhouette.* VITA, *lit in a tight spot of light, addresses audience.*]

VITA:	I adore Virginia, not 'in love', love, devotion, the way I love Harold. Virginia?... Very long walks, excursions to the theatre, the zoo, Kew Gardens, France... Sitting in her little dinghy and marvelling at her capacity to row us, up river! Sitting at her feet in front of the fire, she playing with my hair, my pearl necklace. The heat of the fire glowing on our faces, and talking, talking into the flames.

'Dangerous moments I have sometimes seen
Dangerous passions I have sometimes had'

Walking the streets of London and Paris with Violet on my arm. Not that anyone looked twice, for what did they see – a slightly plump young woman linked to a slightly awkward young... man? 1919 – I never felt so free in all my life. Once we bumped into Gertrude Stein. Afterwards Violet said, 'a pose is a pose is a pose'! Whenever I hear an owl hoot I think of Violet.

Mary conjures up... crushed flowers on a crumpled, fragrant bed; aromatic fingers, long, long after.

Margaret? Her saying, 'I love you,' and then immediately regretting it!

Darling Dotty – who will say 'Yes' without hesitation – even if it's in answer to, 'Come with me to Cairo, in five days?'

Hilda, determined eyes willing me through my first broadcast on the wireless...

And Evelyn! Bold brave Evelyn – ravishing in silks, debonair in trousers. We were a match. Could have killed her when she went off with that other woman!

'Do not forget my Dear, that once we loved.
Remember only, free from stain or smutch,
That passion once went naked and ungloved,
And that your flesh was startled by my touch.'

Passion is challenge, excitement, the violence of a rough possession; the pain of pleasure! Love, I keep quite separate.

[VITA *exits.*]

VIRGINIA: She glides across my horizon like a racing clipper, tossing off novels and articles and biographies in her wake. Fiercely honourable, she publishes only with our Hogarth Press, and so we net up her best sellers by the shoal. *All Passion Spent* has already sold 6000 copies – pre-publication! Each week she sails through the air waves to dispatch a handsome cargo of reviews; gently circum-navigating one book, boldly raising up another. She was seriously considered for Poet Laureate, she deservedly wears the laurels of the Haw-thornden Prize, and she is certainly read by 'the people' for an advertisement quoting her poem is plastered on every bus in London.

I, meanwhile, am to be given a prize of forty pounds for winning the Prix Femina Vie Heur-euse, and so shall have the inverted honour of following in the leaden footsteps of Miss Rad-clyffe Hall! And at sea I shall cause havoc, for copies of my *To The Lighthouse* have been pur-chased by The Seafarers Educational Society!

[VIRGINIA *exits.*]

INTERVAL

ACT TWO

VIRGINIA *enters, dressed as before.* VITA/ORLANDO *enters wearing a very full Victorian crinoline dress –* ORLANDO *is a woman.*

As ORLANDO *enters she spins like a top.* VIRGINIA *watches amused.*

ORLANDO: Oh! Oh! Oh! Of all the clothes that I have worn through all the ages, this crinoline is the drabbest and heaviest. I feel dragged down and pitifully weak and fearful of some terrible danger at every turn. Help! What is to become of me? I am not... myself... at all. I suddenly lack strength and forti-tude. Oh for something to lean upon... or some-one. A husband! A husband! My inheritance for a husband!

[*Pause as she waits for rescue.*]

Oh woe, woe is me to be a woman in such an age. I must sink, for I cannot swim.

[ORLANDO *hereafter interacts with an imaginary character* SHELMERDINE, *while* VIRGINIA *controls the scene from a distance, speaking* SHELMERDINE's *part and sharing the joke with the audience.*]

SHELMERDINE: Madam, you are sick!

ORLANDO: Oh I am a fragile, delicate, feeble, powerless, frail, defenceless woman!

SHELMERDINE: Yes, and fair and soft and lovely.

ORLANDO: I shall faint!

SHELMERDINE: What sensibilities!

ORLANDO: Oh frailty, frailty, all is frailty!

SHELMERDINE: Will you marry me?

ORLANDO: Yes!

SHELMERDINE: Oh great happiness! And will you have sons by me?

ORLANDO: Yes!

SHELMERDINE: Oh jubilation!

ORLANDO: Well at last that's settled, now I can get on. Oh and what's your name?

SHELMERDINE: Marmaduke Bonthrop Shelmerdine, Esquire.

ORLANDO: That'll do. Mine's Orlando.

SHELMERDINE: Yes I had guessed it, for if you see a ship in full sail coming with the sun on it proudly sweeping across the Mediterranean one says at once – Orlando.

ORLANDO: Are you sure you're a man?

SHELMERDINE: Yes.

ORLANDO: Right. And what do you do?

SHELMERDINE: I travel the world and am at this moment waiting for the wind to change so that I can set sail for the East.

ORLANDO: Excellent. I run Knole, my large ancestral home and huge garden, and I write prose and poetry.

SHELMERDINE: Are you sure you're a woman?

ORLANDO: Yes. What is your parentage?

SHELMERDINE: Above my fortunes, yet my state is well. I am a gentleman.

ORLANDO: Viola, *Twelfth Night*!

SHELMERDINE: Act one, scene five.

ORLANDO: We're going to get on splendidly. So you travel and have adventures.

SHELMERDINE: Absolutely.

451

ORLANDO: Me too.

SHELMERDINE: All I ask is a tall ship and a star to steer her by.

ORLANDO: Oh Bonthrop you are a card!

SHELMERDINE: I say, why don't you come with me?

ORLANDO: What fun – but I have to finish my poem first and plant hundreds of bulbs and seedlings – I'll join you later.

SHELMERDINE: Oh drats, and I was so looking forward to it, I had all sorts of games planned out.

ORLANDO: Don't be sad Shelmerdine, I'll come later.

SHELMERDINE: And I've got a pet rabbit.

ORLANDO: Oh that's nice, what's its name?.

SHELMERDINE: Raymond.

ORLANDO: Well I'll meet Raymond when I come later. You know, a woman's got to do what a woman's got to do Shel. We don't have to spend all our time together just because we're married.

SHELMERDINE: No, I 'spose not.

ORLANDO: Friends?

SHELMERDINE: Till death. I say, I'm hungry – can you cook?

ORLANDO: No!!! Can you?

SHELMERDINE: No. Orlando, are you sure you're a woman?

ORLANDO: Of course I'm a woman, are you sure you're a man?

SHELMERDINE: Of course I'm a man.

ORLANDO: Prove it then.

[ORLANDO/VITA *exits as if pursued by* SHELMERDINE.]

VIRGINIA: 'We can merely state that Orlando professed enjoyment in the society of her own sex, and leave it to the gentlemen to prove, as they are very fond of doing, that this is impossible.'
[*Pause.*]
'The Autumn leaves were falling. Orlando changed her skirt for a pair of breeches, then strode down the long corridor and through a dozen drawing rooms and so began a perambulation of the house, attended by such elk hounds and spaniels as chose to follow her. In this window seat she had written her first verses; in that chapel she had been married; and it was

here, she reflected, that she would be buried. She, who believed in no immortality, could not help feeling that her soul would come and go here for ever.

'She read her own notice, "Please do not touch". The house was no longer hers entirely, she sighed. It belonged to time now; to history.'

[VIRGINIA *exits.* VITA *enters wearing her 1930s gardening clothes: silk shirt, breeches, boots and jacket. She addresses the audience.*]

VITA: Gardeners are amongst the few people left in this distressed world who carry on the tradition of charm and elegance – we're useless members of society in terms of economics. Beauty is our aim and we break our backs, our finger nails and sometimes our hearts in the pursuit of it! Surely, a gardener is an artist of sorts.

In the design of our gardens my husband and I have sought to combine the elements of expectation and surprise. What I mean is – there must be a plan, an architectural plan and a colour plan and a seasonal plan.

Now by architecture I don't just mean the lay-out of a garden's paths, hedges and walls, I mean the relation between one group of plants and another, in mass and in height and in colour. It's all a question of shape, and good grouping.

Of course a lot depends on soil and aspect, but gardening is largely a question of mixing one sort of plant with another sort of plant and see-ing how happily they marry, and if they don't happily marry then you must hoick one of them out and be quite ruthless about it. The true gardener must be brutal, and imaginative for the future.

Jot your ideas down in a notebook. If you want something yellow to put with the yellow tulips experiment there and then with a few cut flowers stuck into the garden, and then write down your choice – clearly, so that you're not flummoxed when you come to read it next winter! Oh and if you have to buy – always buy the best.

Since we've moved to Sissinghurst Castle we've had the pleasure of designing a completely new garden out of what had been an ancient rubbish heap! I've experimented with the design of a one colour garden in two of the small internal areas. One of these is a typical cottage garden, a muddle of flowers, but all of them in the range of colour you might find in a sunset; the other is a *white* garden, which looks so cool on a summer evening.

Oh, one last word, don't be too rigid, let things ramp away if they want to. Better to walk around or duck beneath a stray straggle of beauty than to lop it off.

[VITA *exits.* VIRGINIA *has entered during the latter part of* VITA's *speech.*]

VIRGINIA: She cannot write much now, and so she gardens.

She digs and digs, and waters, and walks her dogs, and falls in love with every pretty woman, though I fancy it is Sissinghurst – that castle of her own – that is her true love now.

She has run to seed rather, only kindles about dogs, flowers and new buildings – sixteenth century of course.

Her fruit will ripen, and her leaves golden; and the night will be indigo blue, with a soft gold moon. She lacks only what I have – some cutting edge; some invaluable idiosyncrasy, intensity, for which I would not have all the sons and all the moons in the world.

Knole is besieged by a new master – Edward Sackville-West, her cousin. Such is the justice history hands down to women. She will not go there again.

[VITA *enters.* VIRGINIA *is sitting on a garden seat, she is convalescing.* VITA *carries a folded rug.*]

VITA: Mrs Woolf.

VIRGINIA: Mrs Nicolson. Let us talk about copulation.

VITA: Leonard has given me strict instructions that you are not to be excited, and that you are to sleep.

VIRGINIA: Sleep! Sleep! When you're near me I never want to sleep.

VITA: Do you know what I'd do if you weren't a person to be strict with? I'd speed here in my motor, secretly, in the dead of night and stand beneath your window and halloo your name until you let me in, and, if you did let me in, I'd stay with you till larks rise and scrabble home by half past six. But you being you I can't, more's the pity.

VIRGINIA: You would do much. But what you really mean is that if I weren't such a wet fish, and if I weren't so elderly and valetudinarian – in poor health—

VITA: I know what it means.

VIRGINIA: If I weren't so elderly and valetudinarian, we could spend the night together. When I am well I shall send you a telegram and on it will be two words: come then.

VITA: Ah ha!

VIRGINIA: Ah ha.

VITA: Leonard will be very severe with me, if you do not sleep.

[VIRGINIA *finally accepts the rug and covers herself with it.*]

VIRGINIA: Leonard and Vanessa and Donkey-West have lavished upon me the maternal protection that, for some reason, I have always most wished from everyone.

VITA: Sleep.

VIRGINIA: And it is you Vita, who has broken down more ramparts than anyone.

VITA: Sleep.

VIRGINIA: Potto wants a story.

VITA: No.

VIRGINIA: Potto won't sleep unless Donkey-West tells a story.

VITA: Well … I could tell you about something I've been researching.

VIRGINIA: Is it a story?

VITA:	Yes.
VIRGINIA:	Then begin.
VITA:	Once upon a time there were two women who were mistresses of a girl's boarding school, and their names were Miss Woods and Miss Pirie. One day, in 1811 it was, all the girls disappeared from the school, and do you know why?
VIRGINIA:	Potto hasn't got a brain.
VITA:	Then I'll tell you, it was all because of what little Miss Cumming told big Dame Cumming who subsequently told everyone else, which is what emptied the school.
VIRGINIA:	Did they have vermin?
VITA:	Little Miss Cumming was the eldest girl in the school, and as she was the eldest she shared a bed with Miss Pirie in a dormitory where lots of other girls shared beds.
VIRGINIA:	Mmmmmmmm.
VITA:	This was quite usual in a nineteenth-century school. In the other dormitory Miss Woods slept with the second eldest girl – Miss Bunrow. Now, when Miss Woods and Miss Pirie sued Dame Cumming for defamation of character, little Miss Cumming had to tell her whole story in court, and this is what she said: In the middle of the night Miss Woods would come into their dorm, get into bed on Miss Pirie's side, climb on top of Miss Pirie, and shake the bed! And occasionally she would hear conversations between them.
VIRGINIA:	Potto wants to know what they said.

VITA:	Miss Pirie : Oh, you're in the wrong place!
	 Miss Woods : I know.
	                 : Why are you doing it then?
	                 : For fun.
	                 : Oh. Do it again.

VIRGINIA:	Dirty Buggers.
VITA:	When Miss Bunrow gave evidence the story was corroborated: Miss Pirie had several times slipped under the covers, mounted Miss Woods and shaken the bed, keeping Miss Bunrow awake

till all hours. The case went to the House of Lords and, after lengthy review of the evidence, both actual and historical, Dame Cumming was soundly beaten, because, as the judge said: The crime here alleged has no existence. End of story.

VIRGINIA: Do you mean he didn't see it as a crime or that he couldn't believe such a thing existed?

VITA: What do you think?

VIRGINIA: I think Potto wants a cuddle.

VITA: All right.

VIRGINIA: Potto wants a kiss.

VITA: All right.

[VITA *kisses her.*]

VIRGINIA: And here.

[VITA *kisses where directed.*]

And here.

[*Pause.*]

I'm tired, but I don't want you to leave me.

VITA: I'll stay until you're asleep.

VIRGINIA: Potto loves Donkey-West.

VITA: Donkey-West loves Potto.

[*Pause.*]

Close your eyes and listen to some of my new poem – that's sure to send you off!

VIRGINIA: I'll close my eyes but I certainly won't sleep.

[VITA *enfolds* VIRGINIA *in her arms.*]

VITA: Think about early evening at the end of summer.

'Now will the water-lilies stain the lake
With cups of yellow, chalices of cream,
Set in their saucer leaves of olive-green
On greener water, motionless, opaque,
– This haunt of ducks, of grebes, and poacher herns.
Now is the stillness deeper than a dream;
Small sounds, small movements shake
This quietude, that deeper then returns
After the slipping of the water-snake,
The jump of trout, the sudden cry of coot,
The elegiac hoot

>Of owls within the bordering wood, that take
>The twilight for their own.
>This is their hour, and mine; we are alone;
>I drift; I would that I might never wake.'

[VITA *gently leaves* VIRGINIA *and moves to a separate area on stage.*]

>When I won the Hawthornden Prize for my long poem, 'The Land', I planted a whole field with trees. In fifty years time which will be greater, the trees, or my poem?

[VITA *exits.*]

VIRGINIA: I am walking. I am wearing a woollen jacket with pockets, a full skirt that has two stains and a hole in it and pockets, and a heavy pair of rubber boots. In my hand I have my walking stick. It is spring and the larks are rising and the blossoms buzzing. On my walk towards the river I pass two cows and a bomb crater.

[*Pause.*]

>I am a pacifist in an age of warmongers – they will not hear me.

[*Pause.*]

>Vita...

[VITA's *voice only is heard, as if it is inside* VIRGINIA's *head, like a memory.*]

VITA: Listen I can't come, there's a terrible air battle going on.

VIRGINIA: A terrible what?

VITA: Air battle – they're fighting it out above my head.

VIRGINIA: Where are you?

VITA: Sissinghurst. Under the table!

VIRGINIA: For goodness sake go down into the cellar!

VITA: No, I think I'm better off here – but anyway darling it means I can't come.

VIRGINIA: No, of course not, stay exactly where you are.

VITA: Bombs have been dropping all day so the roads are too dangerous, and anyway I have to stand by to drive the ambulance.

VIRGINIA: Are you on your own?

VITA: Yes.

VIRGINIA:	I was thinking of you, I'd just put flowers in your room... Leonard's playing bowls in the garden...
VITA:	How very Francis Drake!
VIRGINIA:	We had a lot of incendiaries last night... But darling, are you all right?
VITA:	They've desecrated my garden!
VIRGINIA:	What – the bombs?
VITA:	No, army tanks, its a defence line against the invasion.
VIRGINIA:	They've dug in here too...
VITA:	Harold says London is devastated, he says the invasion might come any day. He's ordered me to pack the car ready for escape!
VIRGINIA:	Good idea.
VITA:	Yes but I'm the ambulance driver, I have to stand by in an emergency!
VIRGINIA:	Oh Vita I wish you wouldn't.
VITA:	Don't worry, I'll get out if I have to, one way or another.
VIRGINIA:	We've decided on asphyxiation in the garage!... there'll be no mercy for a Socialist Jew and his wife, not that I have any desire to end my days in the garage...
VITA:	I'll have to go. Are you all right?
VIRGINIA:	Yes.
VITA:	Writing?
VIRGINIA:	No – my head is very stupid at the moment. I've no stimulus, no audience. Nothing to write for. No-one wants to listen to a pacifist.
VITA:	Did you finish *Between the Acts*?
VIRGINIA:	Yes, but its too slight, too sketchy, I won't publish.
VITA:	What does Leonard think?
VIRGINIA:	He likes it but...
VITA:	The birds in my aviary are dying.
VIRGINIA:	Do they die all in an instant?
VITA:	I have to go Virginia.
VIRGINIA:	Am I still third rung on the ladder?
VITA:	Third rung – at least!

[*Pause.*]

VIRGINIA: You have given me enormous happiness, you know that don't you. Isn't it strange, when I need words most, I can't find them.

[*Pause.*]

Holding her hand brought the wildest sensation – making love was stupendous, voluptuous, absurd.

For the most part, I have been very, very happy.

I almost know what my death will be like, for I have attempted it. I know now how to achieve it. But for these terrible voices I would write about it, but then, I have been writing about it all my life.

I feel I am going mad again. I am hearing voices. I am sane, but I fear this madness. I feel it coming, just as it came the first time. I fear it coming, and I know that, this time, I will go under.

I choose death, unvanquished and unyielding. I will walk to the river, the tidal river, the Ouse River and I will fill my pockets with stones and my boots with water, and I will cast off my mind and my life.

[VIRGINIA *exits down stage.* VITA *enters up stage, looking to where* VIRGINIA *has gone, still dressed in gardening clothes.*]

VITA: That lovely mind, that lovely spirit.

[VITA *exits.*]

THE END

1. Violet Trefusis

2. This refers to the journal that Vita wrote at that time. She locked it in a Gladstone bag which her son, Nigel, found after her death and wrote *Portrait of a Marriage* with it.

3. This refers to the novel, *Challenge*, that Vita wrote during her relationship with Violet. It was published in America in 1923, but she got cold feet and withdrew it from publication in England. (Collins published it in 1974.)

Bibliography

The great wealth of material written by and about Virginia Woolf and Vita Sackville-West has been an invaluable source for research. Virginia Woolf's *Orlando* was a major influence in the making of this play and specific quotes have been adapted from it. The primary research material is listed below:

Bell, Anne Olivier (ed.) 1982, *The Diary of Virginia Woolf*. Penguin, London.

Bell, Quentin 1972, *Virginia Woolf*. Hogarth Press, London.

Brown, Jane 1985, *Vita's Other World*. Penguin, London.

DeSalvo, Louise and Mitchell A. Leaska (eds) 1985, *The Letters of Vita Sackville-West to Virginia Woolf*. Papermac, London.

Faderman, Lillian 1985, *Surpassing the Love of Women*. The Women's Press, London.

Glendinning, Victoria 1986, *Vita: The Life of Vita Sackville-West*. Penguin, London.

Nicolson, Nigel 1973, *Portrait of a Marriage*. Weidenfeld & Nicolson, London.

— (ed.) 1977, *The Letters of Virginia Woolf*. Hogarth Press, London.

Sackville-West, Vita 1946, *The Garden*. Michael Joseph, London.

Woolf, Virginia 1974, *Orlando: A Biography*. Penguin, London.

Bibliography

The details of the biographical sources beyond those by Leon Woolf and Virginia Nicolson have been, wherever possible, too poor for reuse. In Virginia Woolf volumes, where sources indicate in the reading of this essay and quotes from those have been adapted material. The primary sources material is listed below.

Bell, Anne Olivier, ed. 1982–1976. *Diary of Virginia Woolf.* Penguin, London.

Bell, Quentin. 1972. *Virginia Woolf.* Hogarth Press, London.

Spater, George. 1985. *James Joyce Woolf.* Pamphlet on Love.

Gordon, Lyndall, and Mitchell A. Leaska, eds. 1985. *The Letters of Virginia Woolf.* Hogarth Press, London.

Edel, Leon. 1979. *Bloomsbury: A House and Group: Two Volumes.* Faber, London.

Glendinning, Victoria. 1983. *Vita: The Life of Vita Sackville-West.* Penguin, London.

Nicolson, Nigel. 1973. *Portrait of a Marriage.* Weidenfeld & Nicolson, London.

——, ed. 1975. *The Flight of the Mind: The Letters of Virginia Woolf.* Hogarth Press, London.

Sackville-West, Vita. 1985. *The Garden.* Michael Joseph, London.

Woolf, Virginia. 1976. *Moments of Being.* Sussex University Press.

BETH YAHP

Beth Yahp was born in Malaysia in 1964. Her
father is Chinese, her mother Eurasian (half-English,
half-Thai). 'I grew up speaking English,' she says.
'Their only common language. In this way I suppose
I am an excellent example of the "multi-cultural."'

She has spent most of her life in Petaling Jaya,
which is a satellite town of Kuala Lumpur, and
where she was educated in a convent.

'At school I was addicted to Enid Blyton and later,
Georgette Heyer. When I was fourteen, Heyer's
Regency England seemed more real to me than
modern day Malaysia. I said things like "Lawks" and
"Lud" quite unselfconsciously. I took it for granted
that heroes and heroines were always "naturally"
white and spoke with English and American accents.
I probably first gravitated to writing as revenge for
all this swamping.'

Having been channelled into a science stream
at school ('Malaysia is a developing country, keen
on "progress" and "technology"') she felt that there
were great gaps in her reading when she arrived in
Sydney in 1984. 'In Australia I discovered Virginia
Woolf and feminism,' she comments. 'And I also
slowly unlearnt my "fear of speaking" which was
a big part of my Malaysian education, which all
Malaysians – or anyone who has lived in a politically
repressive country – will recognise.'

With a B.A. in Communications from the
University of Technology, Sydney, Beth Yahp readily
admits that she is somewhat addicted to television.
'I watch everything, docos, soaps, music videos, ads,

so much so that recently I have had to disconnect
the TV and hide it under the stairs; if I can't see it,
it won't distract me. I also like chopping different
coloured vegetables into tiny bits,' she adds. 'Can
salad-making be called an interest?'

When it comes to politics, Beth Yahp is non-sexist,
non-racist, and pro-equality and pro-environment.
For her, writing is a form of politics, a way of
redressing the balance.

'As a writer I am still learning. I think I always
will be. I want to write all sorts of things but at
present am concentrating on short stories (for
practical reasons – especially limits on writing
time) and a novel. I'm interested in the sounds of
words when they're put together, and the rhythms
they make; perhaps this makes me a rhythmic
writer. I'm certainly an experimental writer. Each
story is not just a way to say something, but an
exploration of the ways in which it can be said. I
like pushing at the limits of narrative convention,
but I am also concerned with telling coherent
stories. Form and content are equally important
to me.

'The fact that I am an Asian writer, writing in
English, makes me feel I have to be doubly good.
I don't want any concessions. No starry-eyed
sentimentality either. I think I am trying to evolve
a new "multicultural" voice, one that is not
"migrant-oppressed", or sentimental. A new way of
seeing, and speaking. That can become part of the
Australian tradition.'

Earning a living from writing is not always easy, as
Beth Yahp makes clear. 'Usually I am engaged in
a juggling act between having to work to live, and
finding the time, energy and concentration to write;
the result is often *not writing*. When you average
about $120 for short stories published, and anything
from nothing to $100 for a reading, then in order to
live, you would have to churn out a lot of stories.
Which I can't. I've always accepted that I will have

to work at other jobs to support my writing. My writing life has been made easier this year by a grant which has enabled me to write full time. I think grants are essential, especially for beginning writers who often don't have enough time to get together a body of work for publication, and who won't make any money to live on until they get published. A Catch 22 situation. Which is why I think a generous, ideologically sympathetic and undemanding patron would be good. I'm still looking.'

Beth Yahp's stories have been widely published in anthologies and literary magazines; with M. Daly and L. Falconer she edited *My Look's Caress; A Collection of Modern Romances* (Local Consumption Press, Sydney, 1990) in which appears her story, 'The Red Pearl'. 'Kuala Lumpur Story' has been published in Sneja Gunew and Jan Mahyuddin (eds) *Beyond the Echo: Multicultural Women's Writing* (University of Queensland Press, St Lucia, 1988) and 'So We Walked Down Abercrombie Street' is in Stephanie Dowrick and Jane Parkin (eds) *Speaking with the Sun* (Allen and Unwin Australia, Sydney, 1991) and 'Homeland' in George Papaellinas (ed), *Homeland*. Allen and Unwin Australia, Sydney, 1991. Her first novel will be published by Collins/Imprint in 1992.

In 1969

In 1969 my mother crawled into a ditch. The sky was low, it was the monsoon season and the winds were blowing. It beat the ends of her hair into her face. Against the back of her neck the creeping began.

That was the year of the floods in Bangau, the driest part of the country, where the wind whipped the houses in lashes and pulled at the roots of trees. It was the night the storm broke the wall of the madhouse and there was singing and dancing in the streets and the slamming of simple folks' doors. It was the year the lizard woman fell over sideways, scraping her skin against the wall in a pattern you can still see today.

The year of disasters.

Where my mother was though, it was quiet. Not a sound in that edge of the city, not even cicadas or crickets. But she knew what a year it would be. She lay in the ditch with one hand clutching at her belly, a squeeze, then release, then another squeeze, and harder, to the beat of her heart. She could tell by the shape of the moon and a cloud above her, like an eye.

My mother, an old mother by now, was used to this smell, the smell of the sour earth and the growing things. Water in the ditch seeped up to caress her. In a high fever my mother saw feet march past her ditch in quick tempo, shiny soldier's feet, in boots to crush a woman's skull. Then shambling feet in worn-out shoes or no shoes at all but toes and mud and soles which were dirty and cracked. Children's feet, running.

My mother heard no sound. There was only this beating of her heart and she squeezed and pushed and breathed in the familiar smells like a charm. Silent armies marched past her but she saw no faces, only the swinging of their fists.

In 1969, there were men on boxes and men crowded on the backs of trucks. There were lorries pasted with party posters and loud-hailers that wound their voices through the city streets, through main streets and sidestreets and lanes that bumped and jolted. My mother's city was filled with symbols – a sailing boat, red rockets in circles, a fat moon against a green sky. The excitement of election time. Boys in caps and printed T-shirts handed out pamphlets my mother crushed against her thigh. They pasted kindly faces on fences and walls and lamp posts wherever she looked. Men came knocking from door to door. Everywhere my mother looked were the words she couldn't read, and smiling faces, and hands held out to pat her shoulder, to squeeze the fleshy part of her palm. My mother crossed her own hands. She held them tightly in her lap.

In rooms where daylight never entered, my mother twisted and turned. She let her hair fall in frizzled curls to her shoulders, she stood in the doorway in clothes tucked care-lessly, hanging this way and that. My mother stood smoking. The smoke curled around her head.

Imagine this room, this mother's room.

In the bowels of the building she stood staring at walls against which the dark earth pushed and seeped. My mother's room: once the cellar of a mad English planter's townhouse, now a room in a shabby hotel: an air-raid shelter he'd built and bricked himself into just before the Japanese invaded in World War II. At night my mother lay twisting, turning. She liked lying deep in the earth, the earth all around her, dozing. She liked the smell of the Englishman's bones. When the cleaning boy had shouted his discovery, my mother had helped to pull the bricks from the doorway with her own hands. Then she had bribed and scolded, and scrubbed and hung and swept, and dragged in her bed.

Here my mother lay like a spider, weaving tendrils of smoke. Here she listened to the rumble of the trucks and the feet marching, the tinkling of bicycle bells and the banners that flapped over the swelling crowds. The speeches on the radio, the demonstration voices that cheered. My mother lay in the yellow light of the naked bulb and she too glowed softly. She too was hot to the touch. She burned so men had to snatch their hands away. My mother, an old mother by now, lay in her room through which the smell of the earth seeped darkly. This smell was the smell of her village, comforting, nothing to do with this city. She lay with her hands crossed in her lap and my father lay beside her.

Years later my mother said: this man is your father, and he dropped a coin in her hand with a gesture of loathing. He walked quickly away. Even then my father didn't believe her. Lying beside my mother he ran his hand over her rounded belly, then made her shut her mouth. He plucked long twirling hairs from his cheek and used her tweezers to pick deep pores at the side of his nose. He worried the skin between his toes until it bled. My father picked and squeezed and scrubbed at his body to remove all traces of human shedding: to be clean. He washed five times a day. His skin was the colour of the deep diggings of earth around my mother's village: darkly golden. His flesh was as soft as her creams. When she pressed his belly the tip of her finger disappeared.

My father's charm was his voice that soothed and rumbled, that brought crowds to a standstill with its reasonable talk, or could rouse them to a frenzy if he chose. His voice that lulled my mother to silence, to sleep. By day my father worked in his air-conditioned office, at night he crumpled exhausted to bed with one of his wives. At lunchtime he brought bracelets and other knick-knacks to my mother's cellar. He ran his fingers over the arch of her back and kissed her ankles, first one, then the other. My father liked best my mother's feet. When they fucked she became hotter and hotter, her cheeks reddened and she sweated and laughed. My father was cool against her, his touch like water. Their skins sizzled together.

That was the year people banded together in groups according to their colour, there was safety in numbers and looking the same, and kitchen knives, *parangs* and pieces of metal swishing the air. It was the night the army fired at shadows that moved in windows and burning rags were thrust through wooden shutters, and the moon hung yellow in a rainy sky. The year a man came home after the curfew to find his house looted and on the doorstep only his grandmother's feet.

Twenty years later the history books said: In 1969 the third federal elections after Malaya's Independence were held. The elections were fought on highly emotional issues – education and language. Each ethnic group saw the elections as a means of preserving its interest against the encroachment of the others. In Selangor the Opposition parties, consisting mainly of non-Malays, won as many seats as the Malay-dominated Alliance government. On 13 May, the day after the elections, jubilant Opposition supporters took to the streets of Kuala Lumpur in a victory celebration. A counter-rally that evening by supporters of the United Malays National Organisation quickly deteriorated into uncontrolled violence. The Constitution was suspended and a national emergency declared. Only after four days of bloody fighting was order finally restored, but for two months after the riots, incidents of communal violence persisted. The riots were officially blamed on the activities of the 'communist-infiltrated' Opposition parties and their followers, whose provocative jeering and taunting of the Malays was the cause of their violent retaliation.

My mother told me things the books didn't say.

In the ditch she whispered words I could hardly hear. She heaved and panted, her breaths came short and sharp, and she held her neck stiffly, and her shoulders, and her belly were dark bruises were already swelling. If my mother lifted her head she would see smoke rising in hasty columns from the cars and houses that burned. If she uncovered her ears she would hear over the other sounds thin cryings like the mewling of wounded cats. If she reached out her hand she could touch the grass that was trampled and bunched together in sticky patches of red. But my mother dug her fingers into her ears. She kept her head down and her body still: only her eyes wide open.

The message my father sent her was: Trouble. Leave immediately. The boy with the message left without explaining. My mother stood in her doorway, smoking, swilling her drink. Feeling the tightening at the back of her neck. In the hotel bar above her were the sounds of drunken celebration. Speeches and cheering, smashing glasses and the popping of corks. My mother shut her bedroom door.

In 1969, although my mother did not know it then, the official figures said 196 dead, 52 killed by gunshots and fifteen found highly decomposed in the Klang River and mining pools. To my mother the number seemed like thousands, the sound of gunfire echoing in her ears. But she did not know this then. In the ditch she did not know that only minutes later there would be a cry she could not stop and the sound of feet turning towards her. That many years later she would be tagged and her story would span six lines on a foreign page:

A Chinese couple, the woman pregnant, were in a motorcar near Circular Road on Tuesday evening when they were surrounded by Malays. The man was dragged out, killed, and the car set on fire. In the excitement the woman managed to slip away. Discovered not far from the scene, she was beaten, stripped, and her breasts cut off. She was left for dead but, later, was found and taken to hospital.

All this, then, my mother did not know.
In the ditch she wept not for all the city's disasters but for

herself and the baby whose waters had broken but who clung to the sides of her belly with claws, with scraping teeth that ripped and pulled. The sound of her heart was the beat to which I kicked her, to which I stuck my elbows, my knees to her softest parts. I smelt her terror, her anger, in the blood she fed me. In the squeezing to my right, to my left, and the insistent pushing to my head and spine. My weeping mother shed tears not for sorrow but for this tearing, cutting pain: a pain to split her so that I would have not one mother but two, and could choose.

The whites of her eyes shone from the ditch like twin stars and she squeezed and pushed and coaxed with her whispered curses. Her eyes unable to close. All those bodies sweeping past. Soon the city would be full. It would be full to bursting, and then it would burst.

That was the year my father stood watching. Imagine this father, my father. Watching from an upstairs window as the crowd in the compound thickened. My father watched with narrowed eyes and a heart that leapt to his mouth. Still the busloads arrived. Young men from the outlying *kampungs*, village men in *sarungs* or western clothes, some with scraps of red or white cloth wrapped around their heads. Men bursting with indignation, shoving and flopping against each other like seals. Their anger swelled the fence around the compound, they crushed the newly-mown grass. They shook their fists in the air. My father traced the outline of the men below on the windowpane with his finger. In the room behind him the leaders milled, they paced and swore and planned, and prepared to speak.

To act.

Years later I walked with my father on a path along the river. The river was the colour of milky coffee, there were bits of plastic and an occasional cat or dog floating by. No larger bodies. Newly released from serving a jail sentence for corruption, my father walked in disguise. He wore large sunglasses and shabby clothes. His skin was raw from rough soaps and too much scrubbing. His gait was changed: he took tiny steps. I ran beside my father, and around him, and backwards and forwards, holding out my hand. My child's T-shirt and close-cropped hair flapped in the evening breeze. My feet danced on the cooling cement. *Encik, Encik,* I said. *Tolong, Encik.* Mister, please. My father threw two coins as far as he could, and I scurried after.

Years later, I learnt to walk like him. Each step a condemnation.

And now rain. Washing the mud from my mother's face so it became streaked and could be seen. My mother burrowed into the ditch. She clung like a slug to its side. Now things began to wash down, sharp stones to scratch her and sticks to break her bones. The water licked at her feet, then covered them, scrubbing vigorously, washing them clean. Two pale feet in a churning ditch, two fine feet with soles soft and pink. Feet used to the finest arched shoes. My mother lay like a corpse in the ditch, only her fingers gripping. Only there, in the crook of her leg, behind the knee: that would give her away. That purple vein, beating and beating, pulling the eye towards it and beating through the current of water like some angry beast. This vein and the one behind her other knee, and the ones on the seat of her bum, and lower. The ones she rubbed and smoothed with balms on a quiet night. These, beating and beating till the sound filled her. These were the ones that would give her away.

Imagine this mother in another place.

Perhaps behind a counter. Imagine the light garish on her upturned face, yellow then purple, then green. Imagine her mouth rimmed with red, her eyes with black and silver, a paper star pinned to her hair. She is smiling, this mother, there is a patch on her chin. A beauty spot: she is beautiful. Laughing. She laughs with her whole body, she leans forward and her breasts shake and that is when the men tickle her to make her laugh the more. My mother behind a counter, moving her fingers deftly as she pours the drinks and wearing a shiny slitted dress.

I imagined this mother. Telling jokes in a bawdy voice and climbing onto a table to sing. Leading a drunken man by his necktie down the stairs to her room. In the street she wore her hair in a bun. She wore her face lightly powdered and that was all. She wore long-sleeved blouses and wrapped a cloth around her that reached from her bosom to her knees. This mother prodded her belly as it grew, in a certain spot she prodded and pinched until she wept. She lay in bed for days, brooding. Threw her half-filled glass at the wall so the stain it made was a trickling of tears. This mother ate powders that shrivelled her breasts and made her gut ache. The oils she rubbed herself with scalded me. This mother slept late and swore loudly, but in the street she walked daintily and people bowed in greeting, and smiled. In the street my mother looked gentle. In lamplight she looked cruel.

When my mother was young she lived in a village surrounded by wire. The British were still in Malaya then, they were the ones who stood guard at the gate. Who herded the Chinese families there, and searched them, and kept them in. Under surveillance. My mother's village was a White Spot, considered free of communist guerilla supporters: that meant more food supplies were allowed in, and a nurse, and day passes to leave. My mother stood at the gate watching the white men that drove up in cars with Malay men, and sometimes a white woman who sweated in a sunhat and shiny white shoes. My mother asked the guards for a fag and a light and leant back in the shade.

Imagine this mother.

This mother so young her belly was flat and her skin creamy like petals of magnolia. Her voice low and singsong lilting, making people turn their heads. My mother never spoke above a whisper so men would have to lean closer to hear. Even then she knew the value of her charms. Her string of yellow thread tied around her wrist to protect her. The goodluck squares of red paper she wore sewn into a pouch, swinging on a chain around her neck. Her red-lipped smile and the seductive tilt of her head. My mother stood at the gate, smoking. Even then she knew the value of hating. She hated the white women in the big cars whose laughter was like the tinkling of bells. She hated the wire fence and the trucks into which her whole village had been bundled and brought to this place.

And the white men outside, and the Malay men, and the Indian labourers who carried baskets of stones on their heads, growing shiny in the noonday sun, unwinding the rolls of wire. The fat Chinese businessmen who came to look. My mother hated everyone outside. She hated the ache of her empty belly.

In 1969, Kuala Lumpur was loosely divided into living areas according to race. The communal groups liked living together: a legacy from the British, who divided and ruled so skilfully that when they left, they left behind them a society famous for its ethnic divisions. Even as a young girl my mother already knew the roles allocated to each race. Her mother told her, and her grandmother, and her aunts and cousins with their stories of the us's and thems. All around my mother, the racial relics of a colonial Malaya remained: the whites who were managers and skilled supervisors; the Chinese who were rich merchants and tin miners; the Indian estate workers and labourers; and the Malays, who didn't forget that this land was named for them – the majority of the Malays who were subsistence farmers.

My mother laughed at these roles, so watertight on paper. In 1969 the government juggled between propagating the idea of a united Malaysia, regardless of race, and redressing the economic imbalance between the races: giving the Malays a greater share of the country's wealth. Special privileges based on colour and name. Not class, or poverty. My mother laughed harshly. In her village, everyone had struggled together. The only rich merchants and tin miners she knew were the ones who rode around the city in chauffeured cars and refused to give her credit at their shops. Who came to the hotel to swill drinks and dance with grinding hips, and stumble downstairs to fuck her.

In 1969 my mother woke to the sounds of splintering wood. The smell of burning. The hotel was on fire. Thumping feet on the floorboards upstairs and the screams of men and women slashed and pierced where they hid. My mother opened her eyes. Next came footsteps racing down the stairs, three at a time. Next the wrenching open of her door: the shadow of the old Malay woman whose room was above my mother's. *Cepat!*

cepat! she cried, throwing Malay clothes at my mother, a *sarung,* a blouse, a shawl to cover her head. Quickly, be quick. She pulled my mother from the bed. The *sarung* stretched across my mother's belly, her arms were thrust into sleeves too tight for her, the blouse left unbuttoned. The shawl wrapped around her shoulders and head. As they finished they heard the sounds on the stairs, the delirious cries: *China keluar! China keluar!* Chinese come out. My mother lowered her head as she was led past the men with knives as long as her arm. *Melayu!* the Malay woman cried. When the men saw her, they let her and my mother pass. As they stumbled out the back, they bumped against the hotel manager, creeping along the corridor, car keys in hand. The woman bundled my mother into his car. My mother's breath came hoarsely as she and the manager sped away. She pulled the shawl tightly around her.

Years later, my mother surprised my father on a street corner. My father stood in his dark glasses, quiet, dignified, absently waiting for the lights to change. My mother, a street away, raced up to meet him. Her breath caught in her throat, her blouse flapped flat against her chest. Each breath my mother took was a rattle, a repetition of the phrase she never spoke. To speak that phrase was illegal: leading to accusations of inciting racial hatred, sedition, to imprisonment without a trial. My mother's voice rattled in her throat. Only in her throat, never aloud. The words went round and round her head. In 1969, in 1969. In 1969, whispered in my ear as I slept. Pinched into ridges on my arms when I wept for hunger, shoved into my mouth with the scraps of food she grudgingly fed me. When my mother reached my father she tugged at his sleeve. How good to see you, my mother said. These days, how do you sleep? My father brushed her hand away. This man is your father, my mother said, and he dropped a coin in her hand with a gesture of loathing. He walked quickly away.

There were not so many now in the army that passed my mother's ditch, only people with dragging feet. The rain fell steadily. Water swirled around her: soon it would carry us away. The tightening at the back of my mother's neck, her danger signal, was a snake, thick and heavy, spreading around and around until it must strangle her. The water sucked and lapped.

At first my mother held her voice tightly inside her. She knew the dangers of the smallest sound. But the water would sweep us away. Later, she said it was her scream that broke the night, that plug-eared silence of her night – even though the wind was howling and all around us were the sounds of running and doors being torn open. Cars crashing one into another and the smashing of windscreens with knives and axes and pieces of wood.

She said it was her scream, but the cry was mine. It roared from my throat, gurgling through her waters through her stomach through her thin shivering diaphragm to her lungs, to push at the air she gulped and swallowed in hopes of drowning me. Air full of her charmed earth.

I pushed and pushed, this sound from my throat to hers so that her chest swelled and the snake tightened around her neck. The snake plunged its mouth to her voicebox and she threw back her head. Her lips tore open, she ground her teeth again and again. My mother's head: a rain-soaked head only full of grinding teeth to hold back the thing that threatened to burst from her. But I pushed and pushed and the snake tightened and her lips fell open like the petals of a flower. Her jaws loosened: she screamed. My cry, for the wind to hear.

And then the sound of feet.

Pausing.

Bibliography

Andaya, Barbara Watson and Leonard Y. Andaya 1982, *A History of Malaysia*. Macmillan, London.

Slimming, J. 1969, *Malaysia: Death of a Democracy*. John Murray, London.

Rahman Putra Al-Haj, Tunku Abdul 1969, *May 13: Before and After*. Utusan Melayu Press, Kuala Lumpur.

SOURCES

For permission to reprint the works in this anthology, grateful acknowledgement is made to the following:

Barbara Jefferis: 'The Drover's Wife', first published in the *Bulletin*, December 23–30, 1980; to the author.

Janette Turner Hospital: 'The Last of the Hapsburgs', first published in *LinQ* magazine; and in *Isobars*, University of Queensland Press, St Lucia, 1990; to the author.

Adele Horin: 'Murder in Adelaide', first published in the *National Times*, July 26, 1980; 'Obsessive Love', first published in the *National Times*, November 29, 1981; to the author.

Finola Moorhead: 'Miss Marple Goes to Ayers Rock', first performed at the Belvoir Street Downstairs Theatre in Sydney during January 1986.

Thea Astley: 'Northern Belle' published in *Hunting the Wild Pineapple*, Penguin Books, 1988; to the author.

Eva Johnson: 'What Do They Call Me?', a part of this was first published under the title 'Alison' in *The Exploding Frangipani*, edited by Cathie Dunsford and Susan Hawthorne, New Women's Press, Auckland, 1990; to the author. First performed as part of the Lesbian Festival, Guild Theatre, University of Melbourne, January 1990 and at Adelaide Fringe Festival, Wetpack Theatre, Adelaide, March 1990.

Jocelynne Scutt: 'Fair Shares of Our Heritage', a lecture given at the Heidelberg Town Hall, October 12, 1986.

Helen Hodgman: 'Roundabout', reprinted here with the kind permission of the Australian Film Commission.

Elizabeth Jolley: 'Supermarket Pavane', previously published in the *Sydney Morning Herald Literary Supplement* in 1988; and in *Tampa Review*, University of Florida; to the author.

Joanne Burns: 'found parable' published in *blowing bubbles in the 7th lane*, FAB Press, Sydney, 1988; to the author.

Elizabeth Riddell: 'Atwood's survival kit' first published in the *Bulletin*, 21 March, 1989; 'A fairy story from NZ' first published in the *Bulletin*, March 14, 1989; to the author.

Sara Hardy: 'Vita! – a fantasy' was first performed at the Universal Theatre, Melbourne, in August, 1989.

Beth Yahp: 'In 1969', a part of this was first published in *Australian Short Stories*, No. 25, 1989; to the author.

Grateful acknowledgement is made to the following for permission to quote from published works:

Eva Johnson's play: to Kitchen Table: Women of Color Press, NY for permission to reprint Jo Carrillo's poem 'And When You Leave Take Your Pictures With You' from *This Bridge Called My Back: Writings by Radical Women of Color*, edited by Cherrie Moraga and Gloria Anzaldúa.

Sara Hardy's play: to Nigel Nicolson for permission to quote freely from the work of Vita Sackville-West including an extract from 'Valediction' quoted in Victoria Glendinning, *Vita: The Life of Vita Sackville-West*, Penguin Books, London, 1986; and from *The Garden* by Vita Sackville-West, Michael Joseph, London, 1946; to Random Century and the Estate of Virginia Woolf and Hogarth Press to publish extracts from *The Waves* and *Orlando* by Virginia Woolf; to Macmillan to quote extracts from *The Letters of Vita Sackville-West to Virginia Woolf*, edited by Louise de Salvo and Mitchell A. Leaska, London, 1985. Other sources include *The Letters of Virginia Woolf*, Vol. 3. Nigel Nicolson (ed). The Hogarth Press, London, 1977; and *The Diary of Virginia Woolf*, Vol. 3. Ann Olivier Bell (ed), Penguin Books, London, 1980.